DIOPHANTINE
EQUATIONS

DIOPHANTINE EQUATIONS

L. J. MORDELL

ST. JOHN'S COLLEGE
CAMBRIDGE, ENGLAND

1969

ACADEMIC PRESS   London and New York

ACADEMIC PRESS INC. (LONDON) LTD.
Berkeley Square House, Berkeley Square, London, W1X 6BA

U.S. Edition published by
ACADEMIC PRESS INC.
111 Fifth Avenue, New York, New York 10003

LIBRARY OF CONGRESS CATALOG CARD NUMBER: 68–9112

PRINTED IN GREAT BRITAIN BY WILLIAM CLOWES AND SONS LTD
LONDON AND BECCLES

Preface

Most books on number theory treat with more or less detail various aspects of Diophantine analysis, a subject which can be described briefly by saying that a great part of it is concerned with the discussion of the rational or integer solutions of a polynomial equation $f(x_1, x_2 \ldots, x_n) = 0$, with integer coefficients. It is well known that for many centuries, no other topic has engaged the attention of so many mathematicians, both professional and amateur, or has resulted in so many published papers. Nevertheless, apart from reports or surveys, there are very few books dealing only with Diophantine equations, and sometimes these are either very elementary or deal only with special aspects of the subject. It seems therefore desirable to produce a more representative account, and an attempt is now made to do this. I have tried to preserve the old spirit and traditions of Diophantine analysis, and to these I attach great importance.

It is hoped that all readers will find herein some results which are of interest to them and which do not require too much knowledge. Some well known elementary results have been included for the sake of completeness. Accounts have been given without undue generality of many results which seemed to me of greatest significance, and most representative of the subject. Note has been taken of various Diophantine problems, both classical and recent ones, which seemed worthy of special attention. I have included a number of results, really part of the subject but not usually found in accounts of Diophantine equations, and indicating something about their role in number theory. The material is arranged in a systematic way such that a basic idea runs through each chapter, and it is hoped that the presentation is reasonably self-contained.

The proofs of the results vary considerably. Some are very elementary and others are rather simple, making little demand upon specialized knowledge. This does not apply to the demonstration of the really important theorems. Many require a knowledge of the fundamental results for an algebraic number field, for example, the basis for the integers, the finite generation of the units and the finiteness of the number of classes of ideals. When more knowledge of algebraic numbers is required as for Fermat's last theorem, I state the results assumed in the proof. Occasionally a brief introductory account is given of relevant results or principles required, for example, of some algebraic geometry and the invariants and covariants of binary cubic and bi-quadratic forms, and also for local or p-adic applications.

This book had its origin in the lectures on Diophantine equations given at Cambridge (England), Toronto (Canada), Varenna (Italy), and Urbana (Illinois), and so the reader must not expect an exhaustive treatise. However, it seemed desirable to enlarge the scope of the book and in particular some mention is made of the more important and worthwhile results, especially recent ones.

A great deal of number theory also arises from the study of the solution in integers of a polynomial equation $f(x_1, x_2, \ldots, x_n) = 0$, and so our subject is coextensive with most of number theory. Hence it becomes necessary to make a choice of material, both classical and modern.

There is no need in this book to go into detail about general Diophantine problems whose study forms part of a general theory to be found in the usual treatises such as the representation of number by quadratic forms in several variables, or by norm forms in algebraic number fields.

No account has been given of theorems whose proofs are of an advanced analytical character such as the applications of the Hardy-Littlewood-Vinogradoff circle method, though many interesting and important results have been found in this way, for example, Waring's theorem on the representation of an integer as a sum of powers, and Davenport's theorem that every homogeneous cubic equation in at least 16 variables has an infinity of integer solutions.

Unless the results are of fundamental importance, arithmetical proofs have also been usually omitted when they are lengthy and complicated, or involve considerable details, or excessive numerical work, or are out of place in this book. Among such instances are Linnik's proof of Waring's theorem, and Siegel's theorem on the solution of the binomial equation $ax^l + by^l = c$. Many striking results on the solution of equations of the form $ax^m + by^n = c$ can be stated very simply but, unfortunately, their proofs require a surprisingly large amount of calculation and so are not discussed here. This applies to proofs of many simple and long sought results given by Ljunggren. An out-line, however, is given of some of the specially interesting ones.

I have also omitted a discussion of results which require too much pre-vious preparation and knowledge such as the modern developments linking Diophantine analysis with the new algebraic geometry and homological algebra. These have led to many new points of view as can be seen from Lang's book and Cassels' recent report.

Most of the book is concerned with the classical theory of the subject, in which the unknowns were in general elements of the rational field Q, and the solution of the equation involved only operations in this field. Occasionally solutions were considered in some quadratic and cubic fields, and more importantly in cyclotomic fields in connection with Fermat's last theorem. Further developments led to emphasis on solutions in fields other than Q, and in particular, in finite fields. This required a discussion of the solvability and the number of solutions of a polynomial congruence,

$$f(x) = f(x_1, x_2, \ldots, x_n) = 0 \quad (\text{mod } p^r),$$

where p is a prime number. Such congruences had previously arisen in the solution of some equations $f(x) = 0$, and in particular in the Hardy-Littlewood analytic solution of Waring's problem that every positive integer n can be expressed as a sum of k r-th powers of non-negative integers where k is independent of n.

Great advances have recently been made by the association of congruences with types of zeta-functions, and many important and suggestive results have been found. In particular, this has led to highly probable conjectures when $f(x) = 0$ is a plane cubic curve of genus one, and a new field of research has been opened up.

Sufficient has been said to show that Diophantine analysis draws upon resources from many branches of mathematics, for example, the higher arithmetic, algebra, geometry, analysis; not only the classical aspects of these subjects but also the most recent developments.

I have much pleasure in acknowledging my great indebtedness to the many writers on Diophantine equations, both ancient and modern, many of whom are not mentioned here. From these, I have learnt much and also derived inspiration. In fact, my interest in the subject was aroused in my school days by reading the chapters on Diophantine equations usually to be found in many of the algebra books of the first half of the nineteenth century. These except for Euler's algebra have long since been forgotten.

Among the writers on Diophantine Equations whom I have studied are Borevich and Shafarevich, Carmichael, Delone and Faddeev, Dickson, Lang, Nagell, Skolem. Many books on number theory also contain useful sections on Diophantine analysis. There may be mentioned those by Bachmann, Hardy and Wright, Landau, Le Veque, Nagell, Sierpenski, Uspensky-Heaslet. I have also consulted many papers and memoirs, in particular those by Billings, Birch and Swinnerton-Dyer, Cassels, Erdös, Fueter, Ljunggren, Nagell, Pocklington, Roth, Selmer, Skolem, Siegel. Many references have been given but the list is by no means complete, especially for the older results. For these Dickson's invaluable "History of the Theory of Numbers" may be consulted.

Nov. 1968   L. J. MORDELL

Contents

  1*

Acknowledgments

I have much pleasure in acknowledging my very great indebtedness to many colleagues for their numerous comments and suggestions. Among these are Dr A. Baker, Prof. Cassels, Prof. Chalk, Prof. Davenport, Mr Makowski, Mr H. Montgomery, Prof. Nagell, Dr M. Newman, Dr A. Rotkiewicz, Prof. Schinzel, Prof. de Witte. I am very grateful to all of them for their valuable assistance with the manuscript and proof sheets and the resulting clarification in the exposition. Prof. de Witt and Mr Montgomery should be given special mention.

Mr Montgomery also prepared the list of equations.

The book has profited from the great knowledge and the generous help of Prof. Nagell in reading the proof sheets.

I am especially indebted to Prof. Schinzel who made a most painstaking reading and careful scrutiny of the proof sheets. He corrected many errors, noted many obscurities, and suggested numerous improvements.

Finally, I should like to thank the Academic Press for the great help they have given me in preparing my manuscript for publication and for meeting my every wish. It has been a great pleasure to deal with them.

Feb. 1969   L. J. MORDELL

CHAPTER 1

Introduction

Preliminary

1. Let $x_1, x_2, \ldots, x_n$, say x, be n variables, and let $f(x_1, x_2, \ldots, x_n)$, say $f(x)$, be a polynomial in these variables with rational coefficients. There will be no loss of generality in supposing that the coefficients are integers since we shall be concerned with equations $f(x) = 0$. An obvious question is the

Problem. To find some or all of the solutions of $f(x) = 0$ in
   I. *rational numbers, i.e. in the field Q;*
   II. *rational integers, i.e. in the ring Z.*

Suppose first that $f(x)$ is a homogeneous polynomial. We ignore the trivial solution $x = 0$. Then the questions I and II are clearly† equivalent, and we can confine ourselves to integer solutions with $(x_1, x_2, \ldots, x_n) = 1$.

Suppose next that $f(x)$ is a non-homogeneous polynomial. On putting

$$x_1 = y_1/y_{n+1}, \ldots, x_n = y_n/y_{n+1},$$

we have a homogeneous equation

$$g(y_1, y_2, \ldots, y_n, y_{n+1}) = 0.$$

There is now a 1–1 correspondence between the rational values of x, and those integer values of y with $y_{n+1} \neq 0$, and $(y_1, y_2, \ldots, y_{n+1}) = 1$.

We may also have simultaneous equations of the type $f(x) = 0$, e.g.

$$f_1(x) = 0, \ldots, f_r(x) = 0.$$

These can be written as the single equation

$$f_1^2(x) + \cdots + f_r^2(x) = 0.$$

More generally we can impose restrictions upon the variables. Thus we can require them to be positive integers. The simplest significant problem then arising is $x_1 x_2 = n$, and the solutions of the natural questions arising from this lead in due course to the classical results on the divisor problem and the theory of prime numbers. We are also led to Waring's problem on the representation of integers as sums of rth powers. We can require variables to be prime numbers and then problems associated with Goldbach's theorem arise. We may also allow the variables to be algebraic integers, for example, Gaussian integers of the form $x + yi$ where x and y are rational integers.

† This statement due to Gauss is disputed by Dickson.[1,2]

The general problem suggests many questions. Can we find reasonably simple necessary conditions for the solvability of $f(x) = 0$? Are these conditions sufficient? Can we, having found some solutions, deduce from these others or an infinity of others, or all the solutions? What can be said about the number of solutions or their magnitudes in terms of the coefficients of $f(x)$? Questions may also be asked about the arithmetical properties of solutions.

2. *Necessary conditions for solvability.*

Theorem 1

Rational or integer solutions of $f(x) = 0$ can exist only if $f(x) = 0$ can be satisfied by real values of x.
Proof. Obvious.

Theorem 2

Integer solutions of the inhomogeneous equation $f(x) = 0$ can exist only if the congruence

$$f(x) \equiv 0 \,(\text{mod } M)$$

has solutions for all integers M.
Proof. Obvious.

The elementary properties of congruences show that we need only consider $M = p^{\alpha}$ where p runs through the primes and $\alpha = 1, 2, \ldots$.

Theorem 3

Integer solutions $x \neq 0$ of the homogeneous equation $f(x) = 0$ can exist only if the congruence

$$f(x) \equiv 0 \,(\text{mod } M),$$

has solutions for which $(x_1, x_2, \ldots, x_n, M) = 1$ for all integers M; and if in particular when $M = p^{\alpha}$, it has solutions for which not all x are divisible by p.

This is obvious since we may suppose $(x_1, x_2, \ldots, x_n) = 1$ in a homogeneous equation, and this x must satisfy $f(x) \equiv 0 \,(\text{mod } M)$.

It is also obvious that if an inhomogeneous equation $f(x) = 0$ implies that $x_1 \equiv x_2 \equiv \cdots \equiv x_n \equiv 0 \,(\text{mod } p^{\alpha})$, for given p and arbitrary large α, then $x = 0$ is the only solution.

Finally, if the equation $f(x) = 0$ implies that one variable, say x_1, is divisible by p for an infinity of primes p, then there can only be solutions with $x_1 = 0$.

REFERENCES

1. L. E. Dickson. Fallacies and misconceptions in diophantine analysis. A new method in diophantine analysis. *Bull. Amer. Math. Soc.*, **27** (1921), 312–319.
2. L. E. Dickson. "Modern Elementary Theory of Numbers". Univ. Chicago Press, Chicago (1939), Chapter IX.

CHAPTER 2

Equations Proved Impossible by Congruence Considerations

1. We now consider the

Problem. To find by congruence considerations, equations $f(x) = 0$, with either no integer solutions or only the solution $x = 0$.

This requires the application of some elementary results in number theory. Many of the results now given are classical. We begin with a preliminary discussion of the equation

$$x_1^r = a + bx_2, \qquad (1)$$

where r is an integer > 1. First, let $r = 2$ and so

$$x_1^2 = a + bx_2. \qquad (2)$$

This is solvable if and only if the congruences

$$x_1^2 \equiv a \,(\text{mod } 2^\alpha), \quad x_1^2 \equiv a \,(\text{mod } p^\beta), \quad x_1^2 \equiv a \,(\text{mod } q^\gamma), \ldots$$

are solvable, where $2^\alpha \,\|\, b$, i.e. 2^α is the highest power of 2 occurring in b, $p^\beta \,\|\, b \ldots$. For simplicity, we suppose $(a, b) = 1$. When $\alpha = 1$, the congruence is always solvable; when $\alpha = 2$ only if $a \equiv 1 \,(\text{mod } 4)$; when $\alpha = 3$ only if $a \equiv 1 \,(\text{mod } 8)$, and then it is also solvable for $\alpha > 3$. The congruence is solvable for all β if it is solvable for $\beta = 1$. Then a is called a quadratic residue of p, i.e. $(a/p) = 1$. If the congruence is insoluble, a is called a quadratic non-residue of p, i.e. $(a/p) = -1$. From these results, it follows that every prime divisor p of $x^2 - a$ for integer x is either a divisor of a, or can be represented by a finite number of arithmetic progressions. Thus if $p \mid (x^2 + c^2)$ and $p \neq 2$, then if $(p, c) = 1$, $p \equiv 1 \,(\text{mod } 4)$, but if $p \equiv 3 \,(\text{mod } 4)$, $p \mid c$.

Theorem 1

The equation

$$f(x_1, x_2, \ldots, x_n) = g(x) \qquad (3)$$

is impossible in integers if $f(x_1, x_2, \ldots, x_n)$ has a prime factor p which cannot be a divisor of $g(x)$, e.g. $g(x) = x^2 - a$ where $(a/p) = -1$.

Proof. Obvious.

Suppose next that $r = 3$ in (1). Then

$$x_1^3 = a + bx_2, \qquad (4)$$

and for simplicity we suppose that $(a, b) = 1$. Let $3^\alpha \parallel b$, $p^\beta \parallel b$, ... Then (4) is solvable if and only if

$$x_1^3 \equiv a \pmod{3^\alpha}, \quad x_1^3 \equiv a \pmod{p^\beta}, \quad x_1^3 \equiv a \pmod{q^\gamma}, \ldots \tag{5}$$

are solvable. When $\alpha = 1$, the first congruence is always solvable. When $\alpha = 2$, it is solvable only when $a \equiv \pm 1 \pmod 9$, and then it is solvable for all α. Take next the second congruence. When $p \equiv 2 \pmod 3$, it is solvable for all β. When $p \equiv 1 \pmod 3$, the condition for solvability is not so simple and it is not easy to specify the values of a for which the congruence is solvable. Then a is called a cubic residue of p and we write $(a/p)_3 = 1$. It might be noted that $(2/p)_3 = 1$ if and only if p can be represented in the form $p = x^2 + 27y^2$ with integers x and y. Similar remarks apply for other values of r.

2. *Congruences* mod M.

We now apply to various equations, congruences mod M, where M is a prime power. We commence with $M = 2^\alpha$.

$M = 4$.

The equation

$$x_1^2 + x_2^2 = 4x_3 + 3 \tag{6}$$

has no integer solutions.

For $x_1^2 \equiv 0, 1$, $x_2^2 \equiv 0, 1$, $x_1^2 + x_2^2 \equiv 0, 1, 2$.

The equation

$$x_1^2 + x_2^2 = (4a + 3)x_3^2 \tag{7}$$

has only the integer solution $x_1 = x_2 = x_3 = 0$.

This is obvious if $a < 0$, and so we need only consider $a \geqslant 0$. From (6), $x_3 \not\equiv 1 \pmod 2$, and so $x_3 \equiv 0 \pmod 2$, and then $x_1 \equiv x_2 \equiv 0 \pmod 2$. Since we may suppose $(x_1, x_2, x_3) = 1$, we have a contradiction unless $x_1 = x_2 = x_3 = 0$.

$M = 8$.

The equations

$$x_1^2 + 2x_2^2 = 8x_3 + 5 \quad or \quad 8x_3 + 7,$$

and
$$x_1^2 - 2x_2^2 = 8x_3 + 3 \quad or \quad 8x_3 + 5 \tag{8}$$

have no solutions.

For to mod 8, $x_1^2 \equiv 0, 1, 4$ and so $x_1^2 + 2x_2^2 \not\equiv 5, 7$, $x_1^2 - 2x_2^2 \not\equiv 3, 5$.

The equation

$$x_1^2 + x_2^2 + x_3^2 = 4^\alpha (8x_4 + 7) \tag{9}$$

has no solutions.

If $\alpha \geqslant 1$, $x_1 \equiv x_2 \equiv x_3 \equiv 0$ (mod 2), and so we need only consider $\alpha = 0$. But then $x_1^2 + x_2^2 + x_3^2 \not\equiv 7$ (mod 8).

The equation

$$ax_1^2 + bx_2^2 + cx_3^2 = 0, \qquad abc \neq 0, \qquad (x_1, x_2, x_3) = 1 \qquad (10)$$

has only the trivial solution $x_1 = 0$, $x_2 = 0$, $x_3 = 0$ *if either*

$$a \equiv b \equiv c \equiv 1 \ (\text{mod } 2) \quad and \quad a \equiv b \equiv c \ (\text{mod } 4),$$

or $\qquad a/2 \equiv b \equiv c \equiv 1 \ (\text{mod } 2) \quad and \quad b + c \equiv a \ or \ 4 \ (\text{mod } 8).$

The result is obvious in the first case since

$$x_1^2 + x_2^2 + x_3^2 \not\equiv 0 \ (\text{mod } 4).$$

In the second case, we write

$$ax_1^2 + bx_2^2 + cx_3^2 \equiv 0 \ (\text{mod } 8).$$

Clearly x_1, x_2, x_3 are not all odd since $a + b + c \not\equiv 0$ (mod 8). Also two of the x cannot be even and so only one can be even. This cannot be x_1 since $b + c \not\equiv 0$ (mod 8), nor x_2 since cx_3 is odd, nor x_3 since bx_2 is odd.

The equation

$$z^2 = (ax^2 + by^2)^2 - 2k(cx^2 + dy^2)^2 \qquad (11)$$

has no integer solutions $\neq (0, 0, 0)$ *if* $a + b \equiv 0$ (mod 2), $cd \equiv 1$ (mod 4), $k \equiv 1$ (mod 2).

Suppose first that $x \equiv 1$ (mod 2), $y \equiv 0$ (mod 2). Then

$$z^2 \equiv a^2 - 2c^2 \equiv -1 \ or \ 2 \ (\text{mod } 4),$$

and this is impossible. Similarly if $x \equiv 0$ (mod 2), $y \equiv 1$ (mod 2).

Suppose next that $x \equiv y \equiv 1$ (mod 2). Then

$$\left(\frac{z}{2}\right)^2 \equiv \left(\frac{a+b}{2}\right)^2 - 2k\left(\frac{c+d}{2}\right)^2 \ (\text{mod } 4)$$

$$\equiv -1 \ or \ 2 \ (\text{mod } 4),$$

since $c + d \equiv 2$ (mod 4).

$M = 16.$

The equation

$$ax_1^4 + bx_2^4 + cx_3^4 + dx_4^4 = 0, \qquad (x_1, x_2, x_3, x_4) = 1 \qquad (12)$$

has only the trivial solution $x = 0$ *if*

    I. $a \not\equiv 0$ (mod 16), *etc.*

    II. $a + b \not\equiv 0$, $a + c \not\equiv 0$ (mod 16), *etc.*

    III. $a + b + c \not\equiv 0$, $a + b + d \not\equiv 0$ (mod 16), *etc.*

    IV. $a + b + c + d \not\equiv 0$ (mod 16).

Since $x_1^4 \equiv 0$ or $1 \pmod{16}$, these conditions exclude in turn one odd value, two odd values etc. for the variables. A simple instance occurs if we take a, b, c, d to be congruent mod 16 to any distinct four of 1, 2, 3, 4, 5, 6.

$M = 2^\alpha$.

The equation

$$ax_1^2 + bx_2^2 + cx_3^2 = 2dx_1x_2x_3, \qquad (13)$$

where $a \equiv b \equiv c \equiv \pm 1 \pmod{4}$ has only the solution $x_1 = x_2 = x_3 = 0$.

Obviously x_1, x_2, x_3 cannot all be odd, for if one is even, so are the others since then

$$x_1^2 + x_2^2 + x_3^2 \equiv 0 \pmod{4}.$$

Put $x_1 = 2X_1, x_2 = 2X_2, x_3 = 2X_3$. Then

$$aX_1^2 + bX_2^2 + cX_3^2 = 4dX_1X_2X_3.$$

Similarly X_1, X_2, X_3 are all even. Hence all the x must be zero since they are divisible by 2^α where α is arbitrary.

$M = 32$.

The equation

$$(a_1x_1^2 + a_2x_2^2 + a_3x_3^2 + a_4x_4^2)(b_1x_1^2 + b_2x_2^2 + b_3x_3^2 + b_4x_4^2)$$
$$= 2k(c_1x_1^2 + c_2x_2^2 + c_3x_3^2 + c_4x_4^2)(d_1x_1^2 + d_2x_2^2 + d_3x_3^2 + d_4x_4^2) \quad (14)$$

has only the trivial solution $x = 0$ if the a, b, c, d are all odd, and

$$a_1 \equiv a_2 \equiv a_3 \equiv a_4 \pmod{8}, \qquad b_1 \equiv b_2 \equiv b_3 \equiv b_4 \pmod{8},$$

$$(c_1 + c_2 + c_3 + c_4)(d_1 + d_2 + d_3 + d_4) \equiv 0 \pmod{16}.$$

We may suppose without loss of generality that

$$a_1x_1^2 + a_2x_2^2 + a_3x_3^2 + a_4x_4^2 \equiv 0 \pmod{2}.$$

Then either

I. $x_1 \equiv x_2 \equiv x_3 \equiv x_4 \equiv 1 \pmod{2}$,

or, say,

II. $x_1 \equiv x_2 \equiv 1 \pmod{2}, x_3 \equiv x_4 \equiv 0 \pmod{2}$.

For I, $a_1x_1^2 + a_2x_2^2 + a_3x_3^2 + a_4x_4^2 \equiv 4 \pmod{8}$, and so the left-hand side of (14) is $\equiv 16 \pmod{32}$. The right-hand side is $\equiv 0 \pmod{32}$, i.e. a contradiction. For II, $a_1x_1^2 + a_2x_2^2 + a_3x_3^2 + a_4x_4^2 \equiv a_1 + a_2 \equiv 2 \pmod{4}$, and so the left-hand side of (14) is $\equiv 4 \pmod{8}$. The right-hand side is $\equiv 0 \pmod{8}$, i.e. a contradiction.

$M = 3^\alpha$.

M = 3.
  The equation

$$(3a + 1)x_1^2 + (3b + 1)x_2^2 = 3c, \quad c \not\equiv 0 \,(\text{mod } 3) \tag{15}$$

has no integer solutions.
  Here $x_1^2 + x_2^2 \equiv 0 \,(\text{mod } 3)$, and since $x_1^2 \equiv 0, 1 \,(\text{mod } 3)$, $x_1 \equiv x_2 \equiv 0 \,(\text{mod } 3)$, and this is impossible.

M = 9.
  The equation

$$x_1^3 + x_2^3 + x_3^3 = 9x_4 \pm 4 \tag{16}$$

has no integer solutions.
This is obvious since $x_1^3 \equiv 0, \pm 1 \,(\text{mod } 9)$.
  The equation

$$x_1^3 + 2x_2^3 + 4x_3^3 = 9x_4^3, \qquad (x_1, x_2, x_3, x_4) = 1 \tag{17}$$

has only the trivial solution $x = 0$.
Here $x_1^3 + 2x_2^3 + 4x_3^3 \equiv 0 \,(\text{mod } 9)$. The only solution of this is $x_1 \equiv x_2 \equiv x_3 \equiv 0 \,(\text{mod } 3)$, and then $x_4 \equiv 0 \,(\text{mod } 3)$.
  The equation

$$ax^3 + 3bx^2y + 3cxy^2 + dy^3 = z^3 \tag{18}$$

has no integer solutions if

$$a \equiv d \equiv 4 \,(\text{mod } 9), \qquad b \equiv 0 \,(\text{mod } 3), \qquad c \equiv \pm 1 \,(\text{mod } 3).$$

  We may suppose $(x, y, z) = 1$. Clearly $xy \not\equiv 0 \,(\text{mod } 3)$, since $4x^3 \equiv z^3 \,(\text{mod } 9)$ requires $x \equiv z \equiv y \equiv 0 \,(\text{mod } 3)$. From (18), $z \equiv ax + dy \,(\text{mod } 3)$,

$$z^3 \equiv a^3x^3 + 3a^2dx^2y + 3ad^2xy^2 + d^3y^3 \,(\text{mod } 9),$$

and so

$$\left(\frac{a - a^3}{3}\right)x^3 + (b - a^2d)x^2y + (c - ad^2)xy^2 + \left(\frac{d - d^3}{3}\right)y^3 \equiv 0 \,(\text{mod } 3).$$

Since to mod 3, $x^3 \equiv x$, $x^2 \equiv 1$, we have

$$x + (b - 1)y + (c - 1)x + y \equiv 0 \,(\text{mod } 3), \quad \text{or} \quad x \equiv 0 \,(\text{mod } 3),$$

and this has been excluded.
  The result implies that the equation

$$ax^3 + 3bx^2y + 3cxy^2 + dy^3 = 1$$

has no rational solutions.

$M = 7$.

The equation

$$(7a + 1)x_1^3 + (7b + 2)x_2^3 + (7c + 4)x_3^3 + (7d + 1)x_1x_2x_3 = 0,$$
$$(x_1, x_2, x_3) \equiv 1, \quad (19)$$

has only the trivial solution $x = 0$.

Here $x_1^3 + 2x_2^3 + 4x_3^3 + x_1x_2x_3 \equiv 0 \pmod 7$.

Also $x_1^3 \equiv 0, \pm 1 \pmod 7$. It suffices to show that $x_1 \equiv x_2 \equiv x_3 \equiv 0 \pmod 7$; if $x_3 \equiv 0$, $x_1^3 + 2x_2^3 \equiv 0$ and then $x_1 \equiv x_2 \equiv 0$: if $x_3 \not\equiv 0$, we can put $x_1 \equiv X_1x_3, x_2 \equiv X_2x_3$, and then

$$X_1^3 + 2X_2^3 + X_1X_2 + 4 \equiv 0.$$

Clearly $X_1X_2 \not\equiv 0$, and so $X_1^3 \equiv \pm 1$, $X_2^3 \equiv \pm 1$. This leads to four impossible cases since

  1. $X_1^3 \equiv X_2^3 \equiv 1$ gives $X_1X_2 \equiv 0$,
  2. $X_1^3 \equiv X_2^3 \equiv -1$ gives $X_1X_2 \equiv -1$, i.e. $X_1^3X_2^3 \equiv -1$,
  3. $X_1^3 \equiv -X_2^3 \equiv 1$ gives $X_1X_2 \equiv 4$, i.e. $X_1^3X_2^3 \equiv 1$,
  4. $X_1^3 \equiv -X_2^3 \equiv -1$ gives $X_1X_2 \equiv 2$, i.e. $X_1^3X_2^3 \equiv 1$.

$M = 7^2$.

The equation

$$x_1^3 + 2x_2^3 = 7(x_3^3 + 2x_4^3), \quad (x_1, x_2, x_3, x_4) = 1 \quad (20)$$

has only the trivial solution $x = 0$.

Here $x_1^3 + 2x_2^3 \equiv 0 \pmod 7$ and so $x_1 = 7X_1, x_2 = 7X_2$. Then

$$7^2(X_1^3 + 2X_2^3) = x_3^3 + 2x_4^3.$$

This gives $x_3 = 7X_3, x_4 = 7X_4$ and then $(x_1, x_2, x_3, x_4) \geqslant 7$.

An obvious deduction is that the equation

$$x^3 + 2y^3 = 7(z^3 + 2) \quad (21)$$

has no rational solutions.

$M = p^\alpha$, p a prime.

The equation

$$x_1^2 + 1 = px_2, \quad p \equiv 3 \pmod 4 \quad (22)$$

is impossible.

Obvious since $(-1/p) = -1$.

The equation

$$x_1^2 + 1 = ax_2, \quad (23)$$

is impossible if a has a prime factor $\equiv 3 \pmod 4$.

So for the equations

$$x_1^2 - 2 = px_2 \quad \text{if} \quad p \equiv \pm 3 \ (\text{mod} \ 8) \tag{24}$$

and
$$x_1^2 + 2 = px_2 \quad \text{if} \quad p \equiv 5, 7 \ (\text{mod} \ 8). \tag{25}$$

The equation

$$x_1^3 - 2 = 7x_2 \tag{26}$$

is impossible.

Proof. Obvious.

It is more difficult to deal with the equation

$$x_1^3 - 2 = px_2 \tag{27}$$

if $p \equiv 1 \ (\text{mod} \ 3)$. As already stated on page 4, (27) is solvable, i.e. 2 is a cubic residue of p if and only if for integers a and b

$$p = a^2 + 27b^2.$$

The equation

$$x_1^2 + x_2^2 - p(x_3^2 + x_4^2) = 0, \qquad p \equiv 3 \ (\text{mod} \ 4), \ (x_1, x_2, x_3, x_4) = 1 \tag{28}$$

has only the solution $x = 0$.

Here $x_1^2 + x_2^2 \equiv 0 \ (\text{mod} \ p)$, and so $x_1 = pX_1$, $x_2 = pX_2$. Then $x_3 = pX_3$, $x_4 = pX_4$ etc.

The equation

$$ax_1^3 + bpx_2^3 + cp^2x_3^3 = 0, \quad (x_1, x_2, x_3) = 1, \ abc \not\equiv 0 \ (\text{mod} \ p) \tag{29}$$

has only the solution $x = 0$.

Here $x_1 \equiv 0 \ (\text{mod} \ p)$ and so $x_1 = pX_1$. Then

$$ap^2X_1^3 + bx_2^3 + cpx_3^3 = 0.$$

Similarly $x_2 \equiv 0 \ (\text{mod} \ p)$ and $x_2 = pX_2$. This leads to $x_3 \equiv 0 \ (\text{mod} \ p)$.

A more general result[1] is given by the

Theorem 2

Let $f(x, y, z)$ be a cubic homogeneous polynomial such that the only solution of $f(x, y, z) \equiv 0 \ (\text{mod} \ p)$, p a prime, is $x \equiv y \equiv z \equiv 0 \ (\text{mod} \ p)$. Let $f_s(x_s, y_s, z_s)$, $s = 1, 2, 3$, be three such polynomials each associated with the same prime p. Then the equation in nine variables

$$f_1(x_1, y_1, z_1) + pf_2(x_2, y_2, z_2)$$

$$+ p^2f_3(x_3, y_3, z_3) + p^3 \sum_{l,m,n=1}^{3} a_{lmn}x_ly_mz_n = 0, \tag{30}$$

where the suffixes l, m, n in any one term are all different, has only the trivial solution $x_s = y_s = z_s = 0$, $(s = 1, 2, 3)$.

A congruence mod p shows that $x_1 = pX_1, y_1 = pY_1, z_1 = pZ_1$. Similarly we obtain $x_2 = pX_2, y_2 = pY_2, z_2 = pZ_2$ and $x_3 = pX_3, y_3 = pY_3, z_3 = pZ_3$, etc.

A similar result holds for equations of the nth degree in n variables.

An application with $p = 7$ is given from (19) by

$$f(x, y, z) = (7a + 1)x^3 + (7b + 2)y^3 + (7c + 4)z^3 + (7d + 1)xyz. \quad (31)$$

For other instances, take an equation irreducible over the rational field Q with three roots θ_1, θ_2, θ_3, and a prime p such that p is a prime in the field $Q(\theta_1, \theta_2, \theta_3)$. Let $\omega_1^{(r)}, \omega_2^{(r)}, \omega_3^{(r)}$ be a basis of the integers in the field $Q(\theta_r)$, $(r = 1, 2, 3)$, the $\omega_1^{(r)}$ denoting the conjugates of $\omega_1^{(1)} = \omega_1$. Then we can take

$$f(x, y, z) = N(x\omega_1 + y\omega_2 + z\omega_3),$$

N denoting the norm in the cubic field, i.e. the product of three conjugate expressions. For if $f(x, y, z) \equiv 0 \pmod{p}$, since p is a prime in $Q(\theta_1, \theta_2, \theta_3)$, we must have for some r

$$x\omega_1^{(r)} + y\omega_2^{(r)} + z\omega_3^{(r)} \equiv 0 \pmod{p}.$$

Since the ω are a basis, $x \equiv y \equiv z \equiv 0 \pmod{p}$.

For the application above, we note that

$$x^3 + 2y^3 + 4z^3 + xyz \equiv 0 \pmod{7}$$

can be written as

$$N(x + y\sqrt[3]{2} + z\sqrt[3]{4}) \equiv 0 \pmod{7}.$$

Since 2 is not a cubic residue of 7, we have $x \equiv y \equiv z \equiv 0 \pmod{7}$.

The method of proof for equation (29) in nine variables is of some interest since Artin has stated the

Conjecture

A homogeneous equation $f(x) = 0$ of degree r with $n > r^2$ variables always has a non-trivial integer solution in any p-adic field, i.e. as a congruence mod p^α, for all primes p and integers $\alpha > 0$.

This has been long known for $r = 2$, $n = 5$ and is proved in Chapter 7; and it has been proved recently for $r = 3$.

A counterexample with $r = 4$, $n = 18$, has just been found by Terjanian[2]:

Theorem 3

Let $f(x) = x_1^4 + x_2^4 + x_3^4 - x_2^2x_3^2 - x_3^2x_1^2 - x_2^2x_1^2 - x_1x_2x_3(x_1 + x_2 + x_3)$. Then the equation

$$f(x) + f(y) + f(z) - 4(f(u) + f(v) + f(w)) = 0, \quad (32)$$

where $(x, y, z, u, v, w) = 1$, has only the trivial zero solution since there is no 2-adic solution.

We prove first that $f(x) \equiv 1 \pmod{4}$, unless $x_1 \equiv x_2 \equiv x_3 \equiv 0 \pmod{2}$. We have three cases.

1. If $x_1 \equiv x_2 \equiv x_3 \equiv 1 \pmod{2}$, say, $x_1 = 2X_1 + 1$, etc.,

$$f(x) \equiv -x_2 x_3 - x_3 x_1 - x_1 x_2 \pmod{4}$$
$$\equiv -\sum (1 + 2X_2 + 2X_3) \pmod{4}$$
$$\equiv -3 \pmod{4}.$$

2. If $x_1 \equiv x_2 \equiv 1 \pmod{2}$, $x_3 \equiv 0 \pmod{2}$,

$$f(x) \equiv 1 - x_2 x_3 - x_1 x_3 \equiv 1 \pmod{4}.$$

3. If $x_1 \equiv 1 \pmod{2}$, $x_2 \equiv x_3 \equiv 0 \pmod{2}$,

$$f(x) \equiv 1 \pmod{4}.$$

Hence $f(x) \equiv 0 \pmod{2}$ only when $x \equiv 0 \pmod{2}$. The equation requires $x \equiv 0 \pmod{2}$, $y \equiv 0 \pmod{2}$, $z \equiv 0 \pmod{2}$ since otherwise the equation is impossible when considered as a congruence $\pmod{4}$. Hence we must have $x = 2\mathscr{X}$, $y = 2\mathscr{Y}$, $z = 2\mathscr{Z}$, and then

$$f(u) + f(v) + f(w) - 4(f(\mathscr{X}) + f(\mathscr{Y}) + f(\mathscr{Z})) = 0.$$

This gives $u = 2\mathscr{U}$, $v = 2\mathscr{V}$, $w = 2\mathscr{W}$, and this contradicts $(x, y, z, u, v, w) = 1$.

It has been shown by Shanuel that for large p, there exists r such that for a form $f(x)$ of degree r, with more than $r^2 + 1$ variables, $f(x) \not\equiv 0 \pmod{p^\alpha}$ for a certain α unless $x = 0$. This has been proved for all p by J. Browkin[3] who has also found other results.

By ideas completely different from those above, a non-constructive proof[4] has been given of the

Theorem 4

For every natural number r, there exists a fixed set $S(r)$ of primes such that for every prime p not in $S(r)$, every homogenous equation $f(x) = 0$ of degree r and with $n > r^2$ variables, always has a non-trivial solution in the p-adic fields.

REFERENCES

1. L. J. Mordell. A remark on indeterminate equations in several variables. *J. Lond. Math. Soc.*, **12** (1937), 127–129.
2. G. Terjanian. Un contre-exemple à une conjecture d'Artin. *Comptes Rendus Acad. Sci. Paris*, **262** (1966), 612.
3. J. Browkin. On forms over p-adic fields. *Bull. Acad. Polon. Sci. Sér. des sci. math. astr. et phys.*, **14** (1966), 489–492.
4. J. Axil and S. Kochen. Diophantine problems over local fields I. *Amer. J. Math.*, **87** (1965), 605–630.

CHAPTER 3

Equations Involving Sums of Squares

Theorem 1

The general integer solution of the equation

$$x_1^2 + x_2^2 + \cdots + x_n^2 = x^2, \quad (x_1, x_2, \ldots, x_n) = 1, \; x > 0, \tag{1}$$

is given by

$$dx_r = 2X_r X_n \; (r = 1, 2, \ldots, n-1), \quad dx_n = X_n^2 - X_1^2 - \cdots - X_{n-1}^2,$$
$$dx = X_n^2 + X_1^2 + \cdots + X_{n-1}^2, \tag{2}$$

where the X are arbitrary integers with $(X_1, \ldots, X_n) = 1$ *and* $d > 0$ *is taken so that* $(x_1, x_2, \ldots, x_n) = 1$. *For given* $x_1, x_2, \ldots, x_n$, *there are two sets of values for the ratios* $X_1 : X_2 : \ldots : X_n$.

Put $\qquad x_1 = tX_1, \ldots, x_{n-1} = tX_{n-1}, \qquad x_n = tX_n - x.$

Then $\qquad\qquad\qquad t(X_1^2 + X_2^2 + \cdots + X_n^2) = 2xX_n,$

$$t(X_n^2 - X_1^2 - \cdots - X_{n-1}^2) = 2x_n X_n,$$

and so

$$\frac{x_1}{2X_1 X_n} = \cdots = \frac{x_{n-1}}{2X_{n-1}X_n} = \frac{x_n}{X_n^2 - X_1^2 \cdots - X_{n-1}^2} = \frac{x}{X_n^2 + X_1^2 \cdots + X_{n-1}^2}, \tag{3}$$

and (2) follows.

Conversely, suppose that the $x_1, \ldots, x_n$ are given in (3). We now solve for the X. From homogeneity considerations, it suffices to take $X_n = 1$, $x = 1$. Then

$$X_1 = vx_1, \ldots, X_{n-1} = vx_{n-1},$$

say, whence from (3),

$$2v = 1 + v^2(x_1^2 + \cdots + x_{n-1}^2),$$

$$v^2(1 \quad \tfrac{2}{n}) - 2v + 1 = 0,$$

$$(v(1 + x_n) - 1)(v(1 - x_n) - 1) = 0,$$

and the result follows.

We now examine some particular cases. We take $n = 2$ and write

$$x^2 + y^2 = z^2, \quad (x, y) = 1, \; z > 0. \tag{4}$$

Here

$$x = \frac{2XY}{d}, \qquad y = \frac{Y^2 - X^2}{d}, \qquad z = \frac{Y^2 + X^2}{d}, \quad (X, Y) = 1. \tag{5}$$

Clearly $d = (2XY, Y^2 - X^2, Y^2 + X^2) = 1$ or 2.

If $d = 1$, then X, Y cannot both be odd or even, and so we have the solution when x is even. If $d = 2$, X, Y are both odd and replacing them by $Y \pm X$ we have from (5),

$$x = Y^2 - X^2, \qquad y = 2XY, \qquad z = Y^2 + X^2. \tag{6}$$

This is the solution when y is even.

The equation

$$x^2 + y^2 = 2z^2, \quad (x, y) = 1, z > 0. \tag{7}$$

We cannot have z even since then $x \equiv y \equiv 0 \pmod 2$.
Hence x, y are both odd, and so we can put

$$x = X + Y, \qquad y = X - Y, \quad (X, Y) = 1,$$

and $$X^2 + Y^2 = z^2.$$

Then $X = a^2 - b^2, \qquad Y = 2ab$ or $X = 2ab, \qquad Y = a^2 - b^2.$

The solution of (4) may also be found by arithmetical considerations. We need only consider non-negative solutions. Clearly x, y are not both odd since then $x^2 \equiv y^2 \equiv 1 \pmod 4$, and $z^2 \equiv 2 \pmod 4$. Hence z is odd. We consider only the solutions with even y. Write

$$y^2 = z^2 - x^2 = (z - x)(z + x),$$

then $(z - x, z + x) = 2$ since x, z are odd. Hence

$$z + x = 2Y^2, \qquad z - x = 2X^2, \qquad y^2 = 4X^2Y^2,$$

and so $$x = Y^2 - X^2, \qquad y = 2XY, \qquad z = Y^2 + X^2.$$

Clearly every non-negative solution (x, y) leads to a non-negative (X, Y).

The general solution of (4) can also be found very simply by applying the arithmetic theory of the Gaussian integers $x + iy$ where x, y are rational integers. The main results required are as follows. The units, that is divisors of unity, are ± 1, $\pm i$. The primes $p \equiv 1 \pmod 4$ can be expressed in the form $x^2 + y^2$ with integers x, y. The primes $q \equiv 3 \pmod 4$ cannot be expressed in this way. Since $2 = i(1 - i)^2$, 2 is not a prime. Hence the primes in the complex theory are typified by the factors $x + iy$ of p, by q, and by $1 - i$. A Euclidean algorithm holds for the Gaussian integers, and so factorization is unique if units and the order of the prime factors are disregarded.

We write (4) as

$$(x + iy)(x - iy) = z^2.$$

As z is odd, the two factors are relatively prime for a common factor would divide $2x$, $2iy$. Hence

$$x + iy = (X + iY)^2 \quad \text{or} \quad i(X + iY)^2,$$

since $-1 = i^2$ can be absorbed in the square. This gives the result.

The equation

$$x^2 + y^2 = pz^2, \quad z > 0, \tag{8}$$

where p is a prime $\equiv 1 \pmod 4$ and so $p = r^2 + s^2$.
All the integer solutions are given by

$$x + yi = (\pm r \pm is)(Z + iW)^2,$$

where Z, W are integers and the $\pm$ signs are independent of each other.

We now take $n = 3$ and write

$$x^2 + y^2 + z^2 = w^2, \quad (x, y, z) = 1, \ w > 0, \tag{9}$$

Clearly only one of x, y, z can be odd, say z, and so it suffices to consider the equation

$$4x^2 + 4y^2 + z^2 = w^2, \quad (x, y, z) = 1. \tag{10}$$

We give a general solution different from (2) by using complex numbers. This has been presented by Carmichael[1] without using them as

$$x = XZ - YW, \qquad y = XW + YZ,$$
$$z = X^2 + Y^2 - Z^2 - W^2, \qquad w = X^2 + Y^2 + Z^2 + W^2. \tag{11}$$

We have $\qquad\qquad 4x^2 + 4y^2 = w^2 - z^2.$

Hence $\qquad\qquad w - z = 2f, \qquad w + z = 2(x^2 + y^2)/f, \tag{12}$

where, by adjusting the sign of z, we may suppose that f is odd. Suppose that $x \equiv y \equiv 0 \pmod{q^\alpha}$, but not $\pmod{q^{\alpha+1}}$, where q is a prime $\equiv 3 \pmod 4$. It follows then that either $(f, q) = 1$ or $f \equiv 0 \pmod{q^{2\alpha}}$. For if $f \equiv 0 \pmod{q^\beta}$, but not $q^{\beta+1}$ and $\beta < 2\alpha$, then also $w \equiv z \equiv 0 \pmod q$. Write

$$x + iy = \prod (a_r + ib),$$

for the decomposition into complex primes. Then f as a divisor of $x^2 + y^2$ is either prime to q or divisible by $q^{2\alpha}$ and so can be expressed as a sum of two squares, and then has a representation

$$f = \prod (a_s^2 + b_s^2) = Z^2 + W^2,$$

where the a_s, b_s are included among the a_r, b_r, and in which we can take

$$Z + iW = \prod (a_s + ib_s).$$

Then $$x + iy = (X + iY)(Z + iW)$$

where X, Y are rational integers. This with (12) gives (11).

The equation

$$x^2 + y^2 = z^2 + w^2. \tag{13}$$

The complete solution is given by

$$2x = d_1 X + d_2 Y, \qquad 2z = d_1 X - d_2 Y,$$
$$2w = d_1 Y + d_2 X, \qquad 2y = d_1 Y - d_2 X, \tag{14}$$

where d_1, d_2 are arbitrary integers.

We deduce this from the solution of

$$AB = CD.$$

Write $\qquad (A, C) = d_1 \quad$ and so $\quad A = d_1 X, \; C = d_1 Z,$

$\qquad\qquad (B, D) = d_2 \quad$ and so $\quad B = d_2 Y, \; D = d_2 W,$

then $\qquad\qquad XY = ZW.$

Since $(Y, W) = 1$, and $(X, Z) = 1$, $X = \pm W$, $Y = \pm Z$, and so $A = d_1 X$, $B = d_2 Y$, $C = \pm d_1 Y$, $D = \pm d_2 X$. Write now

$$(x + z)(x - z) = (w + y)(w - y).$$

Hence $\qquad x + z = d_1 X, \qquad x - z = d_2 Y,$

$\qquad\qquad w + y = \pm d_1 Y, \qquad w - y = \pm d_2 X.$

Then the result follows on replacing $\pm w$, $\pm y$ by w, y.

REFERENCE

1. R. D. Carmichael. "Diophantine Analysis". John Wiley & Sons, New York (1915).

CHAPTER 4

Quartic Equations with only Trivial Solutions

1. We shall consider some quartic equations of the form $f(x^2, y^2, z^2) = 0$ which have only trivial solutions, e.g. those given by $xy = 0$. Equations of the form

$$ax^4 + bx^2y^2 + cy^4 = dz^2 \tag{1}$$

have a long history going back to Fermat and Euler as can be seen from the second volume of Dickson's "History of the Theory of Numbers". Many of them can be dealt with by elementary means requiring only the obvious

Lemma
    Let $k = k_1k_2$ be the factorizations of k with $(k_1, k_2) = 1$. Then the general integer solution of the equation

$$XY = kZ^2, \quad (X, Y) = 1, Z \neq 0,$$

is given by

$$X = \pm k_1 P^2, \qquad Y = \pm k_2 Q^2, \qquad Z = \pm PQ,$$

where P, Q are arbitrary integers with $(Pk_1, Qk_2) = 1$.
The really classical equation is that due to Fermat and given as

Theorem 1
    The equation

$$x^4 + y^4 = z^2 \tag{2}$$

has no integer solutions with $xy \neq 0$ (and so no rational solutions with $xy \neq 0$).
    We need only consider the solutions with $x \geqslant 0, y \geqslant 0, z \geqslant 0$ and $(x, y) = 1$. Clearly x and y cannot both be odd, and so we need only consider $x \equiv 1$, $y \equiv 0 \pmod 2$. Hence by (6) of chapter 3,

$$x^2 = a^2 - b^2, \qquad y^2 = 2ab, \qquad z = a^2 + b^2,$$

$a \geqslant b \geqslant 0, (a, b) = 1; (x, b) = 1; a \equiv 1, b \equiv 0 \pmod 2$.

Hence $\qquad x = p^2 - q^2, \qquad b = 2pq, \qquad a = p^2 + q^2,$

where $p \geqslant q \geqslant 0, (p, q) = 1$, and p and q are not both odd.

Now $\qquad\qquad y^2 = 2ab = 4pq(p^2 + q^2).$

Since $p, q, p^2 + q^2$ are relatively prime to each other in pairs,

$$p = r^2, \qquad q = s^2, \qquad p^2 + q^2 = t^2, \quad r \geqslant 0, s \geqslant 0, t \geqslant 0, (r, s) = 1,$$

and so
$$r^4 + s^4 = t^2.$$

Also

$$x = r^4 - s^4, \qquad y = 2rst, \qquad z = r^8 + 6r^4s^4 + s^8.$$

If $xy = 0$, then $rst(r - s) = 0$. Clearly $r \neq s$ and so solutions with $xy \neq 0$ correspond to solutions with $rs \neq 0$ and *vice versa*. Hence any solution x, y, z with $xy \neq 0$ leads to a solution r, s, t with $rs \neq 0$ and $t < \sqrt[4]{z}$, since $z > (r^4 + s^4)^2 = t^4$. The process can be continued and leads to a new solution r_1, s_1, t_1 with $r_1s_1 \neq 0$ and $t_1 < \sqrt[4]{t}$. The t, t_1, etc., form a sequence of decreasing positive integers and so we arrive at a stage when $t_n = 1$ and a contradiction arises, and then $r_n s_n = 0$.

This method is the so-called method of infinite descent and is due to Fermat. It has many important applications in number theory. The proof could have been slightly shortened if we had assumed in the beginning that x, y, z was a solution of equation (2) with least z, but it is often convenient in some questions to make the descent.

Corollary
   The equation

$$Y^2 = X^4 + 1 \tag{3}$$

has only the rational solutions $X = 0, Y = \pm 1$.
For if $X = x/y$ where $(x, y) = 1$, then $Y = z/y^2$, and

$$x^4 + y^4 = z^2.$$

Theorem 2
   The equation

$$x^4 - y^4 = z^2, \quad (x, y) = 1 \tag{4}$$

has no integer solutions except $x^2 = y^2 = 1$ *and* $x^2 = 1, y = 0$.
For these solutions $xyz = 0$, and we suppose now that $xyz \neq 0$. Let $x > 0, y > 0, z > 0$ be that solution for which x is least. Clearly x is odd and then y may be even or odd.
   If $y \equiv 1 \pmod{2}$, then

$$x^2 = a^2 + b^2, \qquad y^2 = a^2 - b^2, \qquad z = 2ab, \quad (a, b) = 1, a > b > 0,$$

and so
$$x^2y^2 = a^4 - b^4.$$

This is a case of equation (4) and since $a < x$, we have a contradiction.

If $y \equiv 0 \pmod 2$, then

$$x^2 = a^2 + b^2, \qquad y^2 = 2ab, \quad (a, b) = 1, a > 0, b > 0,$$

and we may suppose that a is even and b is odd. Then

$$a = 2p^2, \qquad b = q^2, \qquad q \equiv 1 \pmod 2, \quad (p, q) = 1, p > 0, q > 0$$

and so

$$x^2 = 4p^4 + q^4, \qquad y = 2pq.$$

Hence

$$p^2 = rs, \qquad q^2 = r^2 - s^2, \quad (r, s) = 1, r > s > 0;$$

and so

$$r = u^2, \qquad s = v^2, \quad (u, v) = 1, u > v > 0.$$

Then

$$u^4 - v^4 = q^2.$$

Also

$$u = \sqrt{r} \leqslant p < \sqrt{x},$$

and this contradicts the definition of x.

Corollary

The only integer solutions of

$$x^4 + y^4 = 2z^2, \quad (x, y) = 1 \tag{5}$$

are given by $x^2 = y^2 = 1$.

For x, y are both odd and

$$z^4 - x^4 y^4 = \left(\frac{x^4 - y^4}{2}\right)^2.$$

Corollary

If we replace x, y by $x \pm y$, we see that the only integer solutions of

$$x^4 + 6x^2 y^2 + y^4 = z^2, \quad (x, y) = 1 \tag{6}$$

are given by $x^2 = 1, y = 0$ and $x = 0, y^2 = 1$.

Using this we now prove

Theorem 3

The only integer solutions of

$$x^4 - 6x^2 y^2 + y^4 = z^2, \quad (x, y) = 1 \tag{6'}$$

are given by $x = 0$ or $y = 0$.

We may suppose that $x > y > 0$.

Write

$$(x^2 - y^2)^2 - 4x^2 y^2 = z^2,$$

and so

$$(x^2 - y^2 + z)(x^2 - y^2 - z) = 4x^2 y^2.$$

We show now that 2 is the greatest common divisor of the two left-hand factors. We cannot have $x \equiv 1, y \equiv 1 \pmod 2$, for then $z^2 \equiv -4 \pmod{16}$.

If $x \equiv 1$, $y \equiv 0 \pmod 2$, then z is odd and the greatest common divisor divides $2z$, and so is 2. Similarly, if $x \equiv 0$, $y \equiv 1 \pmod 2$. Both factors are obviously positive and so

$$x^2 - y^2 + z = 2a^2, \quad x^2 - y^2 - z = 2b^2, \quad xy = ab, \, a > 0, \, b > 0, \, (a, b) = 1.$$

Then
$$x^2 - y^2 = a^2 + b^2,$$

and so
$$(x^2 + y^2)^2 = (a^2 + b^2)^2 + 4a^2b^2$$
$$= a^4 + 6a^2b^2 + b^4.$$

Hence $ab = 0$ from equation (6) and then $xy = 0$.

Equations of the form

$$x^4 + kx^2y^2 + y^4 = z^2, \quad (x, y) = 1, \tag{7}$$

where we may suppose that $x \geqslant 0$, $y \geqslant 0$, have played an important part in the early history of the subject and Euler wrote many papers on the equation. The problem has usually been to show that the only solutions are given by $xy = 0$, and occasionally further solutions $x = y = 1$. A list of the values of k for which this is so has been given by Pocklington[1] who has also found some general results. Thus there are only solutions with $xy = 0$ of

$$(x^2 + y^2)^2 - nx^2y^2 = z^2$$

if $n \equiv 1, 5, 7 \pmod 8$, $n - 4 = p^{2n+1}$, p a prime, and if n is not divisible by a prime $\equiv 1 \pmod 4$. We give a few instances.

$k = 1.$

The equation

$$x^4 + x^2y^2 + y^4 = z^2, \quad (x, y) = 1, \tag{7'}$$

has only the solutions $x^2 = 1$, $y = 0$; $x = 0$, $y^2 = 1$.

Here x and y are of different parities and we may suppose that y is odd and has the least possible value.

Write
$$4z^2 - (2x^2 + y^2)^2 = 3y^4,$$

or
$$(2z + 2x^2 + y^2)(2z - 2x^2 - y^2) = 3y^4.$$

The two factors are relatively prime for $(2x^2 + y^2, 3y) = 1$ since y is odd, and we cannot have $x^2 \equiv y^2 \equiv 1 \pmod 3$. Hence, either

$$2z + 2x^2 + y^2 = a^4, \qquad 2z - 2x^2 - y^2 = 3b^4, \quad y = ab,$$
$$\text{or} \quad 2z + 2x^2 + y^2 = 3a^4, \qquad 2z - 2x^2 - y^2 = b^4, \quad y = ab.$$

The first pair of equations gives

$$4x^2 = a^4 - 2a^2b^2 - 3b^4 \equiv -4 \pmod{16}$$

and so is impossible. The second gives

$$4x^2 = 3a^4 - 2a^2b^2 - b^4$$
$$= (a^2 - b^2)(3a^2 + b^2).$$

Since we may assume that $x \neq 0$, and $a \equiv b \equiv 1 \pmod 2$, then

$$a^2 - b^2 = c^2, \qquad 3a^2 + b^2 = 4d^2.$$

Then $\qquad\qquad\qquad a = p^2 + q^2, \qquad b = p^2 - q^2$

and $\qquad\qquad\qquad p^4 + p^2q^2 + q^4 = d^2.$

This is the same as equation (7') and

$$p < \sqrt{a}, q < \sqrt{a} \quad \text{and so} \quad p < \sqrt{y}, q < \sqrt{y},$$

and this contradicts the definition of y.

We deduce another result. From

$$(x^2 + xy + y^2)(x^2 - xy + y^2) = z^2,$$

we have $\qquad x^2 + xy + y^2 = X^2, \qquad x^2 - xy + y^2 = Y^2$

and so $\qquad\qquad 3X^2 - Y^2 = 2(x + y)^2 = 2U^2,$

$$3Y^2 - X^2 = 2(x - y)^2 = 2V^2,$$

whence $\qquad\quad U^2 + 3V^2 = 4Y^2, \qquad V^2 + 3U^2 = 4X^2.$

These equations can only have the solutions $X^2 = Y^2 = 1$, i.e. $U^2 = 1$, $V^2 = 1$.

$k = -1.$

The equation

$$x^4 - x^2y^2 + y^4 = z^2, \quad (x, y) = 1 \qquad\qquad (8)$$

has only the solutions $x^2 = 1$, $y = 0$; $x = 0$, $y^2 = 1$ *and* $x^2 = y^2 = 1$.

Write the equation as

$$(x^2 - y^2)^2 + x^2y^2 = z^2.$$

Suppose first that x and y are not both odd.

Then $\qquad\qquad x^2 - y^2 = a^2 - b^2, \qquad xy = 2ab, \quad (a, b) = 1.$

Let $d_1 = (x, b)$, $d_2 = (y, a)$. Then

$$x = d_1X, \qquad b = d_1B, \qquad y = d_2Y, \qquad a = d_2A, \qquad XY = 2AB.$$

Since $(X, B) = 1$, and $(Y, A) = 1$, then $(X, Y) = (2A, B)$ or $(A, 2B)$.

Hence $\qquad\quad x = 2Ad_1, \qquad b = d_1B, \qquad y = d_2B, \qquad a = d_2A,$

or $\qquad\qquad x = Ad_1, \qquad b = d_1B, \qquad y = 2d_2B, \qquad a = d_2A.$

Then for the first alternative,

$$4A^2d_1^2 - d_2^2B^2 = d_2^2A^2 - d_1^2B^2,$$

and

$$d_1^2(4A^2 + B^2) = d_2^2(A^2 + B^2),$$

and since

$$A^2 + B^2 \not\equiv 0 \pmod 3 \quad \text{and} \quad (A, B) = 1,$$

$$A^2 + B^2 = C^2, \qquad 4A^2 + B^2 = D^2.$$

We may suppose that B is odd since, if B were even, we could put $B = 2B_1$ and have a similar pair of equations. Hence $B = p^2 - q^2$, $A = pq$ and $p^4 - p^2q^2 + q^4 = C^2$. Also $pq \leqslant a \leqslant xy/2$, and so the method of descent applies since p and q are not both odd.

The other alternative gives

$$A^2d_1^2 - 4d_2^2B^2 = d_2^2A^2 - d_1^2B^2$$

and so

$$d_1^2(A^2 + B^2) = d_2^2(A^2 + 4B^2).$$

Now $A = p^2 - q^2$, $B = pq$ and $pq \leqslant b \leqslant xy/2$ and so the method of descent applies to the product xy.

Suppose next that x and y are both odd.

Then

$$xy = a^2 - b^2, \qquad x^2 - y^2 = 2ab, \quad (a, b) = 1,$$

and so a and b are not both odd. Then

$$a^4 - a^2b^2 + b^4 = \left(\frac{x^2 + y^2}{2}\right)^2.$$

Hence $ab = 0$, $x = y$ giving the solution

$$x^2 = y^2 = 1.$$

Corollary

On replacing $2x$, $2y$ by $x \pm y$, we see that the only solutions of

$$x^4 + 14x^2y^2 + y^4 = z^2$$

are given by $x^2 = 1$, $y^2 = 0, 1$, or $y^2 = 1$, $x^2 = 0, 1$.

An interesting corollary is Fermat's

Theorem 3

There cannot be four squares in arithmetical progression.

Let the squares be x^2, y^2, z^2, w^2.

Then

$$x^2 + z^2 = 2y^2, \qquad 2z^2 = y^2 + w^2$$

and so

$$x^2(2z^2 - y^2) = w^2(2y^2 - z^2),$$

$$2(x^2z^2 - y^2w^2) = x^2y^2 - w^2z^2.$$

2+

Put $xz = a$, $yw = b$, $2c = xy + wz$, $2d = xy - wz$. Since obviously x, y, z, w are all odd, c and d are integers.

Then
$$a^2 - b^2 = 2cd, \qquad ab = c^2 - d^2,$$
$$a^4 - a^2b^2 + b^4 = (c^2 + d^2)^2.$$

Hence $a = 0$, $b = 0, 1$, etc.

It is easily shown that other values of k, e.g. $k = \pm 3, -4$, are also easily dealt with in a similar way.

Theorem 4

Let a, b, c be rational numbers where $ac \neq 0$. Then if there are only a finite number of rational solutions of

$$(b^2 - 4ac)X^4 - 2bX^2Y^2 + Y^4 = Z^2, \tag{9}$$

there are only a finite number for

$$ax^4 + bx^2y^2 + cy^4 = z^2. \tag{10}$$

These are given by $y = X$, $z = xY$ and possibly $xy = 0$.

If $x \neq 0$, replace the second equation by

$$ax^4 + bx^2y^2 + cy^4 = x^2z_1^2,$$

Then
$$ax^4 + (by^2 - z_1^2)x^2 + cy^4 = 0.$$

Hence
$$(by^2 - z_1^2)^2 - 4acy^4 = v^2,$$

say, and this is the first equation with $y = X$, $z_1 = Y$. Since $X = 0$, $Y = 1$ is a solution of (9), $y = 0$ is a possible solution of (10).

Take $b^2 - 4ac = 1$ and suppose that the only solutions of

$$X^4 - 2bX^2Y^2 + Y^4 = Z^2,$$

are given by $XYZ = 0$. Then the only possible solutions of

$$ax^4 + bx^2y^2 + cy^4 = z^2$$

are given by $xy = 0$.

Putting $b = \pm 3$, $ac = 2$ in equation (9), the only possible solutions of

$$ax^4 \pm 3x^2y^2 + \frac{2}{a}y^4 = z^2$$

are $xyz = 0$. In particular if $a = 1$ and $b = -3$,

$$(x^2 - y^2)(x^2 - 2y^2) = z^2,$$

and we have $x = \pm 1$, $y = 0$ and $x^2 = y^2 = 1$.

2. An interesting special case of equation (1) is the equation

$$ax^4 + by^4 = cz^2, \quad (x, y) = 1.$$

Most of the results on the impossibility of non-trivial integer solutions do not go too far back. They are due to Pocklington[1], Nagell[2], and Lind[3]. Many of them can be proved by a simple application[4] of infinite descent. Among these are the equations

$$x^4 + dy^4 = z^2, \quad (x, y) = 1, y \neq 0, \tag{11}$$

for the following values of d. Let p be a prime number. Then

I.	$d = p,$	$p \equiv 7, 11 \pmod{16},$
II.	$d = 2p,$	$p \equiv \pm 3 \pmod 8,$
III.	$d = 4p,$	$p \equiv \pm 3, -5 \pmod{16},$
IV.	$d = -p,$	$p \equiv \pm 3, -5 \pmod{16}.$

From Theorem 4, it follows that equation (12) is also impossible when d is replaced by $-4d$ where now d is defined above. Hence III follows from IV. Let us take II,

$$x^4 + 2py^4 = z^2, \quad x > 0, y > 0, z > 0.$$

A congruence mod 8 shows that $y \not\equiv 1 \pmod 2$, and so $x \equiv z \equiv 1 \pmod 2$. From

$$(z \pm x^2)(z \mp x^2) = 2py^4,$$

since the two factors have greatest common divisor 2, we have either

$$z \pm x^2 = 2a^4, \quad z \mp x^2 = 16pb^4, \quad y = 2ab,$$

or $\quad z \pm x^2 = 2pa^4, \quad z \mp x^2 = 16b^4, \quad y = 2ab,$

The first set gives

$$a^4 - 8pb^4 = \pm x^2.$$

The $-$ sign can be rejected, and then

$$(a^2 + x)(a^2 - x) = 8pb^4$$

gives either

$$a^2 + x = 2pc^4, \quad a^2 - x = 4d^4, \quad b = cd,$$

or $\quad a^2 + x = 2c^4, \quad a^2 - x = 4pd^4, \quad b = cd.$

The first of these gives

$$a^2 - 2d^4 = pc^4,$$

and this is impossible since $(2/p) = -1$.

The second gives

$$c^4 + 2pd^4 = a^2,$$

and since $d < \sqrt{a} < \sqrt{y}$, the method of descent applies.
The second set above gives

$$pa^4 - 8b^4 = \pm x^2.$$

A congruence mod 8 shows that the $+$ sign must be rejected. The $-$ sign must also be rejected since $(2/p) = -1$.

We now take IV,

$$x^4 - py^4 = z^2, \quad x > 0, y > 0, z > 0.$$

If $y \equiv 1 \pmod 2$, then $x \equiv z \equiv 1 \pmod 2$ and $x^4 \equiv -2, 4 \pmod 8$. Hence $y \equiv 0 \pmod 2$, $x \equiv z \equiv 1 \pmod 2$. Then

$$(x^2 \pm z)(x^2 \mp z) = py^4,$$

and so $\qquad x^2 \pm z = 2a^4, \qquad x^2 \mp z = 8pb^4, \qquad y = 2ab,$

or $\qquad x^2 \pm z = 2pa^4, \qquad x^2 \mp z = 8b^4, \qquad y = 2ab.$

The first gives

$$a^4 + 4pb^4 = x^2.$$

Here $a \equiv 1 \pmod 2$ and so

$$x \mp a^2 = 2pc^4, \qquad x \pm a^2 = 2d^4, \qquad b = cd,$$
$$d^4 - pc^4 = \pm a^2.$$

The $-$ sign must be rejected since $d^4 \pm 3c^4 \equiv -1 \pmod 8$ is impossible. The $+$ sign gives a descent since $c \leqslant b < y$.
The second gives

$$pa^4 + 4b^4 = x^2.$$

Since $a \equiv x \equiv 1 \pmod 2$, a congruence mod 8 shows that this is impossible if $b \equiv 0 \pmod 2$. Hence $b \equiv 1 \pmod 2$, and

$$p + 4 \equiv x^2 \pmod 8.$$

This is impossible unless $p \equiv -3 \pmod{16}$. But then,

$$x \pm 2b^2 = c^4, \qquad x \mp 2b^2 = pd^4, \qquad a = cd.$$

and so $\qquad\qquad\qquad \pm 4b^2 = c^4 - bd^4.$

A congruence mod 16 shows that the $-$ sign is impossible. For the $+$ sign, the method of descent applies since $cd = a < y$.

Sometimes the application of biquadratic residues may be useful. Let p be a prime $\equiv 1 \pmod 8$ and so $p = a^2 + b^2$ where we may suppose a is even and so $a \equiv 0 \pmod 4$. Then 2 is a biquadratic non-residue or residue mod p according as $a \equiv 4 \pmod 8$ or $a \equiv 0 \pmod 8$. We have now

V. *The equation*

$$x^4 - py^4 = 2z^2$$

has no integer solutions if 2 is a biquadratic non-residue of p.
Let $z = 2^r z_1$, $z_1 \equiv 1 \pmod 2$.

Then
$$1 = \left(\frac{p}{z_1}\right) = \left(\frac{z_1}{p}\right) = \left(\frac{z}{p}\right)$$

by the law of quadratic reciprocity and since $(2/p) = 1$. Hence $z \equiv s^2 \pmod p$ and then $x^4 \equiv 2s^4 \pmod p$, and this means 2 is a biquadratic residue.

It may be remarked that it is well known that solutions of equation (11) can be found when d has special values, e.g. when $d = u(v^2 - u)$, a solution is given by the identity

$$(v^2 - 2u)^4 + u(v^2 - u)(2v)^4 = (v^4 + 4uv^2 - 4u^2)^2.$$

3. A different type of result is given by[5]

Theorem 5

The equation

$$k_1(ax^2 + by^2 + cz^2)(a_1x^2 + b_1y^2 + c_1z^2)$$
$$= k_2(px^2 + qy^2 + rz^2)^2, \quad (x, y, z) = 1, \quad (12)$$

or say, $k_1 F F_1 = k_2 G^2$, has no integer solutions except $(0, 0, 0)$ if the coefficients are integers, $k_1 > 0$, $k_2 > 0$ and have only divisors $\equiv 1 \pmod 8$ and

I. $a > 0$, $b > 0$, $c > 0$, $a \equiv b \equiv c \equiv -1 \pmod 8$
II. *all odd divisors of*

$$\Delta = \begin{vmatrix} a & b & c \\ a_1 & b_1 & c_1 \\ p & q & r \end{vmatrix}$$

are $\equiv 1 \pmod 8$, and either
III. *Δ is odd, or*
IV. *Δ is even, and $a_1 \equiv 0 \pmod 2$, $b_1 \equiv c_1 \equiv 1 \pmod 2$, $b_1 + c_1 \equiv 4, 6 \pmod 8$.*

Any common prime factors of F, F_1 can only be divisors of $k_1 k_2$, and also of G and these are divisors of Δ.
We first consider the solutions with $F_1 \neq 0$. Then $F_1 > 0$.
Suppose first that Δ is odd. Then since $G \neq 0$,

$$F = k_3 w^2, \quad F_1 = k_3 w_1^2, \quad (13)$$

where $k_3 \equiv k_4 \equiv 1 \pmod 8$, are taken from a finite set and w, w_1 are integers. The equation $F = k_3 w^2$ is impossible since it gives

$$x^2 + y^2 + z^2 + w^2 \equiv 0 \pmod 8,$$

and so

$$x \equiv y \equiv z \equiv w \equiv 0 \pmod 2.$$

Suppose next that Δ is even. Then besides equation (13) we have also

$$F = 2k_5 w^2, \qquad F_1 = 2k_6 w_1^2. \tag{14}$$

We consider the first of these; clearly $w \not\equiv 0 \pmod 2$ as this would give

$$x^2 + y^2 + z^2 \equiv 0 \pmod 8, \qquad x \equiv y \equiv z \equiv 0 \pmod 2.$$

Hence $w \equiv 1 \pmod 2$ and

$$x^2 + y^2 + z^2 \equiv 2 \pmod 8.$$

This gives three possibilities typified by $x \equiv 0 \pmod 4$, $y \equiv z \equiv 1 \pmod 2$. The equation $F_1 = 2k_6 w_1^2$ gives the three corresponding congruences

$$b_1 + c_1 \equiv 2w_1^2 \pmod 8, \qquad c_1 + a_1 \equiv 0 \pmod 2,$$
$$a_1 + b_1 \equiv 0 \pmod 2$$

all of which are impossible from IV.

We show now there are no solutions with $F_1 = 0$. Then $G = 0$ and

$$\frac{x^2}{b_1 r - c_1 q} = \frac{y^2}{c_1 p - a_1 r} = \frac{z^2}{a_1 q - b_1 p}.$$

Since $(x, y, z) = 1$, we have with integer d,

$$b_1 r - c_1 q = dx^2, \qquad c_1 p - a_1 r = dy^2, \qquad a_1 q - b_1 p = dz^2.$$

Then

$$\Delta = a(b_1 r - c_1 q) + \cdots$$
$$= d(ax^2 + by^2 + cz^2) = dF,$$

and so the odd factors of d and F are $\equiv 1 \pmod 8$.

Also

$$F \equiv -x^2 - y^2 - z^2 \pmod 8.$$

We can exclude $x \equiv y \equiv z \equiv 1 \pmod 2$ since then $F \equiv -3 \pmod 8$ and so all the factors of F cannot be $\equiv 1 \pmod 8$. Also $x \equiv 1, y \equiv 0, z \equiv 0 \pmod 2$ can be excluded since then $F \equiv -1 \pmod 4$. Similarly $x \equiv 0 \pmod 4$, $y \equiv z \equiv 1 \pmod 2$, since now $F \equiv b + c \pmod 8 \equiv -2 \pmod 8$. Finally let $x \equiv 2 \pmod 4$, $y \equiv z \equiv 1 \pmod 2$. Then there are the three possibilities

$$F_1 \equiv 4a_1 + b_1 + c_1, a_1 + 4b_1 + c_1, a_1 + b_1 + 4c_1 \pmod 8$$
$$\equiv 4, 6 \pmod 8, \equiv 1 \pmod 2, \equiv 1 \pmod 2,$$

and so $F_1 \neq 0$.
We can now deduce

Theorem 6

There are no integer solutions of

$$\left(\frac{br - cq}{a}\right)^3 x^4 + \left(\frac{cp - ar}{b}\right)^3 y^4 + \left(\frac{aq - bp}{c}\right)^3 z^4 = 0, \qquad (15)$$

where

I. $a > 0, \quad b > 0, \quad c > 0,$

$a \equiv b \equiv c \equiv -1 \pmod 8$ $(b, c) = (c, a) = (a, b) = 1,$

II. $p \equiv 0 \pmod 8, \qquad q \equiv r \equiv -1 \pmod 8,$

III. $\dfrac{br - cq}{a} \equiv \dfrac{cp - ar}{b} \equiv \dfrac{aq - bp}{c} \equiv 0 \pmod 1,$

and the positive odd factors of these three terms are all $\equiv 1 \pmod 8$.

To reduce equation (12) to this form, we take $k_1 = k_2$, and

$$b_1 c + bc_1 = 2qr, \qquad c_1 a + ca_1 = 2rp, \qquad a_1 b + b_1 a = 2pq.$$

Then $bca_1 = -aqr + brp + cpq, \quad$ etc.

and so a_1, b_1, c_1 will be integers if III is satisfied.

The equation (12) now takes the form

$$(aa_1 - p^2)x^4 + \cdots = 0,$$

or $a(pb - aq)(pc - ar)x^4 + \cdots = 0.$

On replacing x by $(qc - rb)x/a$, we have equation (15).

Now $-\Delta = \begin{vmatrix} (-aqr + brp + cpq)/bc & \cdot & \cdot \\ a & \cdot & \cdot \\ p & \cdot & \cdot \end{vmatrix},$

also $\Delta = 2 \begin{vmatrix} aqr & brp & cpq \\ 1 & 1 & 1 \\ pbc & qca & rab \end{vmatrix},$

$$\Delta = -2 \left(\frac{br - cq}{a}\right) \left(\frac{cp - ar}{b}\right) \left(\frac{aq - bp}{c}\right).$$

Hence all the odd factors of Δ are $\equiv 1 \pmod 8$.

We have now to show equations (13) and (14) have no integer solutions, and we need only consider (14). We write $F_1 = 2k_1 w_1^2$ in the form

$$(aqr + brp + cpq)\left(\frac{x^2}{bc} + \frac{y^2}{ca} + \frac{z^2}{ab}\right)$$
$$- 2\left(\frac{aqr}{bc}x^2 + \frac{bpr}{ca}y^2 + \frac{cpq}{ab}z^2\right) = 2k_4 w_1^2,$$

and from $F = 2k_3w^2$, this is

$$(qr + rp + pq)w^2 + qrx^2 + rpy^2 + pqz^2 = w_1^2 \pmod 8. \qquad (16)$$

Since from equation (14)

$$x^2 + y^2 + z^2 \equiv -2w^2 \pmod 8,$$

one of x, y, z must be even, say x, and then $x \equiv 2 \pmod 4$ $y \equiv z \equiv w \equiv 1$ (mod 2), etc.

Then (16) becomes

$$5qr + 2rp + 2pq \equiv w_1^2 \pmod 8.$$

Similarly if $y \equiv 2 \pmod 4$, etc.

$$5rp + 2pq + 2qr \equiv w_1^2 \pmod 8,$$

$$5pq + 2qr + 2rp \equiv w_1^2 \pmod 8.$$

These are all impossible if $p \equiv 0 \pmod 8$, $qr \equiv 1, 3, 7 \pmod 8$.

We now examine the conditions that the odd factors of

$$L = \frac{qc - rb}{a}, \qquad M = \frac{ra - pc}{b}, \qquad N = \frac{pb - qa}{c}$$

should be $\equiv 1 \pmod 8$. We take $q \equiv r \equiv -1 \pmod 8$ arbitrarily such that the odd prime factors of $(qc - rb)/a$ are $\equiv 1 \pmod 8$. We take $p \equiv 0 \pmod 8$ so great that

$$bY = pc - ra > 0, \qquad cZ = pb - qa > 0.$$

On putting $\qquad\qquad p = 8bcP + P_1,$

say, where P_1 is a value of $p \equiv 0 \pmod 8$ giving integer values for Y and Z, then

$$Y = 8c^2P + P_2, \qquad Z = 8b^2P + P_3,$$

say, where $P_2 \equiv P_3 \equiv 1 \pmod 8$.

Our problem now is to find P such that $Y > 0$, $Z > 0$, and YZ is divisible only by primes $\equiv 1 \pmod 8$.

Many numerical instances have been given me by Mr. K. Kloss. For example, when $a = 7$, $b = 15$, $c = 23$, we can take

p	q	r	L	M	N
8280,	4991,	13335,	12176,	6473,	-3881,
8280,	16583,	15855,	-20512,	5297,	-353,
11040,	3703,	14175,	18208,	10313,	-6073.

These equations $L^3x^4 + M^3y^4 + N^3z^4 = 0$, which have no solutions, cannot be proved impossible by taking congruences mod 16 since $M + N \equiv 0 \pmod{16}$. Cassels points out that the impossibility of the three equations follows at once by taking congruences to mod 761, 353, 6073 respectively. One would have thought that it should not be difficult to find numerical instances for which congruences considerations do not suffice to show the impossibility. Cassels however finds this is not so for a large number of values for p, q, r.

REFERENCES

1. H. C. Pocklington. Some diophantine impossibilities. *Proc. Camb. Phil. Soc.*, **17** (1914), 110–118.
2. T. Nagell. Sur l'impossibilité de quelques équations à deux indéterminées. *Norsk Mat. For. Skriftern* I No. 13, *Kristiania* 1923.
3. C. E. Lind. Untersuchungen über die rationalen Punkte der ebenen kubischen Kurven vom Geschlecht Eins. *Diss. Uppsala*, (1940).
4. L. J. Mordell. The diophantine equation $x^4 + my^4 = z^2$. *Q. J. Math.*, (2) **18** 1–6 (1967).
5. L. J. Mordell. Some quartic diophantine equations of genus 3. *Proc. Am. Math. Soc.*, **17** (1966), 1152–1158; also **18** (1967), 190.

CHAPTER 5

Some Linear Equations

1. We now discuss some linear equations.

Theorem 1

Integer solutions of the equation

$$a_1x_1 + a_2x_2 + \cdots + a_nx_n = a, \tag{1}$$

where the a's are integers, $a_1a_2\ldots a_n \neq 0$, exist if and only if

$$(a_1, a_2, \ldots, a_n) \mid a.$$

This condition is obviously necessary and so we may assume that $(a_1, a_2, \ldots, a_n) = 1$.

Suppose first that $n = 2$. If $a = 0$, the general solution is $x_1 = -a_2t$, $x_2 = a_1t$ where t is an arbitrary integer. If $a \neq 0$, the equation is equivalent to

$$a_1x_1 + a_2x_2 = a, \quad (a_1, a_2) = 1, \tag{2}$$

where we may suppose that $a_1 > 0$, $a_2 > 0$ on writing $-x_2$ for x_2 if need be.

The solution is given by the Euclidean algorithm for finding the greatest common divisor of a_1 and a_2. We may write

$$a_2 = q_1a_1 + r_1 \quad \text{where } 0 < r_1 < a_1, \ (r_1, a_1) = 1.$$

Then
$$x_1 = -q_1x_2 + \frac{-r_1x_2 + a}{a_1} = -q_1x_2 + x_3,$$

and so
$$r_1x_2 + a_1x_3 = a.$$

Write
$$a_1 = q_2r_1 + r_2, \quad 0 \leqslant r_2 < r_1, \ (r_2, r_1) = 1.$$

Then
$$x_2 = -q_2x_3 + \frac{-r_2x_3 + a}{r_1} = -q_2x_3 + x_4,$$

and so
$$r_2x_3 + r_1x_4 = a.$$

Continuing this process, we have a decreasing set of positive integers $r_1, r_2, \ldots$ until we come to a stage where

$$r_{n-2}x_{n-1} + r_{n-3}x_n = a, \quad r_{n-2} = 1.$$

Then $x_{n-1}, x_{n-2}, \ldots, x_2, x_1$ are given successively in terms of a parameter x_n. If one solution (p, q) is known, all the solutions are given by

$$x = p + ta_2, \qquad y = q - ta_1,$$

where t is an integer parameter.

This is obvious since

$$a_1(x - p) + a_2(y - q) = 0.$$

2. The argument when $n = 2$ can be adapted for the general equation (1), say,

$$L(x) = a_1x_1 + \cdots + a_nx_n = a. \tag{3}$$

We may suppose that a_1 is one of the a_r for which $|a_r|$ is least. We apply a substitution

$$x_1 = X_1 + k_2x_2 + \cdots + k_nx_n,$$

where the k are integers satisfying

$$|a_1k_r + a_r| < |a_1|, \quad (r = 2, \ldots, n).$$

Suppose now that in the new form, a_2 plays the role of a_1. A substitution

$$x_2 = X_2 + l_1X_1 + l_3x_3 + \cdots + l_nx_n$$

makes the new coefficients all have moduli $< |a_2|$. Continuing this process, we arrive at a unimodular integral substitution (since $X_1, X_2, \ldots$ are easily given in terms of $x_1, x_2, \ldots$), which changes $L(x)$ into, say,

$$L(x) = \varepsilon_1X_1 + \cdots + \varepsilon_nX_n,$$

where the $\varepsilon = 0$ or ± 1, and then finally to a stage where, say, $\varepsilon_1 = 1$, $\varepsilon_2 = 0, \ldots, \varepsilon_n = 0$. Then $X_1 = a$ and the general solution is given linearly in terms of the $n - 1$ variables $X_2, \ldots, X_n$.

3. Theorem 2

Let $L_r(x) = a_{r1}x_1 + \cdots + a_{rn}x_n$, $(r = 1, 2, \ldots, n)$, be n linear forms with integer coefficients and determinant $D > 0$. Then the equations

$$L_r(x) = a_r \quad (r = 1, 2, \ldots, n) \tag{4}$$

have an integer solution if and only if the congruences

$$L_r(x) \equiv a_r \pmod{M} \quad (r = 1, 2, \ldots, n) \tag{5}$$

are solvable for all M.

The condition is necessary. For the sufficiency, we reduce the $L_r(x)$ to canonical forms given by the

Lemma

A unimodular integral substitution changes the L's into the forms

$$c_{11}X_1, c_{21}X_1 + c_{22}X_2, \ldots, c_{n1}X_1 + \cdots + c_{nn}X_n,$$

where

$$c_{rr} > 0, 0 \leqslant c_{r1}, c_{r2}, \ldots, c_{rr-1} < c_{rr}.$$

Let c_{11} be the greatest common divisor of the coefficients of L_1. Then L_1 may be transformed into $c_{11}X_1$ by a unimodular integral substitution. This substitution changes L_2 into $c_{21}X_1 + L_2(X_2, X_3, \ldots, X_n)$ where L_2 is a linear form in $X_2, \ldots, X_n$. This can be changed into $c_{22}X_2$ where c_{22} is the greatest common divisor of the coefficients of L_2. Then replacing X_2 by $X_2 + k_2c_{21}X_1$ if need be, we may suppose that $0 \leqslant c_{21} < c_{22}$. This process can be continued and so the lemma follows. It is also clear that $c_{11}c_{22}\ldots c_{nn} = D$.

We now continue with the proof of the theorem. We can replace the equations by

$$c_{11}X_1 = a_1, \; c_{21}X_1 + c_{22}X_2 = a_2, \ldots.$$

Since $c_{11}X_1 \equiv a_1 \pmod{c_{11}}$ is solvable, $a_1 \equiv 0 \pmod{c_{11}}$, and so the equation for X_1 has an integer solution. We eliminate X_1 by writing

$$\xi_1 c_{11}X_1 + \xi_2(c_{21}X_1 + c_{22}X_2) = \xi_1 a_1 + \xi_2 a_2,$$

and taking $\xi_1 c_{11} + \xi_2 c_{21} = 0$. Since the equation is solvable as a congruence to mod $c_{11}c_{22}$ for all ξ_1, ξ_2, X_2 is an integer.

Similarly we can eliminate X_1, X_2 from the first three equations, etc.

It may be noted that the Theorem 1 can be extended to the case when the number m of equations is $< n$. When all the right-hand a are zero, we can find an estimate for the magnitude of a solution.

4. Theorem 3

The m simultaneous equations

$$L_r = a_{r1}x_1 + a_{r2}x_2 + \cdots + a_{rn}x_n = 0, \tag{6}$$

$(r = 1, 2, \ldots, m)$, $(m < n)$ *where the a's are integers, have an integer solution* $x \neq 0$, *for which the x satisfy the inequality*

$$|x_r| \leqslant (A_1 A_2 \ldots A_n)^{1/(n-m)}, \tag{7}$$

where $\qquad A_r = |a_{r1}| + |a_{r2}| + \cdots + |a_{rn}|.$

Let the x run through the integer values in the interval $[0, N]$ where N is an integer defined later. Then if B_r is the sum of the positive $a_{r1}, a_{r2}, \ldots, a_{rn}$ and $-C_r$ is the sum of the negative ones,

$$-C_r N \leqslant L_r \leqslant B_r N.$$

Write $A_r = B_r + C_r$. Then L_r assumes at most $A_r N + 1$ values. Hence if

$$(N + 1)^n > \prod_{r=1}^{m} (A_r N + 1),$$

the L_r take the same set of values for two different x, say x' and x''. Then $x = x' - x''$ is a solution of $L_r = 0$, $(r = 1, 2, \ldots, n)$, and $|x_s| \leqslant N$ for $s = 1, 2, \ldots, n$.

An estimate for N is given by

$$(N + 1)^n > (N + 1)^m \prod_{r=1}^{m} A_r,$$

or

$$N > \left(\prod_{r=1}^{m} A_r \right)^{1/(n-m)} - 1.$$

We can take N to be the integer part of $\prod_{r=1}^{m} (A_r)^{1/(n-m)}$.

It is sometimes useful to know that linear forms can be made to satisfy various inequalities for integer values of the variables. This is a problem in the geometry of numbers and a fundamental result due to Minkowski is given by

Theorem 4

Let $L_r = \sum_{s=1}^{n} a_{rs} x_s$ $(r = 1, 2, \ldots, n)$ be n linear forms with real coefficients and determinant $\Delta = \|a_{rs}\| \neq 0$. Let $l_1, l_2, \ldots, l_n$ be n real numbers such that

$$l_1 l_2 \ldots l_n \geqslant |\Delta|.$$

Then integers $x \neq 0$ exist such that

$$|L_r| \leqslant l_r, \quad (r = 1, 2, \ldots, n).$$

Further any $n - 1$ of the equality signs may be omitted.

CHAPTER 6

Properties of Congruences

1. Congruences play an indispensable role in the discussion of Diophantine equations. They can usually be considered as Diophantine equations in which the variables are elements of a finite field. We have seen in Chapter 2 that many equations

$$f(\boldsymbol{x}) = f(x_1, x_2, \ldots, x_n) = 0$$

have been shown to have no solutions by proving the impossibility of a congruence

$$f(\boldsymbol{x}) \equiv 0 \,(\mathrm{mod}\ p^r).$$

There are, however, many important applications of congruences which give affirmative results. Thus solvability of congruences and the number of their solutions are essential in applying the methods of analytical number theory, not only in proving the existence of solutions of an equation but also formulae for their number. Further, in recent years, it has been shown that there seems to exist for cubic equations $f(x, y) = 0$ a close connection between the number of solutions of $f(x, y) \equiv 0 \,(\mathrm{mod}\ p^r)$ and the existence of rational solutions of $f(x, y) = 0$.

It seems worth while to give some results on congruences required later but also of interest in themselves.

Theorem 1

Let $f(x)$ be a polynomial in one variable with integer coefficients and let p be a prime. Suppose there exist x_1 and $\delta \geqslant 0$ such that

$$f(x_1) \equiv 0 \,(\mathrm{mod}\ p^{2\delta+1}), \qquad \frac{df(x_1)}{dx_1} \equiv 0 \,(\mathrm{mod}\ p^\delta), \not\equiv 0 \,(\mathrm{mod}\ p^{\delta+1}).$$

Then for $s \geqslant 1$, x exists such that

$$f(x) \equiv 0 \,(\mathrm{mod}\ p^{2\delta+s}), \qquad x \equiv x_1 \,(\mathrm{mod}\ p^{\delta+1}). \tag{1}$$

We prove the result by induction. It is true for $s = 1$ with $x = x_1$. We prove that if the result is true for s with $x = x_s$, then it is true for $s + 1$. We write $x = x_{s+1} \equiv x_s \,(\mathrm{mod}\ p^{\delta+s})$ and have to solve

$$f(x) = f(x_s) + (x - x_s)f'(x_s) + \frac{(x - x_s)^2}{2!} f''(x_s) + \cdots \equiv 0 \,(\mathrm{mod}\ p^{2\delta+s+1}).$$

Put $x - x_s = Xp^{\delta+s}$; then $f'(x_s) = Ap^{\delta}$ where $A \not\equiv 0 \pmod{p}$, since

$$f'(x_s) \equiv f'(x_1) + (x_s - x_1)f''(x_1) \pmod{p^{\delta+1}}.$$

Hence $AX + f(x_s)/p^{2\delta+s} \equiv 0 \pmod{p},$

and this has a solution for X. We note $f'(x) \equiv 0 \pmod{p^{\delta}}$, but not $\pmod{p^{\delta+1}}$.

The solvability of $f(x) \equiv 0 \pmod{p^r}$ for all integers $r \geqslant 1$ can be expressed by saying that $f(x) = 0$ has a root, say $x = X$, in the p-adic field Q_p. This means that the solutions of $f(X_r) \equiv 0 \pmod{p^r}$ can be written in the form

$$X_r = x_0 + x_1 p + \cdots + x_{r-1}p^{r-1},$$

where the x are integers with $0 \leqslant x < p$ and where, say,

$$X_{r+1} - X_r = x_r p^r.$$

It proves convenient to mention the solvability of $f(x) = 0$ in real numbers, and then we can say that $f(x) = 0$ is solvable in the p-adic field Q_{p_∞}.

Example

$$x^2 = a,$$

where a is a p-adic unit, i.e. $(a, p) = 1$. If p is an odd prime, the equation has a solution in Q_p if and only if a is a quadratic residue of p, i.e. $(a/p) = 1$. If $p = 2$, the condition is $a \equiv 1 \pmod 8$.

Theorem 2

Let $f(x) = f(x_1, x_2 \ldots, x_n)$ be a polynomial with integer coefficients in n variables and of total degree $l < n$. Then if the congruence

$$f(x) \equiv 0 \pmod{p},$$

p a prime, has one solution, it has another.

In particular if there is a solution $x = x_0$, we can always suppose $x_0 = 0$ on putting $x = X + x_0$.

The theorem is due to Chevalley[1]. For the proof, we recall Fermat's result that if x is any integer then $x^p \equiv x \pmod{p}$. It follows that if $f(x)$ is a polynomial in x such that $f(x) \equiv 0 \pmod{p}$ for all x, then $f(x)$ is divisible mod p by $x^p - x$, and so identically,

$$f(x) \equiv f_1(x)(x^p - x) \pmod{p},$$

where $f_1(x)$ is a polynomial in x with integer coefficients, and the coefficients of the powers of x on both sides are congruent mod p.

Suppose now that $g(x)$ is a polynomial such that

$$g(x) = g(x_1, x_2, \ldots, x_n) \equiv 0 \pmod{p}$$

for all integers $x_1, x_2, \ldots, x_n$. On replacing x_1^p by x_1, x_1^{p+1} by x_1^2, etc., we may suppose that no x occurs in $g(x)$ to a power $\geqslant p$. Then considered as a polynomial in x_1,

$$g(x) \equiv (x_1^p - x_1)g_1(x_2, \ldots, x_n) \pmod{p}$$

$$\equiv (x_1^p - x_1)\ldots(x_n^p - x_n)g_n$$

on continuing the process. Clearly g_n is a constant.

Suppose now that $f(x)$ is a polynomial such that $f(x) \not\equiv 0 \pmod{p}$ except when $x_1 \equiv x_2 \equiv \cdots \equiv x_n \equiv 0 \pmod{p}$. Then the congruence

$$1 - (f(x))^{p-1} \equiv (1 - x_1^{p-1})\ldots(1 - x_n^{p-1}) \pmod{p}$$

holds for all x. It is obviously true for $x = 0$ since $f(x) \equiv 0$. For the other x, $(f(x))^{p-1} \equiv 1$, and at least one of the right-hand factors is $\equiv 0$. The right-hand side is of degree $(p-1)n$ in the variables and so we have a contradiction if $(p-1)n > (p-1)l$, i.e. $n > l$.

An illustration is given by

$$a_1 x_1^l + \ldots + a_n x_n^l \equiv 0 \pmod{p},$$

where $(a_1 a_2 \ldots a_n, p) = 1$, $n > l$. The congruence always has a solution different from $x = 0$.

2. The case $l = 2$ is of special interest and we give a different discussion for

$$f(x, y, z) = ax^2 + by^2 + cz^2 \equiv 0 \pmod{p^r}, \quad (x, y, z, p) = 1. \qquad (2)$$

We prove

Theorem 2

Suppose that a, b, c are relatively prime in pairs, and so $abc \neq 0$, and are square free. Then the congruence

$$ax^2 + by^2 + cz^2 \equiv 0 \pmod{M}$$

is solvable for arbitrary M with $(x, y, z, M) = 1$, if it is solvable for $M = 4abc$.

This implies that integers A, B, C exist such that

$$bA^2 + c \equiv 0 \pmod{a}, \quad cB^2 + a \equiv 0 \pmod{b}, \quad aC^2 + b \equiv 0 \pmod{c}.$$

Suppose first that p is an odd prime and $p^r \| M$. There are two cases according as $(p, abc) = 1$ or p. Suppose first that $r = 1$. Then the congruence is solvable when $(p, abc) = 1$. For, write

$$x^2 \equiv -ba^{-1}y^2 - ca^{-1}z^2 \pmod{p}.$$

Take $z = 1$ and let y run through the values $0, 1, \ldots, p - 1$. Then the right-hand side runs through $1 + (p-1)/2 = (p+1)/2$ values, and so one of these must be either zero or a quadratic residue of p. Since $c \not\equiv 0 \pmod{p}$, we cannot have both $ax \equiv 0$, $by \equiv 0$. Hence Theorem 1 applies for $r > 1$ on considering $f(x, y, 1)$ as a function of x or y.

Suppose next that $p \mid abc$. For simplicity, we suppose that $(p, bc) = 1$, and $p \mid a$. Then

$$by^2 + cz^2 \equiv 0 \pmod{p}.$$

This is solvable with $yz \not\equiv 0 \pmod{p}$ if and only if $(-bc/p) = 1$. Then Theorem 1 applies on considering $f(1, y, 1)$. If, however, $y \equiv z \equiv 0$, the congruence (2) is impossible for $r = 2$.

Suppose next that $p = 2$. We may take $r \geqslant 2$ since the congruence is solvable for $r = 1$. For simplicity, we suppose that at most one of a, b, c is even and that this is not divisible by 4.

Case I. a, b, c are all odd. Then the congruence (2) is solvable for $r = 2$ unless $a \equiv b \equiv c \pmod 4$. If this is not so, then we may assume that $a \equiv -b \pmod 4$ and so a solution is given by $x \equiv y \equiv 1 \pmod 2$, $z \equiv 0 \pmod 2$. A solution is then given when $r = 3$ by taking $z \equiv 0 \pmod 4$ when $a + b \equiv 0 \pmod 8$, and $z \equiv 2 \pmod 4$ when $a + b \equiv 4 \pmod 8$. By Theorem 1, the congruence is solvable for $r > 3$.

Case II. One of a, b, c is even, say $a \equiv 2 \pmod 4$. Then the congruence is solvable unless either $b + c \equiv 4 \pmod 8$ or $b + c \equiv a \pmod 8$. Suppose first that $a \equiv 2 \pmod 8$. Then a solution when $r = 3$ requires $y \equiv z \equiv 1 \pmod 2$, and then $x \equiv 0 \pmod 2$ if $b + c \equiv 0 \pmod 8$, but $x \equiv 1 \pmod 2$ if $b + c \equiv -2 \pmod 8$, i.e. $b + c \equiv -a \pmod 8$. The result for $a \equiv -2 \pmod 8$ follows in the same way. Solvability for $r > 3$ follows by applying the theorem to the congruence applied as a function of y.

3. *The congruence*

$$ax^3 + 3bx^2y + 3cxy^2 + dy^3 \equiv z^3 \pmod 9.$$

This has only the trivial solution $x \equiv y \equiv z \equiv 0 \pmod 3$ if

I. $\qquad a \not\equiv 0, \not\equiv \pm 1 \pmod 9, \qquad d \not\equiv 0, \not\equiv \pm 1 \pmod 9,$

II. $\qquad \dfrac{a - a^3}{3} + c - ad^2 \pm \left(b - a^2d + \dfrac{d - d^3}{3}\right) \not\equiv 0 \pmod 9.$

We have

$$z \equiv ax + dy \pmod 3, \qquad z^3 \equiv (ax + dy)^3 \pmod 9.$$

Then

$$(a - a^3)x^3 + 3(b - a^2d)x^2y + 3(c - ad^2)xy^2 + (d - d^3)y^3 \equiv 0 \pmod 9,$$

and

$$\frac{a - a^3}{3}x^3 + (b - a^2d)x^2y + (c - ad^2)xy^2 + \frac{d - d^3}{3}y^3 \equiv 0 \pmod 3.$$

From I, $xy \not\equiv 0 \pmod 3$, and so $x^2 \equiv y^2 \equiv 1 \pmod 3$, and

$$\frac{a - a^3}{3}\, x + (b - a^2 d)y + (c - ad^2)x + \frac{d - d^3}{3}\, y \equiv 0 \pmod 3.$$

Since $x \equiv \pm y \pmod 3$, the condition for insolubility becomes

$$\frac{a - a^3}{3} + c - ad^2 \pm \left(b - a^2 d + \frac{d - d^3}{3}\right) \not\equiv 0 \pmod 3.$$

Corollary

The congruence

$$ax^3 + 3bx^2 y + 3cxy^2 + dy^3 \equiv 1 \pmod 9$$

has no solutions if I and II hold with the omission of $a \not\equiv 0$ and $d \not\equiv 0$.

The congruence

$$ax^3 + 3bx^2 y + 3cxy^2 + dy^3 \equiv 1 \pmod 7,$$

is impossible if to mod 7, I and either II or III holds.

I.　　　　$a \not\equiv \pm 1,\quad d \not\equiv \pm 1,$

II.　　　　$b \not\equiv 0,\quad \left(\dfrac{c^2 + b(d \pm a - \varepsilon)}{7}\right) = -1,\quad \varepsilon = 1, -1,$

　　　　　$c \not\equiv 0,\quad \left(\dfrac{b^2 + c(d \pm a - \varepsilon)}{7}\right) = -1,$

III.　　　$b \equiv 0,\quad c \equiv 0,\quad d \pm a \not\equiv 0,\quad \pm 1.$

From I, $xy \not\equiv 0$. Hence $x^3 \equiv \pm 1$, $y^3 \equiv \pm 1$. Then we can write the congruence with $X = x/y$, $Z = 1/y$ as

$$aX^3 + 3bX^2 + 3cX + d \equiv Z^3 \equiv \varepsilon,$$

and so　　　　$3bX^2 + 3cX + d \pm a - \varepsilon \equiv 0.$

If $b \not\equiv 0$, this will be impossible if the quadratic character

$$\left(\frac{9c^2 - 12b(d \pm a - \varepsilon)}{7}\right) = -1,$$

or

$$\left(\frac{c^2 + b(d \pm a - \varepsilon)}{7}\right) = -1.$$

If $b \equiv c \equiv 0$, the congruence is impossible if none of the four conditions $d \pm a \pm 1 \equiv 0$ are satisfied.

4. It is often of importance to find estimates for the magnitude of the solutions of congruences. It will suffice to take a particular case[2] given by

Theorem 3

Let $L_1, L_2, \ldots, L_n$ be n homogeneous linear forms in x, y, z with integer coefficients. Let $q_1, q_2, \ldots, q_n$ be any n positive integers and r_1, r_2, r_3 any positive numbers such that $r_1 r_2 r_3 \geqslant q_1 q_2 \ldots q_n$. Then the congruences $L_s \equiv 0 \pmod{q_s}$, $(s = 1, 2, \ldots, n)$ have a non-trivial solution, i.e. not $(0, 0, 0)$, such that

$$|x| \leqslant r_1, \qquad |y| < r_2, \qquad |z| < r_3.$$

Consider the sets of integers (x, y, z) lying in the intervals

$$0 \leqslant x \leqslant r_1, \qquad 0 \leqslant y < r_2, \qquad 0 \leqslant z < r_3.$$

Denote by $[r]$ the integer part of r. Write r' for $[r]$ when r is not an integer, and for $r - 1$ when r is an integer. There are

$$(1 + [r_1])(1 + r_2')(1 + r_3') > r_1 r_2 r_3$$

sets of integers x, y, z lying in the intervals, and so there are more than $q_1 q_2 \ldots q_n$ sets of residues for $L_s \pmod{q_s}$, $(s = 1, 2, \ldots, n)$. Hence at least two different sets (x_1, y_1, z_1) and (x_2, y_2, z_2) have the same residue set, and so the differences $x = x_1 - x_2$, $y = y_1 - y_2$, $z = z_1 - z_2$ are not all zero. For these we have

$$L_s(x, y, z) \equiv 0 \pmod{q_s}, \quad (s = 1, 2, \ldots, n), \quad |x| \leqslant r_1, |y| < r_2, |z| < r_3.$$

In Chapter 2, some equations were proved impossible by congruence considerations. These involved congruences of the form

$$a_1 x_1^{l_1} + a_2 x_2^{l_2} + \cdots + a_n x_n^{l_n} \equiv 0 \pmod{p},$$

p a prime, for which it was shown that at least one of the x, say x_1, is divisible by p. If this holds for an infinity of primes p, then only solutions with $x_1 = 0$ are possible. This possibility can be ruled out from[3]

Theorem 4

The congruence

$$f(x) = a_1 x_1^{l_1} + a_2 x_2^{l_2} + \cdots + a_n x_n^{l_n} \equiv 0 \pmod{p}, \tag{3}$$

where p is a prime, $a_1 a_2 \ldots a_n \not\equiv 0 \pmod{p}$ always has a solution with $x_1 x_2 \ldots x_n \not\equiv 0 \pmod{p}$ if

$$(p - 1)^{n-1} p^{-n/2} > l_1 l_2 \ldots l_n,$$

There is no loss of generality if we suppose that

$$l_1 > 0, \ldots, l_n > 0, \qquad l_1 \mid p - 1, \ldots, l_n \mid p - 1.$$

Denote by $N(a) = N(a_1, a_2, \ldots, a_n)$ the number of solutions of (3) with $x_1 x_2 \ldots x_n \not\equiv 0 \pmod{p}$. Write $e(X) = e(2\pi i X/p)$. Then the number of solutions can be written in the form

$$pN(a) = \sum_{t=0}^{p-1} \sideset{}{'}\sum_{x}^{x=p-1} e(tf(x)), \tag{4}$$

since the sum is zero if $f(x) \not\equiv 0 \pmod p$, and is p if $f(x) \equiv 0 \pmod p$. Here $\sum'$ means that no x is zero.

Write this as

$$pN(a) - (p-1)^n = \sum_{t=1}^{p-1} \sum_{x}^{p-1}{}' e(tf(x)).$$

Then $\qquad |pN(a) - (p-1)^n|^2 = \sum_{t_1,t_2=1}^{p-1} \sum_{x,y}^{p-1}{}' e(t_1 f(x) - t_2 f(y)). \qquad (5)$

Sum now for each a with $0 \leqslant a < p$. The sum is zero except when the x, y satisfy

$$t_1 x_1^{l_1} \equiv t_2 y_1^{l_1}, \ldots, t_1 x_n^{l_n} \equiv t_2 y_n^{l_n}, \quad \pmod p. \qquad (6)$$

Denote by M the number of solutions for t_1, t_2, x, y. Then t_1, t_2 can take at most $(p-1)^2$ sets of values, and x can take at most l values for given y. Hence

$$M \leqslant (p-1)^{2+n} l_1 l_2 \ldots l_n.$$

For each solution, the sum for the a gives p^n.

Hence $\qquad \sum_{(a)} |pN(a) - (p-1)^n|^2 \leqslant p^n(p-1)^{2+n} l_1 l_2 \ldots l_n.$

On replacing x_1 by $f_1 x_1, \ldots,$ x_n by $f_n x_n$, we see there are at least $(p-1)^n / l_1 l_2 \ldots l_n$ congruences with the same $N(a)$ if $a_1 a_2 \ldots a_n \not\equiv 0 \pmod p$, since f^l assumes only $(p-1)/l$ values for $f = 1, 2, \ldots, p-1$. Hence

$$\frac{(p-1)^n}{l_1 l_2 \ldots l_n} |pN(a) - (p-1)^n|^2 \leqslant p^n(p-1)^{2+n} l_1 l_2 \ldots l_n,$$

and so $\qquad |pN(a) - (p-1)^n| \leqslant p^{n/2}(p-1) l_1 l_2 \ldots l_n.$

Hence $N(a) \neq 0$ if

$$(p-1)^n > p^{n/2}(p-1) l_1 l_2 \ldots l_n,$$

and so if

$$(p-1)^{n-1} p^{-n/2} > l_1 l_2 \ldots l_n.$$

Theorem 5

The congruence

$$f(x) = a_1 x_1^{l_1} + \cdots + a_n x_n^{l_n} + a \equiv 0 \pmod p,$$

where p is a prime, $a a_1 a_2 \ldots a_n \not\equiv 0 \pmod p$ always has a solution with $x_1 x_2 \ldots x_n \not\equiv 0$ if

$$(p-1)^{n-1/2} p^{-n/2} > l_1 l_2 \ldots l_n.$$

The proof proceeds as for Theorem 4 except that now $t_1 \equiv t_2 \pmod{p}$. Then $M \leqslant (p - 1)^{1+n} l_1 l_2 \ldots l_n$, and the exponent $2 + n$ is replaced by $1 + n$.

A result[4] required in Chapter 14 for the integer solutions of the equation $z^3 = ax^2 + by^2 + c$ is given by

5. Theorem 6

The congruence

$$y^2 \equiv x^3 + k \pmod{a},$$

when a is odd, has a solution with $(y, a) = 1$ *except when* $a \equiv 0 \pmod 7$, $k \equiv 6 \pmod 7$.

It suffices to consider the case $a = p^r$ where p is an odd prime and r is a positive integer. If there is a solution (x_0, y_0) with $(y_0, p) = 1$ when $r = 1$, then by Theorem 1 there is a solution for $r > 1$.

Three cases arise, $p = 3$, $p \equiv 2 \pmod 3$, $p \equiv 1 \pmod 3$ when $r = 1$. When $p = 3$, since $x^3 \equiv x \pmod 3$, $y^2 \equiv x + k \pmod 3$ and this has a solution $y = 1$.

When $p \equiv 2 \pmod 3$, the congruence $x^3 = y^2 - k \pmod p$ is solvable for arbitrary y.

When $p \equiv 1 \pmod 3$, we can use an estimate for N the number of solutions of the congruence given by Theorem 4, but there will be less numerical detail if we use the fairly deep estimate[5] given by Hasse and Davenport,

$$|N - p| < 2\sqrt{p}, \quad \text{or} \quad N > p - 2\sqrt{p}.$$

Then if $p \geqslant 13$, $N > 4$ and so there will be at least two different residues of $x^3 \pmod p$, and so there exists a value of $y \not\equiv 0 \pmod p$. The only prime $p < 13$ is 7, and it is easily verified that a solution $y \not\equiv 0 \pmod 7$ exists except when $k \equiv 6 \pmod 7$.

When a is even and $a/2^r$ is odd, there are solutions with $(y, a) = 1$ if there are solutions of $y^2 = x^3 + k \pmod{2^r}$ with y odd. When $r = 1$, we can take $y = 1$. When $r = 2$, we have solutions if $k \not\equiv 3 \pmod 4$ since we can take y odd. When $r = 3$, we have solutions with y odd if $k \not\equiv 3, 5, 7 \pmod 8$. This result holds for $r \geqslant 3$.

REFERENCES

1. C. Chevalley. Démonstration d'une hypothèse de M. Artin. *Abh. Math. Sem. Hamburg*, **11** (1935), 73–75.
2. L. J. Mordell. On the equation $ax^2 + by^2 - cz^2 = 0$. *Monatshefte für Math.*, **55** (1951), 323–327.
3. L. J. Mordell. The number of solutions of some congruences in two variables. *Math. Z.*, **37** (1933), 193–209.
4. L. J. Mordell. Note on cubic equations in three variables with an infinity of integer solutions. *Annali mat. pura appl.* (4) **29**, (1949), 301–305.
5. H. Davenport and H. Hasse. Die Nullstellen der Kongruenzetafunktionen in gewissen zyklischen Fällen. *J. Reine Angew. Math.*, **172** (1934), 151–182.

CHAPTER 7

Homogeneous Equations of the Second Degree

1. Let

$$f(x) = \sum_{r,s=1}^{n} a_{rs} x_r x_s, \quad a_{rs} = a_{sr} \tag{1}$$

be an indefinite quadratic form with integer coefficients and of determinant $D = \|a_{rs}\| \neq 0$. We discuss the solvability in integers of the equation $f(x) = 0$.

Results for $n = 3$ were given by Legendre for the diagonal forms, i.e. $a_{23} = a_{31} = a_{12} = 0$, and various modifications of his proof have been given by other writers. Results for diagonal forms in four and five variables were found by Meyer nearly a hundred years after Legendre's work. The general case was considered by Minkowski and Hasse[1] culminating in the latter's result given below as Theorem 1, and embodying a new and important principle, namely, that solvability of the equation $f(x) = 0$ for all local (i.e. p-adic) fields implied global solvability (i.e. solution in integers).

Other results give estimates for the magnitude of a solution in terms of the coefficients. For $n = 3$, the first sharp results are due to Holzer[2]. His method is rather advanced, and so further on we shall give the less sharp results due to Mordell[3] which can be proved by elementary means. These were also found later by Skolem.[4] Mordell[5] has since found a very elementary proof of Holzer's results also given further on. An estimate sometimes better than Holzer's and depending upon results in quadratic fields was given by M. Kneser[6].

Estimates for the magnitude of a solution of the general quadratic equation have been given by Cassels[7], Davenport[8], Birch and Davenport[9], but they have no place here. These results are of great importance in many investigations.

Theorem 1

The equation $f(x) = 0$ is solvable in integers if and only if the congruence $f(x) \equiv 0 \pmod{p^r}$ is solvable for all primes p and integers $r \geqslant 1$ with $(x_1, x_2, \ldots, x_n, p) = 1$.

Stated otherwise the conditions imposed upon $f(x)$ mean that the equation $f(x) = 0$ is solvable in every p-adic field including of course the real field p_∞.

The condition is obviously necessary.

It is well known that by means of a linear substitution

$$X_r = c_{rr} x_r + \cdots + c_{rn} x_n, \quad (r = 1, \ldots, n),$$

where the c are integers and $c_{rr} \neq 0$, that the solution of the equation $f(x) = 0$ is equivalent to that of an equation

$$F(\mathscr{X}) = A_1 X_1^2 + \cdots + A_n X_n^2 = 0. \tag{2}$$

This is easily proved by induction. We may suppose that $a_{11} \neq 0$ by a linear substitution if need be.

Then
$$a_{11} f(x) = X_1^2 + f_1(x),$$

where
$$X_1 = \sum_{r=1}^{n} a_{1r} x_r, \qquad f_1(x) = \sum_{r,s=2}^{n} b_{r,s} x_r x_s.$$

Similarly
$$b_{22} f_1(x) = X_2^2 + f_2(x),$$

where
$$X_2 = \sum_{r=2}^{n} b_{2r} x_r, \quad \text{etc.}$$

It can be shown that the substitution does not affect p-adic solubility.
2. The case $n = 2$ is trivial and so we commence with $n = 3$ and write

$$f(x, y, z) = ax^2 + by^2 + cz^2 = 0. \tag{3}$$

We now may suppose that a, b, c have no common factor, and also that x, y, z have no common factor. We also suppose that a, b, c do not all have the same sign and that $f(x, y, z) \equiv 0 \pmod{p^r}$ is solvable for all primes p and integers $r \geqslant 1$ with $(x, y, z, p) = 1$.

We now reduce $f(x, y, z)$ to a canonical form. Firstly, we may suppose that a, b, c are square-free. For let $a = a_1 \alpha^2$, $b = b_1 \beta^2$, $c = c_1 \gamma^2$ where a_1, b_1, c_1 are square-free. We have now a 1–1 correspondence between the solutions of equation (3) and of

$$f_1(x_1, y_1, z_1) = a_1 x_1^2 + b_1 y_1^2 + c_1 z_1^2 = 0$$

given by

$$d_1 x_1 = \alpha x, \qquad d_1 y_1 = \beta y, \qquad d_1 z_1 = \gamma z, \quad (x_1, y_1, z_1) = 1,$$
$$dx = \beta \gamma x_1, \qquad dy = \gamma \alpha y_1, \qquad dz = \alpha \beta z_1, \quad (x, y, z) = 1.$$

Clearly if $f(x, y, z) = 0$ is p-adically solvable so is $f_1(x, y, z) = 0$ and conversely.

Next we may suppose in equation (3) that $(b, c) = (c, a) = (a, b) = 1$. For let p be a prime factor of (b, c) and so $b = pb_1$, $c = pc_1$. Then $ax^2 \equiv 0 \pmod{p}$, and so $x = px_1$. Hence with $a_1 = pa$, (3) becomes

$$a_1 x_1^2 + b_1 y^2 + c_1 z^2 = 0.$$

Here $a_1 b_1 c_1 = abc/p$ and so $|a_1 b_1 c_1| < |abc|$. Clearly the process, applied to all the prime factors of (b, c), (c, a), (a, b), must terminate at a stage when $(b, c) = (c, a) = (a, b) = 1$. Further the final equation is solvable as a congruence for all p^r.

We now write equation (3) in the form

$$ax^2 + by^2 - cz^2 = 0, \quad a > 0, b > 0, c > 0. \tag{4}$$

Let p be an odd prime divisor of a. Then $by^2 - cz^2 \equiv 0 \pmod{a}$ is solvable and so as in Mordell[3] and Skolem[4],

$$by^2 - cz^2 \equiv b(y + kz)(y - kz) \pmod{p},$$

say, and so $\qquad\qquad f(x, y, z) \equiv L_1 M_1 \pmod{p},$

identically in x, y, z where L_1, M_1 are linear forms in x, y, z.

Similarly if q, r are odd prime divisors of b, c, respectively.

$$f(x, y, z) \equiv L_2 M_2 \pmod{q},$$

$$f(x, y, z) \equiv L_3 M_3 \pmod{r}.$$

Also $\qquad\qquad ax^2 + by^2 - cz^2 \equiv (ax + by + cz)^2 \pmod{2}.$

Hence since abc is square-free, on taking into account the various p, q, r, we have by the Chinese remainder theorem,

$$f(x, y, z) \equiv LM \pmod{abc},$$

where L, M are linear forms.

We show now that we can find integers $x, y, z \neq 0, 0, 0$, such that

$$ax^2 + by^2 - cz^2 \equiv 0 \pmod{abc}, \tag{5}$$

and $\qquad 0 \leqslant |x| < \sqrt{bc}, \qquad 0 \leqslant |y| < \sqrt{ca}, \qquad 0 \leqslant |z| < \sqrt{ab},$

provided we exclude the trivial case $a = b = c = 1$. Here the numbers $\sqrt{bc}, \sqrt{ca}, \sqrt{ab}$ are irrational. The number of sets of integers x, y, z with $0 \leqslant x < \sqrt{bc}, 0 \leqslant y < \sqrt{ca}, 0 \leqslant z < \sqrt{ab}$ is $\Pi (1 + [\sqrt{bc}]) > \Pi (\sqrt{bc}) = abc$. But L has only abc residues mod abc, and so for two sets of values for x, y, z, say, x_1, y_1, z_1 and x_2, y_2, z_2,

$$L(x_1, y_1, z_1) \equiv L(x_2, y_2, z_2) \pmod{abc}.$$

Hence $\qquad L(x_1 - x_2, y_1 - y_2, z_1 - z_2) \equiv 0 \pmod{abc},$

and $\qquad |x_1 - x_2| < \sqrt{bc}, \qquad |y_1 - y_2| < \sqrt{ca}, \qquad |z_1 - z_2| < \sqrt{ab}.$

Then for $x = x_1 - x_2$, etc.

$$-abc < ax^2 + by^2 - cz^2 < 2abc,$$

and so $\qquad\qquad ax^2 + by^2 - cz^2 = 0 \text{ or } abc.$

In the second case,

$$(ax^2 + by^2)(z^2 + ab) = c(z^2 + ab)^2,$$

or
$$a(xz + by)^2 + b(yz - ax)^2 = c(z^2 + ab)^2.$$

i.e.
$$aX^2 + bY^2 = cZ^2.$$

This proves the solvability of equation (4).

The result gives an estimate for the magnitude of the solution, but a better one is given by Mordell's

Theorem 2

There exists a non-trivial solution with

$$|x| \leqslant \sqrt{2bc}, \qquad |y| < \sqrt{2ca}, \qquad |z| < 2\sqrt{ab}. \tag{6}$$

This is not so precise as Holzer's[2] result $|x| \leqslant \sqrt{bc}, |y| \leqslant \sqrt{ca}, |z| \leqslant \sqrt{ab}$, where the equality signs can be omitted unless two of a, b, c, are equal to one. It suffices for a proof of this to show that we can find a solution not $(0, 0, 0)$ of the congruence

$$f(x, y, z) = ax^2 + by^2 - cz^2 \equiv 0 \;(\text{mod } 4abc),$$

with
$$|x| \leqslant \sqrt{2bc}, \qquad |y| < \sqrt{2ca}, \qquad |z| < 2\sqrt{ab}.$$

Then
$$|f(x, y, z)| < 4abc, \quad \text{i.e.} \quad f(x, y, z) = 0.$$

We do this by applying Theorem 3 of Chapter 6 to five linear congruences.

Suppose first that a, b, c are all odd. Then there exist integers A, B, C such that

$$bA^2 - c \equiv 0 \;(\text{mod } a), \quad -cB^2 + a \equiv 0 \;(\text{mod } b), \quad aC^2 + b \equiv 0 \;(\text{mod } c).$$

Three of the congruences are given by

$$y - Az \equiv 0 \;(\text{mod } a), \qquad z - Bx \equiv 0 \;(\text{mod } b), \qquad x - Cy \equiv 0 \;(\text{mod } c).$$

Then from the first,

$$ax^2 + by^2 - cz^2 \equiv (bA^2 - c)z^2 \equiv 0 \;(\text{mod } a).$$

Similarly for mod b, mod c.

We can satisfy $f(x, y, z) \equiv 0 \;(\text{mod } 4)$ by taking two linear congruences each to mod 2. We cannot have both $a - c \equiv 2 \;(\text{mod } 4)$, $b - c \equiv 2 \;(\text{mod } 4)$ for then $a \equiv b \equiv -c \;(\text{mod } 4)$, and so $f(x, y, z) \equiv 0 \;(\text{mod } 4)$ is not solvable. We may suppose that $b - c \equiv 0 \;(\text{mod } 4)$, and then the two congruences are

$$x \equiv 0 \;(\text{mod } 2), \qquad y \equiv z \;(\text{mod } 2).$$

It now suffices to take

$$r_1 = \sqrt{2bc}, \qquad r_2 = \sqrt{2ca}, \qquad r_3 = 2\sqrt{ab}.$$

in Theorem 3 of Chapter 6.

Suppose next that one of a, b, c is even, say a. We can now make $f(x, y, z) \equiv 0 \pmod{\tfrac{1}{2}abc}$ if x, y, z satisfy the three congruences:

$$y - Az \equiv 0 \pmod{\tfrac{1}{2}a}, \qquad z - Bx \equiv 0 \pmod b, \qquad x - Cy \equiv 0 \pmod c.$$

We now satisfy $f(x, y, z) \equiv 0 \pmod 8$ by taking two linear congruences one to mod 2 and the other to mod 4.
These are

$$x \equiv ly \pmod 2, \qquad z = my \pmod 4,$$

where l, m satisfy

$$al^2 + b - cm^2 \equiv 0 \pmod 8.$$

If $a + b - c \equiv 0 \pmod 8$, we take $l = m = 1$. If $b - c \equiv 0 \pmod 8$, we take $l = 0, m = 1$. Then as before, Theorem 3 of Chapter 6 gives a solution. The equation is impossible when $b - c \equiv 4$ or $a \pmod 8$ as follows on taking congruences mod 8.

This finishes the proof.

To summarize, we have proved

Theorem 3

If a, b, c are square free, $(a, b) = (b, c) = (c, a) = 1$, and a, b, c do not have the same sign, then the equation

$$ax^2 + by^2 + cz^2 = 0$$

has non-trivial integer solutions if and only if $-bc$ is a quadratic residue of a, and so for every prime factor of a, i.e. $x^2 + bc \equiv 0 \pmod a$ is solvable, and similarly for $-ca$ and $-ab$, and if

$$ax^2 + by^2 + cz^2 \equiv 0 \pmod 8$$

is solvable.

These give N, say, necessary and sufficient conditions. It can be shown that if any $N - 1$ of these conditions are satisfied, so is the remaining one. This is a consequence of the laws of quadratic reciprocity and the supplementary laws, namely, that if p, q are two different odd primes

$$\left(\frac{p}{q}\right)\left(\frac{q}{p}\right) = (-1)^{(p-1)(q-1)/4},$$

and $\qquad \left(\frac{-1}{p}\right) = (-1)^{(p-1)/2}, \qquad \left(\frac{2}{p}\right) = (-1)^{(p^2-1)/8}.$

There is, however, no need here to go into details. The result is well known from Hilbert's theory of the norm-residue symbol.

Theorem 4

If one integer solution not $(0, 0, 0)$ *of the irreducible equation*

$$f(x, y, z) = ax^2 + by^2 + cz^2 + 2fyz + 2gzx + 2hxy = 0 \qquad (7)$$

exists, then the general solution with $(x, y, z) = 1$ *is given by a finite number of expressions of the form*

$$x = A_1 p^2 + B_1 pq + C_1 q^2, \qquad y = A_2 p^2 + B_2 pq + C_2 q^2,$$
$$z = A_3 p^2 + B_3 pq + C_3 q^2, \qquad (8)$$

where p, q *take all integer values with* $(p, q) = 1$, *and the* A, B, C *are integer constants.*

For let a solution (x_0, y_0, z_0) be known. Write

$$x = rx_0 + p, \qquad y = ry_0 + q, \qquad z = rz_0,$$

where p, q, r are rational numbers. Then we have a linear equation in r from which $r = f(p, q, 0)/L(p, q)$ where L is a linear function of p and q. Hence ignoring denominators, we have with an appropriate factor δ,

$$\delta x = f_1(p, q), \qquad \delta y = f_2(p, q), \qquad \delta z = f_3(p, q),$$

where f_1, f_2, f_3 are binary quadratics with integer coefficients, and we may now suppose that p, q are integers and that $(p, q) = 1$. A simple elimination procedure shows that the common factors of f_1, f_2, f_3 are independent of p, q. These and δ can be removed on replacing p, q by a linear substitution on p, q.

The method of Theorem 4 has been used by Mordell[5] to give an elementary proof of Holzer's

Theorem 5

The solvable equation $ax^2 + by^2 + cz^2 = 0$ *taken in the canonical form with* $a > 0, b > 0, c < 0$ *has a non-trivial solution with*

$$|x| \leq \sqrt{b|c|}, \qquad |y| \leq \sqrt{|c|a}, \qquad |z| \leq \sqrt{ab}$$

It is easily seen that all the equality signs may be removed unless two of the a, b, c are unity.

Let (x_0, y_0, z_0) be a solution with $(x_0, y_0, z_0) = 1$. We show that if for this solution, $|z_0| > \sqrt{ab}$, then another solution (x, y, z) can be found with $|z| < |z_0|$. Hence there exists a solution (x, y, z) with $|z| \leq \sqrt{ab}$. The inequalities for x, y are now obvious. Put

$$x = x_0 + tX, \qquad y = y_0 + tY, \qquad z = z_0 + tZ,$$

where X, Y, Z, are integers to be determined later. Then

$$(aX^2 + bY^2 + cZ^2)t + 2(ax_0 X + by_0 Y + cz_0 Z) = 0.$$

Hence, on neglecting a denominator, a solution, say, (x, y, z), is given by

$$\left.\begin{aligned}
\delta z &= z_0(aX^2 + bY^2 + cZ^2) - 2Z(ax_0X + by_0Y + cz_0Z),\\
\delta x &= x_0(aX^2 + bY^2 + cZ^2) - 2X(ax_0X + by_0Y + cz_0Z),\\
\delta y &= y_0(aX^2 + bY^2 + cZ^2) - 2Y(ax_0X + by_0Y + cz_0Z),
\end{aligned}\right\} \tag{9}$$

where δ is a common divisor of the three expressions on the right.
Further x, y, z are integers if

$$\delta \mid c, \qquad \delta \mid (Xy_0 - Yx_0),$$

For from

$$ax_0^2 + by_0^2 + cz_0^2 = 0,$$

it easily follows that $(\delta, abx_0y_0) = 1$. From (9) it suffices to show that

$$P = ax_0X + by_0Y \equiv 0 \; (\text{mod } \delta), \qquad Q = aX^2 + bY^2 \equiv 0 \; (\text{mod } \delta).$$

Since $\qquad X \equiv x_0Y/y_0, \qquad P \equiv Y(ax_0^2 + by_0^2)/y_0 \equiv 0 \; (\text{mod } \delta);$

also $\qquad Q \equiv (ax_0^2 + by_0^2)Y^2/y_0^2 \equiv 0 \; (\text{mod } \delta).$

From (9)

$$\frac{-\delta z}{cz_0} = \left(Z + \frac{ax_0X + by_0Y}{cz_0}\right)^2 + \frac{ab}{c^2z_0^2}(y_0X - x_0Y)^2. \tag{10}$$

Suppose now that $z_0^2 > ab$. Take X, Y as a solution of $y_0X - x_0Y = \delta$.
First let c be even. Take $\delta = \frac{1}{2}c$, and Z so that

$$\left| Z + \frac{ax_0X + by_0Y}{cz_0} \right| \le \tfrac{1}{2}.$$

Then

$$\frac{1}{2}\left|\frac{z}{z_0}\right| < \tfrac{1}{4} + \tfrac{1}{4} \quad \text{and} \quad |z| < |z_0|. \tag{11}$$

Hence on continuing the process we have a solution with $z^2 \le ab$. Secondly let c be odd. Now impose the condition

$$aX + bY + cZ \equiv 0 \; (\text{mod } 2).$$

This defines the parity of Z. Since δ is odd, the three expressions on the right-hand side of (9) are divisible by 2δ, and so we now have (10) with δ replaced by 2δ. Take $\delta = c$ and Z with assigned parity so that

$$\left| Z + \frac{ax_0X + by_0Y}{cz_0} \right| \le 1.$$

Then (11) is replaced by

$$2\left|\frac{z}{z_0}\right| < 1 + 1 \quad \text{and} \quad |z| < |z_0|.$$

This completes the proof.

3. *Quaternary quadratic equations*[10].

By means of a linear substitution, we may take the equation in the form

$$f(x) = a_1 x_1^2 + a_2 x_2^2 + a_3 x_3^2 + a_4 x_4^2 = 0,$$

where the a's are integers.

Theorem 6

The equation $f(x) = 0$ is solvable in rational integers if and only if $f(x) \equiv 0 \pmod{p^r}$ is solvable for all primes p and for all r with $(x_1, x_2, x_3, x_4, p) = 1$, and $f(x) = 0$ is solvable in real numbers.

We may suppose that the a are square free since if $a_1 = A_1 \alpha_1^2$ etc. where A_1 etc. are square free, a 1–1 correspondence is established between the solutions of

$$\sum_{r=1}^{4} a_r x_r^2 = 0, \qquad \sum_{r=1}^{4} A_r X_r^2 = 0,$$

by the relations

$$X_1 = \alpha_1 x_1, \ldots, \qquad x_1 = \alpha_2 \alpha_3 \alpha_4 X_1 \ldots$$

We may also suppose as in the case of the ternary quadratic that no three of the a's have a common factor.

Since the coefficients a_1, a_2, a_3, a_4 do not all have the same sign, we may suppose that $a_1 > 0$, $a_4 > 0$. Write

$$g = a_1 x_1^2 + a_2 x_2^2, \qquad h = -a_3 x_3^2 - a_4 x_4^2.$$

We shall prove the theorem by showing the existence of an integer a representable by both g and h. This will follow from the p-adic solvability of $f(x) = 0$.

Let $p_1, p_2, \ldots, p_s$ be all the different odd primes dividing $a_1 a_2 a_3 a_4$. Then for every p from among $p_1, \ldots, p_s$, and for $p = 2$ there is a p-adic solution of

$$a_1 \xi_1^2 + a_2 \xi_2^2 + a_3 \xi_3^2 + a_4 \xi_4^2 = 0.$$

We may suppose in this solution $(\xi_1', \xi_2', \xi_3', \xi_4')$ that none of the ξ' are zero. For if $\xi_4' = 0$, the p-adic equation is solvable for arbitrary ξ_4. This is obvious on replacing ξ_1, ξ_2, ξ_3 by $t\xi_1' + \eta_1, t\xi_2' + \eta_2, t\xi_3' + \eta_3$, where the η are arbitrary, and this gives a linear equation in t.

Write

$$b_p = a_1 \xi_1^2 + a_2 \xi_2^2 = -a_3 \xi_3^2 - a_4 \xi_4^2.$$

We can choose the solution ξ so that $b_p \neq 0$ in the p-adic field Q_p. For if $b_p = 0$, then both g and h represent any integer in Q_p since g and h

factorize in the p-adic field. We may also suppose that $b_p \equiv 0 \pmod{p^{\lambda_p}}$ but not $p^{\lambda_p + 1}$, and also when $p = 2$. Consider the congruences with $a > 0$,

$$a \equiv b_2 \pmod{2^{\lambda_2 + 3}}, \qquad a \equiv b_p \pmod{p^{\lambda_p + 1}}, \qquad p = p_1, \ldots, p_s.$$

These determine a uniquely $\bmod\ m = 2^{\lambda_2 + 3} p_1^{\lambda_1 + 1} \ldots p_s^{\lambda_s + 1}$. Since $b_p \not\equiv 0$ $\pmod{p^{\lambda_p + 1}}$, $b_p a^{-1} \equiv 1 \pmod{p}$. Hence the quadratic character $(b_p a^{-1}/p) = 1$, and so $b_p a^{-1}$ is a quadratic residue in Q_p and so is a p-adic square. Similarly $b_2 a^{-1} \equiv 1 \pmod 8$ and so $b_2 a^{-1}$ is a quadratic residue in Q_2 and so is a 2-adic square. Since b_p and a differ by a square factor in all the fields Q_p, Q_2, both the forms

$$-aX_0^2 + a_1 X_1^2 + a_2 X_2^2, \qquad -aX_0^2 - a_3 X_3^2 - a_4 X_4^2$$

represent zero in all the Q_p and Q_2. These forms have a zero in every p-adic field, except possibly when $p \mid a$. Also the forms are indefinite since $a_1 > 0$, $a_4 < 0$. Hence if a has only one prime factor q different from 2, $p_1, \ldots, p_s$, the forms will also have a zero in Q_q. Then from the ternary case of Theorem 1, we have

$$a = a_1 c_1^2 + a_2 c_2^2, \qquad a = -a_3 c_3^2 - a_4 c_4^2,$$

with rational c, and so finally

$$a_1 c_1^2 + a_2 c_2^2 + a_3 c_3^2 + a_4 c_4^2 = 0.$$

The existence of such an a is proved by Dirichlet's theorem that there are an infinity of primes in an arithmetical progression in which the first term is prime to the difference. Let a' be an arbitrary one of the a defined by the congruences above; write $d = (a', m)$. Then there exists an integer $k \geq 0$ such that $a'/d + km/d$ is a prime q. We take $a = a' + km = qd$.

We now state without proof the conditions for the p-adic solvability of the equation

$$f(x) = a_1 x_1^2 + a_2 x_2^2 + a_3 x_3^2 + a_4 x_4^2 = 0,$$

where $f(x)$ is in the normal form, i.e. the a are square free integers and no three of the a have a common factor.

The a of course must not all have the same sign. The p-adic equation is solvable for all p when $(p, a_1, a_2, a_3, a_4) = 1$, as is obvious from the result for the ternary quadratic. Next let $p = p_{12}$ be an odd common prime factor of a_1 and a_2 for which $(-a_3 a_4/p) = 1$. Then we must have $((-a_1 a_2 p^{-2})/p) = 1$. Similarly for the other p_{rs}.

Finally 2-adic solvability is required. This is easily seen to be the solvability of $f(x) \equiv 0 \pmod 8$. The conditions are as follows.

If $a_1 a_2 a_3 a_4 \equiv 1 \pmod 8$, then we require $a_1 + a_2 + a_3 + a_4 \equiv 0 \pmod 8$. There are no conditions if

$$a_1 a_2 a_3 a_4 \equiv 2, 3, 5, 6, 7 \pmod 8.$$

Suppose next that

$$a_1 a_2 a_3 a_4 \equiv 4 \pmod 8 \quad \text{and} \quad a_1 \equiv a_2 \equiv 0 \pmod 2,$$

say. Then if

$$\tfrac{1}{4} a_1 a_2 a_3 a_4 \equiv 1 \pmod 8,$$

we require

$$\tfrac{1}{2} a_1 + \tfrac{1}{2} a_2 + a_3 + a_4 \equiv \tfrac{1}{2}(a_3^2 a_4^2 - 1) \pmod 8.$$

No conditions are required if

$$\tfrac{1}{4} a_1 a_2 a_3 a_4 \equiv 3, 5, 7 \pmod 8.$$

We prove now the

4. Theorem 7

Every indefinite quadratic form $f(x)$ in five variables represents zero.
It suffices to take

$$f(x) = a_1 x_1^2 + \cdots + a_5 x_5^2,$$

where the a are square free, $a_1 > 0$, $a_5 < 0$.
Write

$$g = a_1 x_1^2 + a_2 x_2^2, \qquad h = -a_3 x_3^2 - a_4 x_4^2 - a_5 x_5^2.$$

We argue as in the case of four variables. We find by Dirichlet's theorem a positive rational integer a which is represented by both g and h in the real field, and in all p-adic fields Q_p with the exclusion perhaps of a field Q_q where q is an odd prime number not dividing any of the coefficients $a_1, a_2, \ldots$. Then g represents a by the theory of the ternary quadratic. Also since h represents zero in Q_q, it represents a rationally by the theory of the quaternary quadratic. The theorem follows as for $n = 4$.

It is now trivial that an indefinite form $f(x_1, x_2, \ldots, x_n)$ with $n > 5$ variables represents zero. It is also easily proved that solutions exist with $x_1 x_2 \ldots x_n \neq 0$.

5. A much more difficult question is to investigate the solvability of two simultaneous homogeneous quadratic equations $f(x) = 0$, $g(x) = 0$ in n variables. Mordell[11] has shown by an application of Meyer's theorem that subject to some simple natural conditions, for example, that $\lambda f(x) + \mu g(x)$ is not a definite form for all real values of λ, μ not both zero, that non-trivial solutions, i.e. not all zeros, exist if $n \geqslant 13$. Swinnerton-Dyer[12] has improved this to $n \geqslant 11$. It is conjectured that $n = 9$ is the best possible result, but some equations in 9 variables are such that four of the variables must be zero.

An interesting question is whether the two simultaneous equations in five variables are solvable when they are solvable in every p-adic field including p_∞.

REFERENCES

1. H. Hasse. Über die Darstellbarkeit von Zahlen durch quadratische Formen im Körper der rationalen Zahlen. *J. reine angew. Math.*, **152** (1923), 129–148; also 205–224.

2. L. Holzer. Minimal solutions of diophantine equations. *Can. J. Math.*, **11** (1950), 238–244.

3. L. J. Mordell. On the equation $ax^2 + by^2 - cz^2 = 0$. *Monatshefte für Math.*, **55** (1951), 323–327.

4. T. Skolem. On the diophantine equation $ax^2 + by^2 + cz^2 = 0$. *Rendiconti di Matematica e delle sue applicazioni* (5), **11** (1952), 88–102.

5. L. J. Mordell. On the magnitude of the integer solutions of the equation $ax^2 + by^2 + cz^2 = 0$. *J. number theory*, **I** (1968), 1–3.

6. M. Kneser. Kleine Lösungen der diophantischen Gleichung $ax^2 + by^2 = cz^2$. *Abh. Math. Sem. Hamburg*, **23** (1959), 163–173.

7. J. W. S. Cassels. Bounds for the least solution of homogeneous quadratic equations. *Proc. Camb. Phil. Soc.*, **51** (1955), 262–264. Addendum, *ibid.* **52** (1956), 664.

8. H. Davenport. Note on a theorem of Cassels. *Proc. Camb. Phil. Soc.*, **53** (1957), 539–540. Addendum, *ibid.* **52** (1956), 664.

9. B. J. Birch and H. Davenport. Quadratic equations in several variables. *Proc. Camb. Phil. Soc.*, **54** (1958), 135–138.

10. Z. I. Borevich and I. R. Shafarevich. "Number-theory", Chapter I. Academic Press, New York and London (1966).

11. L. J. Mordell. Integer solutions of simultaneous quadratic equations. *Abh. Math. Sem. Hamburg*, **23** (1959), 124–143.

12. H. P. F. Swinnerton-Dyer. Rational zeros of two quadratic forms. *Acta Arith.*, **9** (1964), 260–270.

CHAPTER 8

Pell's Equation

1. Theorem 1

Let D be a positive integer which is not a perfect square. Then the equation

$$y^2 - Dx^2 = 1 \tag{1}$$

has an infinity of integer solutions. If $(x, y) = (U, T)$ where $T > 0$, $U > 0$ is the solution with least positive x, all the solutions are given by

$$xy\sqrt{D} = \pm(T + U\sqrt{D})^n, \tag{2}$$

where n is an arbitrary integer.

We ignore the trivial solution $y = \pm 1$, $x = 0$ given by $n = 0$.

The proof of (1) follows easily from a result on Diophantine approximation given by

Lemma 1

Let θ be an irrational number and $q > 1$ an arbitrary positive integer. Then there exist integers x and y such that if $L = y - x\theta$,

$$|L| < 1/q, \qquad 0 < x \leqslant q. \tag{3}$$

Let x take the values $0, 1, 2, \ldots, q$ and let y be such an integer that $0 \leqslant L < 1$. Then $q + 1$ values for L arise lying in the q semi-open intervals

$$\left[\frac{r}{q}, \frac{r+1}{q}\right), \qquad r = 0, 1, \ldots, q - 1.$$

Hence two of the values of L corresponding to say (x_1, y_1) and (x_2, y_2), where $x_1 \neq x_2$, say $x_1 > x_2$, lie in the same interval and so

$$|y_1 - y_2 - (x_1 - x_2)\theta| < 1/q.$$

Then (3) follows on putting $y = y_1 - y_2$, $x = x_1 - x_2$. On replacing (3) by

$$|y - x\theta| < 1/x,$$

it follows that there are an infinity of integer solutions of this inequality.

Lemma 2

A number $m = m(D)$, e.g. $m = 1 + 2\sqrt{D}$, exists such that

$$|y^2 - Dx^2| < m,$$

for an infinity of integers, x, y.

3+

Take $\theta = \sqrt{D}$ in (3) and so integers (x, y) exist such that

$$|y - x\sqrt{D}| < 1/|x|.$$

Then

$$|y + x\sqrt{D}| = |y - x\sqrt{D} + 2x\sqrt{D}|$$

$$< 2|x|\sqrt{D} + 1/|x|,$$

and so

$$|y^2 - Dx^2| < 2\sqrt{D} + 1/x^2$$

$$< 2\sqrt{D} + 1.$$

We now deduce the existence of an integer solution of equation (1). There exists an integer k such that $|k| < m$ and

$$y^2 - Dx^2 = k$$

has an infinity of integer solutions. We may suppose there are two, say (x_1, y_1) and (x_2, y_2), such that

$$x_2 \equiv x_1, \qquad y_2 \equiv y_1 \pmod{k}, \qquad (x_2, y_2) \neq (-x_1, -y_1).$$

From

$$y_1^2 - Dx_1^2 = k, \qquad y_2^2 - Dx_2^2 = k,$$

we have by multiplication,

$$(y_1 y_2 - Dx_1 x_2)^2 - D(y_1 x_2 - y_2 x_1)^2 = k^2.$$

Write

$$y_1 y_2 - Dx_1 x_2 = kY, \qquad y_1 x_2 - y_2 x_1 = kX.$$

Clearly X, Y are integers, $X \neq 0$ and

$$Y^2 - DX^2 = 1.$$

We now deduce an infinity of solutions. Let $(x, y) = (U, T)$ where $U > 0$, $T > 0$, and U is the least value of X. Then an infinity of solutions (x_n, y_n) with $x_n > 0, y_n > 0$ are given by taking

$$y_n + x_n\sqrt{D} = (T + U\sqrt{D})^n, \qquad y_n - x_n\sqrt{D} = (T - U\sqrt{D})^n,$$

where n is any positive integer.

All such solutions are given by these formulae.

For suppose (x, y) is a solution not so given. Then for some positive integer n,

$$(T + U\sqrt{D})^n < y + x\sqrt{D} < (T + U\sqrt{D})^{n+1}.$$

Then

$$1 < (y + x\sqrt{D})(y_n - x_n\sqrt{D}) < T + U\sqrt{D}.$$

Write

$$(y + x\sqrt{D})(y_n - x_n\sqrt{D}) = Y + X\sqrt{D}.$$

and so

$$Y + X\sqrt{D} < T + U\sqrt{D}, \qquad Y^2 - DX^2 = 1.$$

Since $Y + X\sqrt{D} > 1$, and $0 < Y - X\sqrt{D} < 1$, then $X > 0$, $Y > 0$. This contradicts the definition of T, U.

The solutions with

$x < 0, y < 0$ are given by $y + x\sqrt{D} = -(T + U\sqrt{D})^n$,

$x < 0, y > 0$ are given by $y + x\sqrt{D} = (T + U\sqrt{D})^{-n}$,

$x > 0, y < 0$ are given by $y + x\sqrt{D} = -(T + U\sqrt{D})^{-n}$,

where n is a positive integer.

Corollary

If d is a given integer, there exists an infinity of solutions with $x \equiv 0$ (mod d).
This is obvious from $Y^2 - Dd^2 X^2 = 1$.

In the study of the units of quadratic fields, say $Q(\sqrt{d})$, a Pellian equation
takes the form

$$y^2 - dx^2 = 4.$$

If now $(x, y) = (u, t)$, $u > 0$, $t > 0$ is the solution with least x, then it can be
shown similarly that the general solution is given by

$$\frac{y + x\sqrt{d}}{2} = \pm\left(\frac{t + u\sqrt{d}}{2}\right)^n,$$

where n takes all integer values.

The solution of the equation

$$y^2 - Dx^2 = -1 \tag{4}$$

is a much more difficult question and simple explicit conditions for solvability
are not known. A necessary condition is that D is not divisible by 4 or by any
prime $\equiv 3$ (mod 4). It is easily proved that the equation is solvable when
$D = p$ is a prime $\equiv 1$ (mod 4).

For let $(x, y) = (U, T)$ be the fundamental solution of $y^2 - px^2 = 1$.
Then $U \equiv 0$, $T \equiv 1$ (mod 2). Write

$$\frac{T + 1}{2} \cdot \frac{T - 1}{2} = p\left(\frac{U}{2}\right)^2.$$

Then either

$$\frac{T + 1}{2} = pa^2, \qquad \frac{T - 1}{2} = b^2,$$

or

$$\frac{T + 1}{2} = a^2, \qquad \frac{T - 1}{2} = pb^2,$$

where a, b are integers. The second set gives $a^2 - pb^2 = 1$, and contradicts
the definition of the fundamental solution.

The first gives

$$b^2 - pa^2 = -1.$$

Then an infinity of solutions is given by

$$Y + X\sqrt{p} = (b + a\sqrt{p})^{2n+1},$$

where n is an arbitrary integer.

The fundamental solution U, T above is obviously given by

$$T + U\sqrt{p} = (b + a\sqrt{p})^2.$$

Pell's equation arises very naturally in the study of the units in a quadratic field say $Q(\sqrt{d})$, where $d > 0$ and is square free. We have the known results for the units ε,

$$d \equiv 2, 3 \text{ (mod 4)}, \qquad \varepsilon = y + x\sqrt{d}, \qquad y^2 - dx^2 = 1,$$

$$d \equiv 1 \text{ (mod 4)}, \qquad \varepsilon = y + \frac{1 + \sqrt{d}}{2} x, \qquad y^2 + xy + \frac{1 - d}{4} x^2 = \pm 1,$$

where x and y are rational integers. Both equations are included under the form $Y^2 - dX^2 = \pm 4$. The fundamental unit ε_0 corresponds to the solution with smallest positive X and Y. Of course when $d \equiv 2, 3 \text{ (mod 4)}$, $\varepsilon_0 = T + U\sqrt{d}$. The result for $d \equiv 1 \text{ (mod 4)}$ can be proved in a similar way.

The study of the class number of the field has led to the

Conjecture (Ankeny, Artin, Chowla)

Let p be a prime $\equiv 1$ (mod 4) and so now

$$Y^2 - pX^2 = -4.$$

Let u be the least positive value of X. Then $u \not\equiv 0$ (mod p).

This has been verified for $p < 2000$ when $p \equiv 5 \text{ (mod 8)}$, and for $p < 100{,}000$ by Dr Goldberg when $p \equiv 1 \text{ (mod 8)}$. It has been shown by Mordell[1] when $p \equiv 5 \text{ (mod 8)}$, and by Chowla when $p \equiv 1 \text{ (mod 8)}$, that $u \not\equiv 0 \text{ (mod } p)$ if and only if

$$B_{(p-1)/4} \not\equiv 0 \text{ (mod } p),$$

where the Bernouilli numbers are defined by the expansion

$$\frac{t}{e^t - 1} = 1 - \frac{t}{2} + \sum_{n=1}^{\infty} (-1)^{n-1} \frac{B_n x^{2n}}{(2n)!}.$$

There is also the further

Conjecture

Let p be a prime $\equiv 3$ (mod 4) and so now

$$Y^2 - pX^2 = 1.$$

Let U be the least positive value of X. Then $U \not\equiv 0$ (mod p).

This has been verified by K. Goldberg for $p < 18,000$. It has been shown by Mordell[2] that $U \not\equiv 0 \pmod{p}$ if and only if the Euler number

$$E_{(p-3)/4} \not\equiv 0 \pmod{p},$$

where E_n is defined by

$$\sec t = \sum_{n=0}^{\infty} \frac{E_n t^{2n}}{(2n)!}.$$

There is a similar conjecture when $p \equiv 1 \pmod 4$.

2. Theorem 2 (Gauss)

Given one integer solution (x_0, y_0) of the equation

$$f(x, y) = ax^2 + bxy + cy^2 + dx + ey + f = 0, \tag{5}$$

where the coefficients are integers, there exists an infinity of integer solutions if

$$D = b^2 - 4ac > 0,$$

is not a perfect square, and if the discriminant

$$\Delta = 4acf + bde - ae^2 - cd^2 - fb^2 \neq 0.$$

The equation can be written as

$$Y^2 - DX^2 = M,$$

where $M \neq 0$ since $\Delta \neq 0$, and

$$Y = px + qy + r, \qquad X = sy + t,$$

say, where the coefficients are integers. From

$$Y_0^2 - DX_0^2 = M, \qquad T^2 - DU^2 = 1,$$

where now T, U is any integer solution of Pell's equation,

$$(TY_0 - DUX_0)^2 - D(TX_0 - UY_0)^2 = M.$$

Then new values of X, Y are given by

$$X = TX_0 - UY_0, \qquad Y = TY_0 - DUX_0.$$

These give values of x, y satisfying

$$px + qy + r = T(px_0 + qy_0 + r) - DU(sy_0 + t),$$

$$sy + t = T(sy_0 + t) - U(px_0 + qy_0 + r). \tag{6}$$

There are an infinity of solutions of Pell's equation with $U \equiv 0 \pmod{ps}$, and so $T^2 \equiv 1 \pmod{ps}$.

We may suppose $T \equiv 1 \pmod{ps}$, for if $T \not\equiv 1 \pmod{ps}$, we need only take a new solution given by

$$T_1 + U_1\sqrt{D} = (T + U\sqrt{D})^2, \quad \text{or} \quad T_1 = T^2 + DU^2, \ U_1 = 2TU.$$

Then
$$px + qy + r \equiv px_0 + qy_0 + r \pmod{ps},$$

$$sy + t \equiv sy_0 + t \pmod{ps}.$$

This gives $y \equiv y_0 \pmod{p}$, $p(x - x_0) + q(y - y_0) \equiv 0 \pmod{ps}$, and so an integer value for x. Hence equation (6) is satisfied by integer values of x, y.

If $\Delta = 0$, the equation (5) is reducible. Then either both linear factors have rational coefficients, and so at least one linear factor is zero for an infinity of integer values of x, y, or both linear factors have coefficients in the quadratic field $Q(\sqrt{D})$. Then there exists only the solution given by $X = 0$, $Y = 0$.

If D is a perfect square or if $D < 0$, there are obviously only a finite number of solutions.

There are many interesting applications[3] of Pell's equation to Diophantine equations.

Theorem 3

The equation

$$x^3 + y^3 + z^3 + w^3 = n \tag{7}$$

has an infinity of integer solutions if there exists one solution (a, b, c, d) such that

$$-(a + b)(c + d) > 0,$$

is not a perfect square, and $a \neq b$, or $c \neq d$.

Put $\quad x = a + X, \quad y = b - X, \quad z = c + Y, \quad w = d - Y.$

Then $\quad (a + b)X^2 + (a^2 - b^2)X + (c + d)Y^2 + (c^2 - d^2)Y = 0.$

Write

$$(a + b)\left(X + \frac{a - b}{2}\right)^2 + (c + d)\left(Y + \frac{c - d}{2}\right)^2$$
$$- \frac{(a + b)(a - b)^2}{4} - \frac{(c + d)(c - d)^2}{4} = 0.$$

The result now follows from equation (1) since
$$D = -(a + b)(c + d), \quad \text{and} \quad (a + b)(a - b)^2 + (c + d)(c - d)^2 \neq 0$$

unless $a = b$, $c = d$.

It is very surprising that this is the only known method of proving the existence of an infinity of integer solutions of the general equation (7).

Another application of Pell's equation is given in Chapter 13 where it is shown that the equation

$$a(x^3 + y^3) + b(z^3 + c^3) = 0,$$

where a, b, c are integers, has an infinity of integer solutions other than $x + y = 0$.

3. Of special interest is the application of the Pell equation to the discussion of the integer solutions of the simultaneous equations

$$ax_1^2 + bx_1x_2 + cx_2^2 = d, \tag{8}$$

$$a_1x_1^2 + b_1x_1x_2 + c_1x_2^2 = d_1z^2, \tag{9}$$

where the constants are integers. We may suppose that none of the left-hand sides are perfect squares, and that

$$b^2 - 4ac = D > 0$$

is not a perfect square.

These equations include as particular cases many equations of current interest.

We first of all note that the equations have only a finite number of integer solutions. For from Chapter 7, the general solution of equation (9) with $(x_1, x_2, z) = 1$, is given by a finite number of expressions of the form

$$x_r = l_rx^2 + m_rxy + n_ry^2, \quad (r = 1, 2),$$

where the l, m, n are integer constants and x, y are integers. On substituting in equation (8), we have a finite number of binary quartic equations of the form $f(x, y) = f$, say. By a theorem of Thue in Chapter 20, there are only a finite number of integer solutions for x, y. To find these is in general a difficult problem, and most results require detailed and complicated proofs. However, A. Baker has recently found estimates (very large ones, indeed) for the magnitude of the solutions.

The Pellian method of approach is to note that the general solution of equation (8) can be written in the form

$$x = pu + qv, \qquad y = ru + sv,$$

where the p, q, r, s refer to a finite set of rational numbers, and u, v are integer solutions of a Pellian equation. Then from equation (9), we have a finite set of equations

$$z^2 = Au^2 + Buv + Cv^2,$$

where A, B, C are rational numbers.

Suppose for simplicity that the Pellian equation takes the form

$$u^2 - Dv^2 = \pm 1,$$

and denote by u_0, v_0 the fundamental solution. Then the general solution is given by

$$u + v\sqrt{D} = (u_0 + v_0\sqrt{D})^n.$$

Write $\alpha = u_0 + v_0\sqrt{D}, \qquad \beta = u_0 - v_0\sqrt{D}, \quad \alpha\beta = \pm 1,$

Then $2u = \alpha^n + \beta^n, \qquad 2v\sqrt{D} = \alpha^n - \beta^n, \quad z = z_n,$

and $z_n^2 = A_1\alpha^{2n} + B_1\beta^{2n} + C_1(\pm 1)^n.$ (10)

Hence we are led to the following

Problem

   Let a sequence u_n be given by a recurrence formula

$$u_{n+2} + au_{n+1} + bu_n = c,$$ (11)

where the a, b, c are given integer constants. When is u_n a perfect square?

   We give some applications to the Fibonacci sequence u_n, where $u_0 = 0$, $u_1 = 1$, and

$$u_{n+2} = u_{n+1} + u_n,$$

and to the Lucas sequence v_n, where $v_0 = 2$, $v_1 = 1$, and

$$v_{n+2} = v_{n+1} + v_n.$$ (12)

Theorem 4

$$v_n = x^2 \text{ only when } n = 1, 3, \pm x = 1, 2,$$

$$v_n = 2x^2 \text{ only when } n = 0, \pm x = 1, 2.$$

Theorem 5

$$u_n = x^2 \quad \text{only when } n = 0, \pm 1, 2, 12, \pm x, = 0, 1, 12.$$

$$u_n = 2x^2 \text{ only when } n = 0, \pm 3, 6, \text{ and } \pm x = 0, 1, 2.$$

   Proofs for $u_n = x^2$ were given about the same time by Cohn[4] and Wylie[5]. We give here the later proof by Cohn[6] who also proved the other results.

   We need some properties of u_n and v_n. From equation (12), on taking the residues of v_n mod 4, we have a periodic sequence of order 6 given by

$$2, 1, 3, 0, 3, 3, 2, 1, \ldots,$$

and so $v_n \equiv 0 \pmod 2$ only when $n \equiv 0 \pmod 3$, and $v_k \equiv 3 \pmod 4$ when $k \equiv \pm 2 \pmod 6$. We see that $v_n \equiv 0 \pmod 3$ only if $n \equiv 2 \pmod 4$, since the residues of v_n mod 3 form a periodic sequence of order 8 given by

$$2, 1, 0, 1, 1, 2, 0, 2, 2, 1, 0, \ldots.$$

We note that

$$v_n = \alpha^n + \beta^n, \qquad \sqrt{5}u_n = \alpha^n - \beta^n,$$

$$\alpha = \frac{1 + \sqrt{5}}{2}, \qquad \beta = \frac{1 - \sqrt{5}}{2}, \qquad \alpha\beta = -1.$$

Hence

$$v_{-n} = (-1)^n v_n, \qquad u_{-n} = (-1)^{n-1} u_n.$$

Also

$$(v_n, u_n) = 1 \quad \text{if} \quad n \not\equiv 0 \pmod 3,$$

$$(v_n, u_n) = 2 \quad \text{if} \quad n \equiv 0 \pmod 3,$$

follows from

$$v_n^2 - 5u_n^2 = 4(-1)^n.$$

We easily deduce the relations

$$2u_{m+n} = u_m v_n + u_n v_m, \qquad 2v_{m+n} = 5u_m u_n + v_m v_n,$$

$$v_{2m} = v_m^2 + 2(-1)^{m-1}, \qquad u_{2m} = u_m v_m.$$

We denote hereafter by k an integer positive or negative for which $k \equiv \pm 2 \pmod 6$. We have now two results fundamental for the proofs of the theorem,

$$v_{n+2kt} \equiv (-1)^t v_n \pmod{v_k},$$

$$u_{n+2kt} \equiv (-1)^t u_n \pmod{v_k}.$$

For

$$2v_{n+2k} = 5u_n u_{2k} + v_n v_{2k}$$

$$= 5u_n u_k v_k + v_n(v_k^2 - 2)$$

$$\equiv -2v_m \pmod{v_k}.$$

The first result above follows since v_k is odd.

So

$$2u_{n+2k} = u_n v_{2k} + u_{2k} v_n$$

$$= u_n(v_k^2 - 2) + u_k v_k v_n$$

$$\equiv -2u_n \pmod{v_k}.$$

The second result now follows.

We proceed to the proof of the theorems.

First for $v_n = x^2$. There are no solutions if $n = 2m$ is even since

$$v_{2m} = v_m^2 \pm 2.$$

We show there are solutions $n = 1, 3, x = 1, 2$ if n is odd.

3*

Write $n \equiv c \pmod 4$, $c = 1, 3$. We exclude $n = 1, 3$ and write with $k > 0$, $n = c + 2.3^r k$, where $r \geqslant 0$, $k \equiv \pm 2 \pmod 6$ and when $c = 1$, $v_c = 1$ and when $c = 3$, $v_c = 4$.

Then
$$v_n \equiv (-1)^{3^r} v_c \equiv -v_c \pmod{v_k}$$

$$\equiv -1, -4 \pmod{v_k}.$$

Since $v_k \equiv 3 \pmod 4$, $(v_n/v_k) = -1$ and so v_n cannot be a square.

Take next $v_n = 2x^2$. There are now only the solutions $n = 0, \pm 6$ and $\pm x = 1, 3$. Suppose first that n is odd. Since

$$v_n^2 = 5u_n^2 - 4,$$

then
$$x^4 = 5(\tfrac{1}{2}u_n)^2 - 1.$$

A congruence mod 8 shows that this is impossible.

Suppose next that n is even. Take first $n \equiv 0 \pmod 4$. Then excluding $n = 0$, we can write

$$n = 2.3^r k, \qquad k \equiv \pm 2 \pmod 6.$$

Hence
$$2v_n \equiv -2v_0 \pmod{v_k}$$

$$\equiv -4 \pmod{v_k}.$$

and so $v_n \neq 2x^2$.

Take next $n \equiv 6 \pmod 8$, $n \neq 6$. Then we can write

$$n = 6 + 2.3^r k, \qquad k \equiv 2 \pmod 6.$$

Hence
$$2v_n \equiv -2v_0 \equiv -36 \pmod{v_k},$$

and so
$$v_n \neq 2x^2.$$

Take finally $n \equiv 2 \pmod 8$. Since $v_{-n} = v_n$ and $-n \equiv 6 \pmod 8$, $v_n = 2x^2$ only if $-n = 6$ (and so also $n = 6$).

We come next to Theorem 5. Now $u_n = x^2$ only for $n = 0, \pm 1, 2, 12$ and $\pm x = 0, 1, 1, 12$.

Suppose first that $n \equiv 1 \pmod 4$. Since $u_1 = 1$, we exclude $n = 1$, and write

$$n = 1 + 2.3^r k, \qquad k \equiv \pm 2 \pmod 6.$$

Then
$$u_n \equiv -u_1 \equiv -1 \pmod{v_k},$$

and so
$$u_n \neq x^2.$$

If $n \equiv 3 \pmod 4$; $u_{-n} = u_n$ and so $u_n = x^2$ only if $-n = 1$ (and so also if $n = 1$).

Suppose next that $n = 2m$ is even. Then $u_{2m} = u_m v_m = x^2$.

If $m \equiv 0 \pmod 3$, $u_m = 2y^2$, $v_m = 2z^2$.

The second gives only $m = 0, -6$, and $m = -6$ gives no value for y.

If $m \not\equiv 0 \pmod 3$, $u_m = y^2$, $v_m = z^2$. The second gives only $m = 1, 3$ and $m = 3$ gives no value for y.

In a similar way it can be shown that if $u_n = 2x^2$, then $n = 0, \pm 3, 6$ and $\pm x = 0, 1, 2$.

Of special interest is the application of such ideas to the equation

$$dy^2 = ax^4 + bx^2 + c,$$

which reduces to a particular case of equations (8), (9). Write $z = 1$ and

$$dy^2 = ax^4 + bx^2 z + cz^2.$$

Then x^2 and z are given by a finite number of expressions of the form $lX^2 + mXY + nY^2$.

Alternatively,

$$4ady^2 = (2ax^2 + b)^2 + 4ac - b^2,$$

and so

$$2ax^2 + b = \lambda \gamma^n + \mu \delta^n.$$

where

$$\gamma, \delta \text{ are of the form } u_0 \pm v_0 \sqrt{D},$$

and λ, μ are a finite set of conjugate constants in $Q(\sqrt{D})$. We have then an equation of the form (10).

Some simple illustrations due to Cohn[6] are given now, but some of the results are due to Ljunggren[9] and Mordell[8].

The equation

$$y^2 = 5x^4 + 1$$

has only the solutions $x = 0, \pm 2$.

For

$$y + x^2\sqrt{5} = (9 + 4\sqrt{5})^n = \left(\frac{1 + \sqrt{5}}{2}\right)^{6n},$$

and then $2x^2 = u_{6n}$.

The equation

$$y^2 = 5x^4 - 1$$

has only the solution $\pm x = 1$.

Here

$$y + x^2\sqrt{5} = (2 + \sqrt{5})^{2n-1} = \left(\frac{1 + \sqrt{5}}{2}\right)^{6n-3},$$

and then $2x^2 = u_{6n-3}$.

The equation

$$y^2 = 5x^4 + 4$$

has only the solutions $\pm x = 0, 1, 12$.

Here $\quad \dfrac{y + x^2\sqrt{5}}{2} = \left(\dfrac{3 + \sqrt{5}}{2}\right)^n = \left(\dfrac{1 + \sqrt{5}}{2}\right)^{2n}$, and $x^2 = u_{2n}$.

The equation

$$y^2 = 5x^4 - 4$$

has only the solutions $\pm x = 1$.

Here $\quad \dfrac{y + x^2\sqrt{5}}{2} = \left(\dfrac{1 + \sqrt{5}}{2}\right)^{2n-1}$, and $x^2 = u_{2n-1}$.

The preceding results arose from the discussion of the case $a = 1$ of the more general sequence

$$u_{n+2} = au_{n+1} + u_n.$$

Cohn[7] has discussed this in detail and has found results similar to those given here. In the course of his investigation, the equation

$$2y^2 = 3x^4 - 1$$

arises. His method could not prove that the only integer solutions are given by $\pm x = 1, 3$. This was however, proved by Bumby[10] by an extension of Cohn's method. For now with $a = 5 + 2\sqrt{6}$,

$$x^2 = \frac{a^n + a^{1-n}}{1 + a}.$$

The proof depends upon an application of the law of quadratic reciprocity in the quadratic field $Q(\sqrt{-2})$.

Other methods of dealing with quartic equations are given in Chapter 28.

REFERENCES

1. L. J. Mordell. On a Pellian equation conjecture. *Acta Arithmetica*, **6** (1960), 137–144.
2. L. J. Mordell. On a Pellian equation conjecture. *J. Lond. Math. Soc.*, **36** (1961), 282–288.
3. L. J. Mordell. On the four integer cube problem. *J. Lond. Math. Soc.*, **11** (1936), 208–218. Addendum **12** (1937), 80. Corrigendum **32** (1957), 383.
4. J. H. E. Cohn. On square Fibonacci numbers. *J. Lond. Math. Soc.*, **39** (1964), 537–540.
5. O. Wylie. Solution of the problem. In the Fibonacci series $F_1 = 1$, $F_2 = 1$, $F_{n+1} = F_n + F_{n-1}$, the first, second and twelfth terms are squares. Are there any others? *Am. Math. Monthly*, **71** (1964), 220–222.
6. J. H. E. Cohn. Lucas and Fibonacci numbers and some diophantine equations. *Proc. Glasgow Math. Assoc.*, **7** (1965), 24–28.
7. J. H. E. Cohn. Eight diophantine equations. *Proc. Lond. Math. Soc.*, **16** (1966), 153–166. Addendum, *ibid*, **17** (1967), 381.

8. L. J. Mordell. The diophantine equation $y^2 = Dx^4 + 1$. *J. Lond. Math. Soc.*, **39** (1964), 161–164.

9. W. Ljunggren. Some remarks on the diophantine equations $x^2 - Dy^4 = 1$, $x^4 - Dy^2 = 1$. *J. Lond. Math. Soc.*, **41** (1966), 542–544.

10. R. T. Bumby. The diophantine equation $3x^4 - 2y^2 = 1$, *Math. Scan.*, **21** (1967) 144–148.

CHAPTER 9

Rational Solutions Derived from Given Ones

1. *Problem*

Given a rational solution of $f(x_1, x_2, \ldots, x_n) = 0$, where f is a polynomial with rational coefficients, to deduce other solutions.

Suppose first that the equation represents a curve, say $f(x, y) = 0$. We refer to a rational solution (x, y) of $f(x, y) = 0$ as a rational point P on the curve $f(x, y) = 0$. If we write the equation in the homogeneous form $F(X, Y, Z) = 0$, where $x = X/Z$, $y = Y/Z$, we still refer to rational points (X, Y, Z) on the curve $F(X, Y, Z) = 0$ when the ratios X/Z, Y/Z are rational. We have a 1–1 correspondence between (x, y) and (X, Y, Z) except when $Z = 0$. We can, however, say this corresponds to an infinite rational point (x, y).

Theorem 1

Let $f(x, y) = 0$, $g(x, y) = 0$ be two curves of degrees r, s. If $rs - 1$ of their intersections are rational points, then the remaining intersection is also a rational point.

On eliminating y, x is determined by an equation of the rsth degree with rational coefficients. Since $rs - 1$ of its roots are known, the remaining one is determined by an equation of the first degree and so is also rational, as was to be proved.

If, however, only $rs - 2$ of the intersections are rational, the remaining two are determined by a quadratic equation and so belong to a quadratic field.

Theorem 2

Let $f(x, y, z) = 0$, $g(x, y, z) = 0$, $h(x, y, z) = 0$ be three surfaces of degrees r, s, t. If $rst - 1$ of their intersections are rational points, then the remaining intersection is also a rational point. If $rst - 2$ of their intersections are rational, then the remaining two intersections have coordinates in a quadratic field. If one of the surfaces is a cubic surface, then the line joining these points meets it in a rational point.

The last part is obvious since the line can be defined by two planes with rational coefficients.

Applications will be given in Chapters 12 and 13.

We come back to curves.

Let $f(x, y) = 0$ be a conic with the known rational point $P(x_0, y_0)$. We take for $g(x, y) = 0$, the line $y - y_0 = t(x - x_0)$ through P, where t is a rational parameter. This line meets the conic in one other point Q, and so Q is a rational point whose coordinates are given in terms of the parameter t. All the rational points Q on $f(x, y) = 0$ are given in this way since the slope of the line PQ defines t. There is also a 1–1 correspondence between the points Q and the rational values of t including $t = \infty$. Also P corresponds to itself for the value of t for which the line is a tangent at P. The intersection of the line $x = x_0$ other than P corresponds to $t = \infty$, but when $x = x_0$ is a tangent, P then corresponds to $t = \infty$.

On eliminating y, we find, say,

$$x = \frac{A_1 t^2 + B_1 t + C_1}{At^2 + Bt + C}, \qquad y = \frac{A_2 t^2 + B_2 t + C_2}{At^2 + Bt + C},$$

where the A, A_1, A_2 etc. are integer constants.

Hence the solution of $F(X, Y, Z) = 0$ is given by putting $x = X/Z$, $y = Y/Z$, $t = p/q$, where p, q are coprime integers, and then

$$dX = A_1 p^2 + B_1 pq + C_1 q^2, \qquad dY = A_2 p^2 + B_2 pq + C_2 q^2,$$

$$dZ = Ap^2 + Bpq + Cq^2.$$

The factor d can be removed by an appropriate substitution $p \rightarrow \lambda p + dq$. Then the solutions X, Y, Z are given by a finite set of binary quadratic forms.

Theorem 3

All the rational points on an irreducible cubic curve with a double point can be expressed in terms of a rational parameter.

There can be only one double point P, for if P, P_1 were both double points, the line PP_1 would meet the curve in four points. Also P is a rational point, say (x_0, y_0). This is easily proven since P is determined by the equations,

$$\frac{\partial f}{\partial x} = \frac{\partial f}{\partial y} = 0 = f,$$

Then every other rational point Q on the curve is determined parametrically by the equation

$$y - y_0 = t(x - x_0),$$

since the double point counts for two of the intersections of the line and the curve.

Example 1

$$ax^3 + bx^2 y + cxy^2 + dy^3 = ex^2 + fxy + gy^2,$$

say $g(x, y) = h(x, y)$.

Here $y = tx$ gives

$$x = h(1, t)/g(1, t), \qquad y = th(1, t)/g(1, t).$$

We note that the origin $(0, 0)$ corresponds to both $t = 0$ and $t = \infty$.

Theorem 4

From a known set S of rational points P_1, P_2, ..., P_n on a cubic curve, others can in general be found.

The tangent at P_1 meets the cubic in three points. Two of these are at P_1 and so the third point, say $P_{1,1}$, being determined by an equation of the first degree, is rational and is different from P if P_1 is not a point of inflexion. So the tangent at $P_{1,1}$ may be expected to lead to a new rational point $P_{11,11}$ etc. Next the line P_1P_2 meets the curve in a third rational point $P_{1,2}$, in general, different from P_1 and P_2. This tangential and chord process can be applied to all the points of S and also to all of the points found in this way. In general, one would expect an infinity of rational points to arise, but this must be proved in each case.

The method above suggests the conjecture that all the rational points on a cubic curve of genus one can be deduced from a finite number by the chord and tangent process. This will be proved later, in Chapter 16.

2. We now give a number of classic instances due to Diophantus, Fermat, Euler, Lagrange, Cauchy.

Example 2

$$y^2 = x^3 + k.$$

Let $P(p, q)$, $q \neq 0$ be a rational point. The tangent at P is

$$y - q = \frac{3p^2}{2q}(x - p),$$

and so

$$x^3 + k = \left(q + \frac{3p^2}{2q}(x - p)\right)^2.$$

Since two roots are $x = p, q$, the sum of the roots of this equation gives for the third root, x,

$$x = \frac{9p^4}{4q^2} - 2p, \quad \text{and then} \quad y = q + \frac{3p^2}{2q}\left(\frac{9p^4}{4q^2} - 3p\right).$$

Alternatively, put $x = p + X$, and

$$y^2 = q^2 + 3p^2 X + 3p X^2 + X^3,$$

and take

$$y = q + \frac{3p^2}{2q} X.$$

Then

$$\frac{9p^4}{4q^2} = 3p + X, \quad \text{etc.}$$

When $k = -2$, $p = 3$, $q = 5$, we find $x = 129/100$.
Fermat asserted that an infinity of rational solutions will arise by this method of Bachet, but this statement requires proof, which will be given later in Chapter 23.

When $q = 0$, the equation takes the form $y^2 = x^3 - p^3$. Now the tangent at $P(p, 0)$ meets the curve again at infinity, i.e. $x = \infty$, $y = \infty$, and this must be considered as a rational point. The homogeneous form of the equation is $Y^2 Z = X^3 - p^3 Z^3$, and P is the point $(p, 0, 1)$. The tangent at P is $X - pZ = 0$, and meets the cubic again at the point $(0, 1, 0)$. The tangent at this point is $Z = 0$ and so the point $(0, 1, 0)$ is a point of inflexion, and so the process cannot be continued.

Example 3

$$y^3 = a^3 + bx + cx^2 + dx^3, \quad a \neq 0.$$

A solution is given by putting $y = a + bx/3a^2$.

Example 4

$$y^3 = a + bx + cx^2 + d^3 x^3, \quad d \neq 0.$$

A solution is given by $y = dx + c/3d^2$.

Example 5

Let $\qquad\qquad y^2 = ax^4 + bx^3 + cx^2 + dx + e,$

with the rational solution (p, q), $q \neq 0$.
On putting $x = p + X$, we may suppose that the solution is $(0, q)$ and that $e = e_1^2$, $e_1 \neq 0$. Put

$$y = Ax^2 + Bx + e_1,$$

where $2e_1 A + B^2 = c$, $2e_1 B = d$.

Then $\qquad\qquad A^2 x + 2AB = ax + b,$

giving in general a new value for x.

Example 6

$$y^2 = ax^4 + bx^3 + cx^2 + dx + e.$$

Let $a = a_1^2 \neq 0$ be a perfect square. Put

$$y = a_1 x^2 + Cx + D,$$

where $\qquad\qquad 2a_1 C = b, \qquad 2a_1 D + C^2 = c.$

Then $\qquad\qquad 2CDx + D^2 = dx + e, \quad$ etc.

Example 7

$$y^2 = ax^4 + bx^3 + cx^2 + dx + e.$$

Let two rational points (p, q), (p_1, q_1) be known. Put

$$x = \frac{pX + p_1}{X + 1}, \qquad y = \frac{Y}{(X + 1)^2}.$$

Then the equation takes the form

$$Y^2 = q^2 X^4 + bX^3 + cX^2 + dX + q_1^2,$$

and now both of the methods above can be applied.

Example 8

$$y^2(ax^2 + bx + c) + y(a_1 x^2 + b_1 x + c_1) + a_2 x^2 + b_2 x + c_2 = 0.$$

Solve for y. Then

$$2y(ax^2 + bx + c) + a_1 x^2 + b_1 x + c_1 = z,$$

say, where

$$z^2 = (a_1 x^2 + b_1 x + c_1)^2 - 4(ax^2 + bx + c)(a_2 x^2 + b_2 x + c_2),$$

a quartic curve in z, x.

We may proceed more simply as follows. Let (x_1, y_1) be a known solution. If we put $x = x_1$ in the equation, the quadratic in y has two roots one of which is y_1. The other is a rational number y_2 given by

$$y_2 + y_1 = -(a_1 x^2 + b_1 x + c_1)/(ax^2 + bx + c).$$

Hence in general we have a new solution (x_1, y_2) different from the first. We can continue the process. Put $y = y_2$ in the equation. Then the quadratic in x gives us a rational x_2 where

$$x_2 + x_1 = -(by_2^2 + b_1 y_2 + b_2)/(ay_2^2 + a_1 y_2 + a_2).$$

Then in general we have a new solution (x_2, y_2). So we find rational solutions

$$(x_2, y_3), (x_3, y_3), (x_3, y_4), (x_4, y_4), \ldots.$$

Example 9
The simultaneous equations

$$y^2 = a_1 x^2 + b_1 x + c_1, \qquad z^2 = a_2 x^2 + b_2 x + c_2.$$

Suppose that a rational solution (x_1, y_1, z_1) is known. On putting $x = x_1 + X$, we may take $x_1 = 0$ and then replace c_1, c_2 by c_1^2, c_2^2. In the first equation, put $y = tx + c_1$. Then

$$t^2 x + 2tc_1 = a_1 x + b_1, \qquad x = (b_1 - 2c_1 t)/(t^2 - a_1).$$

Then

$$z^2(t^2 - a_1)^2 = s^2 = a_2(b_1 - 2c_1 t)^2 + b_2(b_1 - 2tc_1)(t^2 - a_1) + c_2^2(t^2 - a_1)^2.$$

The quartic in t becomes a square when $b_1 - 2tc_1 = 0$, i.e. for $t = b_1/2c_1$ unless $c_1 = 0$, and so in general other rational values of t can be found.

If, however, $c_1 = c_2 = 0$, put $y = Y/X$, $z = Y/X$, $x = 1/X$.

Then $$Y^2 = a_1 + b_1X, \qquad Z^2 = a_2 + b_2X.$$

and $$b_2Y^2 - b_1Z^2 = a_1b_2 - a_2b_1.$$

The solution of this equation is given by the classical theory of quadratic forms.

An alternative method is to note that

$$c_2^2y^2 - c_1^2z^2 = x((a_1c_2^2 - a_2c_1^2)x + b_1c_2^2 - b_2c_1^2) = x(px + q), \quad \text{say.}$$

Take $$c_2y + c_1z = 2c_1c_2(px + q)/q,$$

$$c_2y - c_1z = qx/2c_1c_2,$$

Then $y = c_1 + rx$, say, and $(rx + c_1)^2 = a_1x^2 + b_1x + c_1^2$, etc.

An ancient problem which had its origin[1] among the Arab scholars before 972 A.D. is, when $k = 5$, to find rational solutions of the simultaneous equations:

Example 10

$$y^2 = x^2 + k, \qquad z^2 = x^2 - k.$$

It is easily verified that if k can be written in the form

$$k = ab(a + b)(a - b),$$

then a solution is given by

$$2x = a^2 + b^2, \qquad 2y = a^2 + 2ab - b^2, \qquad 2z = a^2 - 2ab - b^2.$$

From this solution, others can be derived by the method of Example 9.

For $a = 5$, $b = 4$, $k = 5 \cdot 6^2$, $x = 41/2$. Hence when $k = 5$, a solution is given by

$$x = \frac{41}{12}, \qquad y = \frac{49}{12}, \qquad z = \frac{31}{12}.$$

This solution was found by Leonardo of Pisa, about 1220 A.D. and also by Euler who considered the general equation.

The equations can be dealt with by arithmetical considerations on writing them in the following forms:

$$x^2 - 5y^2 = u^2, \qquad x^2 + 5y^2 = v^2.$$

Then Genocchi has shown that from a solution (x, y, u, v), another (X, Y, U, V) is given by

$$X = u^2x^2 + 5v^2y^2, \qquad Y = 2xyuv,$$
$$U = u^2x^2 - 5v^2y^2, \qquad V = u^4 - 2x^4.$$

From the first solution of Leonardo's equation, we find the second solution

$$x = \frac{3{,}444{,}161}{1{,}494{,}696}, \qquad y = \frac{4{,}728{,}001}{1{,}494{,}696}, \qquad z = \frac{113{,}279}{1{,}494{,}696}.$$

A complete solution can be found[2] by more complicated arithmetical methods which show that all the solutions can be derived from the first by rational operations. The third solution has 15 digits in the numerators and denominators.

3. One of the first results in which the method of infinite descent of Chapter 4 shows that all integer solutions can be derived from rational functions of one solution, was given by Euler and Lagrange.

Theorem 5

All the integer solutions of the equation

$$x^4 - 2y^4 = -z^2, \qquad x > 0,\, y > 0,\, z > 0, \quad (x, y) = 1,$$

can be so derived from the solution $(x, y, z) = (1, 1, 1)$.

Suppose x, y is the solution with least y and $x > 1$. If $z \equiv 0 \pmod 2$, then $x \equiv y \equiv 0 \pmod 2$, and so we have

$$x \equiv y \equiv z \equiv 1 \pmod 2.$$

Since

$$\left(\frac{x^2 + z}{2}\right)^2 + \left(\frac{x^2 - z}{2}\right)^2 = y^4,$$

we have

$$\frac{x^2 \pm z}{2} = a^2 - b^2, \qquad \frac{x^2 \mp z}{2} = \pm\, 2ab,$$

$$y^2 = a^2 + b^2, \quad a \geqslant 0,\, b \geqslant 0,\, (a, b) = 1.$$

Clearly $ab \neq 0$, since then $z = x^2 = y^2 = 1$. First, for $+2ab$, we have

$$x^2 = a^2 - b^2 + 2ab, \qquad y^2 = a^2 + b^2.$$

The first equation shows that $a \not\equiv 0 \pmod 2$, and so $a \equiv 1 \pmod 2$, $b \equiv 0 \pmod 2$. Hence from the second equation

$$a = p^2 - q^2, \qquad b = 2pq, \qquad y = p^2 + q^2, \quad (p, q) = 1.$$

Also $pq \neq 0$. Then

$$x^2 + 2b^2 = (a + b)^2,$$

and so

$$x = \pm(c^2 - 2d^2), \qquad b = 2cd, \qquad a + b = c^2 + 2d^2,$$

$c \geqslant 0,\, d \geqslant 0,\, (c, d) = 1$ and $cd \neq 0$. Hence

$$p^2 - q^2 + 2pq = c^2 + 2d^2, \qquad pq = cd.$$

From the second

$$p = rc/s, \qquad q = sd/r, \quad (r, s) = 1, \; rs \neq 0,$$

and so

$$c = sX, \quad d = rY, \quad p = rX, \quad q = sY, \quad (X, Y) = 1, \quad XY \neq 0.$$

Substituting in above, we have

$$(r^2 - s^2)X^2 + 2rsXY - (s^2 + 2r^2)Y^2 = 0.$$

Hence $\qquad \dfrac{X}{Y} = -\dfrac{(rs \pm w)}{r^2 - s^2}, \qquad X = -\dfrac{(rs \pm w)}{\delta}, \qquad Y = \dfrac{r^2 - s^2}{\delta},$

$$\delta = (rs \pm w, r^2 - s^2),$$

where $\qquad\qquad r^2 s^2 + (r^2 - s^2)(s^2 + 2r^2) = w^2,$

or $\qquad\qquad\qquad\quad s^4 - 2r^4 = -w^2.$

Here $\qquad y = p^2 + q^2 = r^2 X^2 + s^2 Y^2 > r^2, \quad$ or $\quad r < \sqrt{y},$

and so we have, from the solution (x, y), deduced a smaller solution (r, s). Take next $-2ab$ above. Then

$$x^2 = a^2 - b^2 - 2ab, \qquad a > b.$$

Hence $a - b = c^2 + 2d^2$ and so

$$p^2 - q^2 - 2pq = c^2 + 2d^2, \qquad pq = cd.$$

As before we deduce a smaller solution (r, s).

We finally come to a stage with $r = 1$, $s = 1$ and so all the solutions can be expressed rationally in terms of this.

We now prove an associated

Theorem 6

All the integer solutions of the equation

$$x^4 - 2y^4 = z^2, \quad x > 0, \; y > 0, \; (x, y) = 1,$$

except $x = 1$, $y = 0$, can be deduced by rational processes from the solution $(x, y) = (3, 2)$ *and the solution* $(x, y) = (1, 1)$ *of* $x^4 - 2y^4 = -z^2$.

Clearly x, z are odd and y is even. Hence

$$x^2 + z = 2a^4, \qquad x^2 - z = 16b^4, \qquad y = 2ab,$$

$ab \neq 0$, $(a, b) = 1$, and so $a \equiv 1 \pmod 2$ and

$$a^4 + 8b^4 = x^2.$$

Hence $\qquad \pm a^2 = p^2 - 2q^2, \qquad b^2 = pq, \quad pq \neq 0, \; (p, q) = 1.$

Then $p = c^2$, $q = d^2$, and

$$c^4 - 2d^4 = \pm a^2.$$

The equation with the $-$ sign has been dealt with. For the equation with the $+$ sign, $d^2 \leqslant b^2 \leqslant \frac{1}{4}y^2$ or $d \leqslant \frac{1}{2}y$, i.e. there is a solution of the original equation with a smaller y. Continuing the process, we have two equations such as

$$e^4 - 2f^4 = \pm g^2.$$

It may be remarked that the solution $x = 1$, $y = 0$ leads to $b = 0$.

In all these examples, new rational solutions were derived from known rational solutions. It is sometimes possible to deduce rational solutions from known solutions given as numbers in an algebraic number field. We have Heegner's[3]

4. Theorem 7

If the equation

$$y^2 = ax^4 + bx^3 + cx^2 + dx + e, \tag{1}$$

where a, b, c, d, e are rational numbers, has a solution (p, q) in an algebraic number field K of odd degree $\geqslant 3$, then there exists a rational solution.

We may suppose that p satisfies an equation with rational coefficients of degree r, say $f_r(p) = 0$, and that K is generated by p. For if p generates a subfield K_1 of K of degree r_1, then from equation (1), q must be an element of an algebraic number field of degree $2r_1$ and so of r_1 since r is odd. Then $q = f_{r-\delta}(p)$, a polynomial of degree $r - \delta$ with rational coefficients, and where in general $\delta = 1$. Since the relation

$$f^2_{r-\delta}(p) = ap^4 + bp^3 + cp^2 + dp + e$$

is a consequence of $f_r(p) = 0$, we have if now x is an arbitrary variable, the identical relation

$$f^2_{r-\delta}(x) - ax^4 - bx^3 - cx^2 - dx - e = f_r(x)f_{r-2\delta}(x),$$

where $f_{r-2\delta}(x)$ is a polynomial of degree $r - 2\delta$.

Hence a solution of equation (1) is given by taking x to be a root of the equation $f_{r-2\delta}(x) = 0$. Since $r - 2\delta$ is odd, the process can be continued until a stage is reached when $r - 2\delta = 1$.

In Heegner's applications, the field K is derived by very abstruse and complicated considerations depending upon equations connecting various modular functions. He gives a number of equations which are said to have rational solutions. Among these, where p is a prime, are

$$py^2 = x^3 + 27, \quad p \equiv 3 \ (\text{mod } 4), \ y \neq 0;$$

$$py^2 = 2x^4 + 1, \quad p \equiv 3 \ (\text{mod } 8);$$

$$py^2 = 4x^4 - 1, \quad p \equiv 3 \ (\text{mod } 8);$$

$$py^2 = 8 - x^4, \quad p \equiv -1 \ (\text{mod } 8).$$

REFERENCES

1. L. E. Dickson. "History of the Theory of Numbers". Carnegie Institute, Washington, **2** (1920), 459–472, for the history and accounts of the subject and references.

2. J. V. Uspensky and M. A. Heaslet. "Elementary number theory". McGraw-Hill, London. (1939), 419–427.

3. Kurt Heegner. Diophantische Analysis und Modulfunktionen. *Math. Z.*, **56** (1952), 227–253.

CHAPTER 10

Rational Points on Some Cubic Curves

1. *Equivalent curves.* Two curves are called equivalent if they can be transformed into each other by a birational transformation with rational coefficients. This means that if the curves are given by $f(x, y) = 0$, $F(X, Y) = 0$, we have, except for a finite set of values for the variables,

$$x = a(X, Y), \quad y = b(X, Y); \qquad X = A(x, y), \quad Y = B(x, y),$$

where a, b, A, B are rational functions of their arguments with rational coefficients.

Theorem 1[1]

A cubic curve $f(x, y) = 0$ with a rational point is equivalent to a cubic whose equation is in the Weierstrass normal form

$$y^2 = 4x^3 - g_2 x - g_3.$$

If the curve is written in the homogeneous form, $F(X, Y, Z) = 0$, then g_2, g_3 are well known invariants of the ternary form $F(X, Y, Z)$. We give Nagell's[2] proof.

Let P be the rational point and take as origin Q, the point where the tangent at P meets the curve again. The line $y = tx$ through Q, where t is a parameter, meets the cubic in two other points determined by the equation,

$$Lx^2 + 2Mx + N = 0,$$

where L, M, N are polynomials in t of respective degrees $3, 2, 1$, and with rational coefficients. Hence

$$(Lx + M)^2 = M^2 - LN.$$

Since P and Q are rational points, and QP is a tangent, the quartic in t, $M^2 - LN = 0$ has a rational root, say $t = t_0$. Write to $t = t_0 + 1/T$. Then

$$(Lx + M)^2 = F(T)/T^4,$$

where $F(T)$ is a cubic in T. Apply a linear substitution $T = CX + D$ with rational coefficients C, D, and put $Lx + M = NY/(CX + D)^2$, and then we have an equation of the form

$$Y^2 = 4X^3 - g_2 X - g_3.$$

Then t takes the form

$$t = (FX + G)/(CX + D) \quad \text{and} \quad y = tx.$$

Clearly rational X, Y lead to rational x, y and conversely.

It proves convenient to regard $(X, Y) = (\infty, \infty)$ as a rational point. This arises from the homogeneous form of the equation

$$Y^2Z = 4X^3 - g_2XZ^2 - g_3Z^3,$$

which has the rational point $(X, Y, Z) = (0, 1, 0)$, so that $Y/Z = \infty$, $X/Z = \infty$.

Theorem 2

If the quartic curve

$$y^2 = ax^4 + bx^3 + cx^2 + dx + e$$

has a rational point, it is equivalent to a cubic curve

$$Y^2 = 4X^3 - g_2X - g_3.$$

We may assume that e is a perfect square. Then on writing $x = 1/X$, $y = Y/X^2$, we may assume that a is a perfect square. If $a = 0$, the result is obvious. If $a \neq 0$, we may assume that $a = 1$ on writing $x = X/\sqrt{a}$, $y = Y/\sqrt{a}$. Then on replacing x by $X - \frac{1}{4}b$, we may assume that $b = 0$. We now write the quartic as

$$y^2 = x^4 - 6cx^2 + 4dx + e.$$

A 1–1 correspondence between this quartic and the cubic is given by

$$y = -x^2 + 2X + c, \qquad 2x = (Y - d)/(X - c).$$

For on substituting for y,

$$x^4 - 6cx^2 + 4dx + e = x^4 - 2x^2(2X + c) + (2X + c)^2,$$

$$x^2(X - c) + dx = X^2 + cX + \tfrac{1}{4}(c^2 - e).$$

$$2x(X - c) = -d \pm (d^2 + 4(X^3 - c^2X) + (c^2 - e)(X - c))^{1/2}$$

$$= -d \pm (4X^3 - g_2X - g_3)^{1/2},$$

where $g_2 = e + 3c^2$, $g_3 = -ce - d^2 + c^3$, $d^2 = 4c^3 - g_2c - g_3$. Hence we can write

$$Y^2 = 4X^3 - g_2X - g_3, \qquad 2x(X - c) = Y - d.$$

We note that this normal cubic has the rational point $(X, Y) = (c, d)$.

A sometimes more convenient form for the quartic is

$$z^2 = ax^4 + 4bx^3y + 6cx^2y^2 + 4dxy^3 + ey^4 = F(x, y).$$

The binary quartic $F(x, y)$ has the two well known invariants g_2, g_3 given by

$$g_2 = ae - 4bd + 3c^2, \qquad g_3 = \begin{vmatrix} a & b & c \\ b & c & d \\ c & d & e \end{vmatrix}.$$

Suppose now that the normal cubic has no double point.

We notice some obvious consequences of these results. If the cubic curve $F(X, Y, Z) = 0$ has one rational point, then all the rational points can be found if all the rational points of the normal cubic are known. Further if the curve $F(X, Y, Z) = 0$ has a finite number $\geqslant 1$ of solutions, the normal cubic has only a finite number of solutions and so any other cubic curve $F_1(X, Y, Z) = 0$ with the same invariants as $F(X, Y, Z)$ can have only a finite number of rational points.

Similar results apply to the quartic $z^2 = F(x, y)$.

2. One would expect that the general cubic curve has an infinity of rational points if it has one, but this requires proof for any given curve.

Theorem 3

Let a, b, c be square-free integers, relatively prime in pairs, $abc \neq 0$ and d an integer. Then the curve

$$ax^3 + by^3 + cz^3 + dxyz = 0,$$

when at most one of a, b, c is ± 1, has either none or an infinity of rational points.

When $a = b = 1$, $c \neq \pm 1$, the curve has either one or two or an infinity of integer solutions. Only two solutions may be possible when $d = -(c \pm 2)$ or $d = -(4c \pm 1)$, and so if such an equation has a third solution, there will be an infinity of solutions.

When $a = b = c = 1$, and $d \neq 1, -3, -5$, the curve has either three rational points or an infinite number. Three of the points are $(1, -1, 0)$ etc. The case $d = -3$ is trivial since then $x + y + z = 0$. When $d = 1$, there are only six solutions, $(1, -1, 0)$ and $(1, 1, -1)$ etc. When $d = -5$, there are only the six $(1, -1, 0)$, $(1, 1, 2)$, etc.

The results for $d = 1, -5$ are due to Mordell[3], the others are due to Hurwitz[4].

We prove first that the tangential $Q(X, Y, Z)$ of any point $P(x, y, z)$ on the curve is given by

$$\delta X = x(by^3 - cz^3), \qquad \delta Y = y(cz^3 - ax^3), \qquad \delta Z = z(ax^3 - by^3),$$

where δ is an integer such that $(X, Y, Z) = 1$. On writing $x = X\sqrt[3]{a}$ etc., it suffices to prove the result when $a = b = c = 1$, and then to verify that Q

lies on the tangent at P and also on the curve. The first is obvious since the tangent at P is in current coordinates $\bar{x}, \bar{y}, \bar{z}$

$$\bar{x}(3x^2 + dyz) + \cdots = 0,$$

and $$\sum x^3(y^3 - z^3) = 0, \qquad \sum xyz(y^3 - z^3) = 0.$$

The second follows from

$$\sum x^3(y^3 - z^3)^3 + dxyz \prod (y^3 - z^3)$$
$$= (x^3 + y^3 + z^3 + dxyz) \prod (y^3 - z^3) = 0.$$

We may suppose that $(x, y, z) = 1$. Then x, y, z are relatively prime in pairs. For if a prime p divides x and y, then $p^2 \mid cz^2$, i.e. $p \mid z$ contrary to hypothesis. Suppose now that there are only a finite number $\geqslant 1$ of rational points on the curve, and denote by (x, y, z) one for which $|xyz|$ has its greatest value.

We return to the point Q and show that $(\delta, xyz) = 1$. For if a prime p divides δ and x, then $(p, yz) = 1$. Then since p divides both cyz^3 and bzy^3, $p \mid b, p \mid c$ contrary to hypothesis. Hence

$$\delta \mid (by^3 - cz^3), \qquad \delta \mid (cz^3 - ax^3), \qquad \delta \mid (ax^3 - by^3).$$

Now suppose $|ab| > 1$. Then $xyz \neq 0$, for if $x = 0$, then $by^3 + cz^3 = 0$ whose only solution is $y = z = 0$ since $(b, c) = 1$ and b and c are square free. Similarly for $y = 0$ etc. Hence $|XYZ|/|xyz| \leqslant 1$ and so

$$\left| \frac{by^3 - cz^3}{\delta} \cdot \frac{cz^3 - ax^3}{\delta} \cdot \frac{ax^3 - by^3}{\delta} \right| \leqslant 1.$$

Then $$by^3 - cz^3 = 0, \pm \delta; \qquad cz^3 - ax^3 = 0, \pm \delta,$$
$$ax^3 - by^3 = 0, \pm \delta,$$

where the signs are independent of each other. The 0 can be rejected since $(y, z) = 1$, and $(b, c) = 1$ etc. Finally the $\pm \delta$ can be rejected since the sum of the left-hand sides of the equations is zero.

Suppose next that $a = \pm 1$, $b = \pm 1$, $|c| > 1$, say $a = b = 1$. The curve has a rational point $(1, -1, 0)$ and this is a point of inflexion and is also the only rational point for which $xyz = 0$. Excluding this point, we have a contradiction unless $XYZ|xyz$. Then

$$x = y = 1, \qquad 2 + cz^3 + dz = 0.$$

Hence either

$$z = \pm 1, \qquad 2 \pm (c + d) = 0,$$
or $$z = \pm 2, \qquad 1 \pm (4c + d) = 0.$$

This means that a finite number of rational points are possibly only for the four equations,

$$x^3 + y^3 + cz^3 - (c \pm 2)xyz = 0,$$

satisfied by $\qquad (x, y, z) = (1, -1, 0), (1, 1, \pm 1),$

and $\qquad x^3 + y^3 + cz^3 - (4c \pm 1)xyz = 0,$

satisfied by $\qquad (x, y, z) = (1, -1, 0), (1, 1, \pm 2).$

     Finally let $a = b = c = 1$. As before, we must have $XYZ|xyz$ and so two of x, y, z must be equal, say $x = y = 1$.

Then $\qquad\qquad\qquad\qquad 2 + z^3 + dz = 0,$

giving $\qquad z = \pm 1, \qquad 2 \pm (1 + d) = 0, \qquad d = 1, -3;$

or $\qquad\quad z = \pm 2, \qquad 2 \pm (8 + 2d) = 0, \qquad d = -5, -3.$

This completes the proof of the Hurwitz results.

Example
     The equation

$$x^3 + y^3 + z^3 - xyz = 0$$

has only the trivial solutions with $xyz = 0$.

     This was proved by Cassels[5] by extending a method similar to that used by Mordell for $d = 1, -5$. He and Sansone also gave another proof[6]. Their proof involves algebraic number theory and will be discussed in Chapter 15.

     We note that all the equations

$$ax^3 + by^3 + cz^3 = 0 \qquad\qquad\qquad (1)$$

with $abc = k$ have the same invariants. We deduce from Theorem 1 that if the equation

$$x^3 + y^3 + kz^3 = 0 \qquad\qquad\qquad (2)$$

has only the trivial solution $x = 1, y = -1, z = 0$, then the equations (1) have only a finite number of solutions. It also follows at once that if a, b, c satisfy Hurtwitz's conditions, namely, that a, b, c are square free, relatively prime in pairs, and at most one of them is 1, then the equations (1) have no rational solutions. It is easily verified that the equation (2) has rational solutions with $z \neq 0$ if and only if

$$XY(X + Y) + kZ^3 = 0$$

has rational solutions with $Z \neq 0$. Thus we can take

$$X = x^3, \qquad Y = y^3, \qquad Z = xyz,$$

or

$$x = X^3 + 6X^2Y + 3XY^2 - Y^3, \qquad y = -X^3 + 3X^2Y + 6XY^2 + Y^3$$
$$z = 3Z(X^2 + XY + Y^2).$$

Fueter's result on the infinity of solutions of the equation $y^2 = x^3 + k$, will be given in Chapter 23.

REFERENCES

1. L. J. Mordell. Indeterminate equations of the third and fourth degrees. *Q. J. Pure Appl. Math.*, **45** (1913), 170–181.
2. T. Nagell. Sur les propriétés arithmétiques des cubiques planes du premier genre. *Acta Math.*, **52** (1929), 93–126.
3. L. J. Mordell. The diophantine equation $x^3 + y^3 + z^3 + kxyz = 0$. "Colloque sur la théorie des nombres". Bruxelles (1955), pp. 67–76.
4. A. Hurwitz. Ueber ternare diophantische Gleichungen dritten Grades. *Viertel jahrschrift Naturf. Ges. Zurich.* **62** (1917) 207–229. Math. Werke (Birkhäuser Cie, Basel) **2** (1933), 446–468.
5. J. W. S. Cassels. On a diophantine equation. *Acta Arithmetica*, **6** (1960), 47–51.
6. G. Sansone and J. W. S. Cassels. Sur la probleme de M. Werner Mnich. *Acta Arithmetica*, **7** (1962), 187–190.

CHAPTER 11

Rational Points on Cubic Surfaces

1. Let $f(x, y, z)$ be a cubic polynomial and $g(x, y, z, w)$ a homogeneous cubic polynomial, both with rational coefficients. In Chapter 1, we have shown that some equations $f = 0$ and $g = 0$ have only the trivial solution, e.g. if p is a prime,

$$ax^3 + bpy^3 + cp^2z^3 = 0, \quad abc \not\equiv 0 \,(\text{mod } p),$$

$$x^3 + 2y^3 = 7(z^3 + 2w^3).$$

No method is known for determining whether rational points exist on a general cubic surface $f(x, y, z) = 0$, or for finding all of them if any exist. Geometric considerations may prove very helpful, and sometimes by their help an infinity of solutions and even all the solutions may be found. Thus it is known that a cubic surface may have four double points, i.e. points for which

$$f = 0, \quad \frac{\partial f}{\partial x} = 0, \quad \frac{\partial f}{\partial y} = 0, \quad \frac{\partial f}{\partial z} = 0.$$

Suppose that one of these points, say $P_1(x_1, y_1, z_1)$ is rational. Then obviously all the rational points on the surface are given by the third intersection with the surface of the line

$$\frac{x - x_1}{l} = \frac{y - y_1}{m} = \frac{z - z_1}{n},$$

where l, m, n are rational parameters.

Results may also be deduced[1] when the double points are defined by irreducible equations of the second, third and fourth degrees.

When one rational point P_1 is known, an infinity of rational points can in general be found. Thus any tangent line to the surface at P_1 meets it at a point P_2 different in general from P_1. The process can be continued. Further, the tangent plane at P_1 meets the surface in a cubic curve with a singular point at P_1. The curve, if irreducible, has a double point and so its coordinates can be expressed rationally in terms of a rational parameter. A similar result holds if the cubic splits into a conic and a straight line. A more interesting case, considered further on, arises when the cubic curve splits into three straight lines and then these are defined by a reducible or irreducible cubic equation. The tangential process may be continued by taking another rational point on the cubic curve defined by P_1, but there seems no analogue corresponding to the finite basis theorem for cubic curves. In fact, Segre[2] has proved the surprising result that cubic surfaces exist containing a rational point P_1 which cannot be obtained by the tangent plane process starting from any given set of rational points of the surface not including P_1.

The existence of straight lines on a cubic surface may prove useful. In general, there are 27 such lines, determined by an equation of the 216th degree, and various sets of these lines may be determined by equations of lower degrees.

Theorem 1

All the rational points on a cubic surface can be found if it contains two lines whose equations are defined by conjugate numbers of a quadratic field and in particular by rational numbers.

Let P_1, P_2 be a pair of conjugate points on conjugate lines L_1, L_2 on the surface. Then the line P_1P_2 meets it in a third point P whose coordinates are rational since if a cubic equation with rational coefficients has a rational quadratic factor, it will also have a rational linear factor. Conversely let a rational point P be given. A plane drawn through P and L_1 will meet L_2 in a point P_2. Then PP_2 meets L_1 in a point P_1 and clearly P_1, P_2 are conjugate points in the quadratic field.

Before the later general results were found, solutions of some equations[3] were found by special devices.

The equation

$$(x + y + z)^3 - dxyz = m. \tag{1}$$

We can find easily the special solutions with $m = dyz^2$. Then the equation can be written as

$$(x + y + z)^3 = dyz(x + z).$$

This equation defines a cubic curve in homogeneous coordinates. It has a double point at $x + z = 0$, $y = 0$, and so its coordinates can be expressed rationally in terms of a parameter.

Put $\qquad\qquad x + z = py,\quad$ and $\quad (p + 1)^3y = dpz.$

Then $\qquad\qquad m = dyz^2 = d^2pz^3/(p + 1)^3.$

This requires $p = dmt^3$ and then x, y, z are rationally expressable in terms of a parameter t.

This equation was the first really significant equation for which a parametric solution was found in the 115 years since the time of Ryley, who in 1825 found a parametric solution of

$$X^3 + Y^3 + Z^3 = n. \tag{2}$$

This equation is included in the equation (1) on putting $d = 24$, $m = 8n$, $x = Y + Z$, etc.

Richmond[4] has given other solutions of Ryley's equation, namely

$$3(1 - t + t^2)X = s(1 + t^3), \quad 3(1 - t + t^2)Y = s(3t - 1 - t^3), \quad (3)$$

$$3(1 - t + t^2)Z = s(3t - 3t^2), \quad t = 3n/s^3.$$

A particular case of Ryley's equation is

Euler's equation

$$x^3 + y^3 + z^3 = 1. \tag{4}$$

The complete solution can be found from Theorem 1 since two lines on the surface are given by

$$x + \rho y = 0, \quad z = \rho; \qquad x + \rho^2 y = 0, \quad z = \rho^2,$$

where $\rho^2 + \rho + 1 = 0$. Alternatively, write the equation as

$$(x + y)(x + \rho y)(x + \rho^2 y) = (1 - z)(1 - z\rho)(1 - z\rho^2).$$

The solution in terms of rational parameters p, q is given by

$$\frac{x + \rho y}{1 - \rho z} = p + \rho q, \qquad \frac{x + \rho^2 y}{1 - \rho^2 z} = p + \rho^2 q. \tag{5}$$

$$(x + y)(p + \rho q)(p + \rho^2 q) = 1 - z. \tag{6}$$

This also holds when $p = q = 0$ giving $z = 1$, $x = y = 0$.

On excluding $p = q = 0$, we can write equations (5), (6) as

$$x + \rho y + \rho(p + \rho q)z = p + \rho q,$$

$$x + \rho^2 y + \rho^2(p + \rho^2 q)z = p + \rho^2 q, \tag{7}$$

$$(x + y)(p^2 - pq + q^2) = 1 - z.$$

Eliminating x, y from the first two equations, we find

$$x = p + qz, \qquad y = q + (q - p)z,$$

$$z((p - q)^3 - q^3 - 1) = p^3 + q^3 - 1. \tag{8}$$

Then
$$x((p - q)^3 - q^3 - 1) = (p^2 - pq + q^2)^2 - p - q,$$

$$y((p - q)^3 - q^3 - 1) = 1 - (p^2 - pq + q^2)^2 + p - 2q. \tag{9}$$

It is obvious on solving equations (8) that (p, q) are uniquely determined when (x, y, z) are given since the denominator $1 + z + z^2 \neq 0$. Conversely let (p, q) be given. Since the only solutions of

$$(p - q)^3 - q^3 - 1 = 0,$$

are given by $p = q = 1; p = 1, q = 0$ as will be shown in Chapter 15, then the equations (7) are inconsistent.

2. We return to the general equation $f(x, y, z) = 0$. We suppose that $f(x, y, z)$ is an algebraically irreducible cubic polynomial and is not a function of two independent variables, nor a homogeneous polynomial in linear functions X, Y, Z of x, y, z. In the latter case, the equation takes the form $F(X, Y, Z) = 0$, which is a cone, but which in homogeneous coordinates represents a cubic curve. This may contain only a finite number of rational points or an infinite number. We give now a proof of Segre's [5]

Theorem 2

If $f(x, y, z)$ is as above, the general cubic equation, $f(x, y, z) = 0$ has either none or an infinity of rational solutions.

Take the equation in the homogeneous form $F(X, Y, Z, W) = 0$, and suppose there is a rational solution $(X_1, Y_1, Z_1, W_1) \neq (0, 0, 0, 0)$, and we may assume that $Z_1 \neq 0$.

Put

$$X = X_1\zeta + \xi, \qquad Y = Y_1\zeta + \eta, \qquad Z = Z_1\zeta, \qquad W = W_1\zeta + \rho.$$

The equation becomes

$$\zeta^2 L_1 + \zeta L_2 + L_3 = 0, \tag{10}$$

where L_1, L_2, L_3 are homogeneous forms of degrees 1, 2, 3, respectively, in ξ, η, ρ, and L_1, L_2 are not both identically zero. If L_1 is identically zero, the equation in ζ gives at once all the rational solutions of $F(X, Y, Z, W) = 0$. Suppose next that L_1 is not identically zero. An infinity of solutions arise on imposing the condition $L_1 = 0$ on ξ, η, ρ, provided that L_2 is not identically divisible by L_1. When this is so, a linear substitution on ξ, η, ρ, replaces L_1 by ρ, say. Then the ζ equation takes the form

$$\left(\frac{\zeta}{\rho}\right)^2 + M_1\left(\frac{\zeta}{\rho}\right) + M_3 = 0,$$

where M_1, M_3 are linear and cubic polynomials in $\xi/\rho, \eta/\rho$. On solving for ζ/ρ, we see that the problem of finding the rational solutions of this equation is equivalent to that of finding rational solutions of the equation

$$z^2 = f(x, y), \tag{11}$$

where $f(x, y)$ is the general cubic polynomial in x, y. This is the type of equation which would have arisen when the tangent plane at a rational point of the surface $F(X, Y, Z, W) = 0$ meets the surface in three straight lines. We give Whitehead's [5] solution of equation (11).

Write

$$z^2 = ax^3 + bx^2y + cxy^2 + dy^3 + ex^2 + fxy + gy^2 + hx + iy + j, \tag{12}$$

4+

where we may suppose that $a \neq 0$ by a linear transformation if need be, and then that $a = 1$ on replacing x, z by x/a, z/a.

On replacing x by $x - py - q$, say, we may suppose that the equation takes the form

$$z^2 = x^3 + x(ay^2 + by + c) + dy^3 + ey^2 + fy + g.$$

The right-hand side is a function of only one variable, which can only be $x + ky$, k a constant, if and only if,

$$a = b = d = e = f = 0,$$

a case we have excluded.

Put $x = y^2 + 2ty$ where t is a parameter. Then

$$z^2 = y^6 + 6ty^5 + (12t^2 + a)y^4 + (8t^3 + 2at + b + d)y^3$$
$$+ (2bt + c + e)y^2 + (2ct + f)y + g.$$

Put now $$z = y^3 + Ay^2 + By + C,$$

where

$$2A = 6t, \quad 2B + A^2 = 12t^2 + a, \quad 2C + 2AB = 8t^3 + 2at + b + d.$$

and so $$A = 3t, \quad 2B = 3t^2 + a, \quad 2C = b + d - at - t^3.$$

Substituting for z^2, we have

$$Py^2 + Qy + R = 0,$$

where $\quad P + \frac{1}{4}(3t^2 + a)^2 + 3t(b + d - at - t^3) = 2bt + c + e.$

or $\quad P = \frac{3}{4}t^4 + \frac{3}{2}at^2 - (b + 3d)t + c + e - \frac{1}{4}a^2.$

So $\quad Q + \frac{1}{2}(3t^2 + a)(b + d - at - t^3) = 2ct + f,$

or $\quad Q = \frac{3}{2}t^5 + 2at^3 - \frac{3}{2}(b + d)t^2 + \frac{1}{2}(a^2 + 4c)t + f - \frac{1}{2}a(b + d).$

Finally $$R = g - \frac{1}{4}(b + d - at^2 - t^3)^2$$
$$= -\frac{1}{4}t^6 + \cdots.$$

We note that

$$2Pt - Q = at^3 - \frac{1}{2}(b + 9d)t^2 + (2e - a^2)t + \frac{1}{2}a(b + d) - f,$$

and this is not identically zero unless $a = e = f = 0$, $b + 9d = 0$.

On solving the quadratic for y, we have two values of y which are finite and different, except for a finite number of values of t since neither P nor $\Delta = Q^2 - 4PR = 3t^{10} + \cdots$ is identically zero.

Hence
$$2Py = -Q \pm \sqrt{\Delta},$$

$$2P^2x = 2P^2y^2 + 4P^2ty$$

$$= -2PQy - 2PR + 4P^2ty$$

$$= y(4P^2t - 2PQ) - 2PR$$

$$= (-Q \pm \sqrt{\Delta})(2Pt - Q) - 2PR$$

$$= Q^2 - 2PR - 2PQt \pm (2Pt - Q)\sqrt{\Delta}.$$

Since $z = y^3 + \cdots$, we have, say,

$$x = \alpha \pm \alpha_1\sqrt{\Delta}, \qquad y = \beta \pm \beta_1\sqrt{\Delta}, \qquad z = \gamma \pm \gamma_1\sqrt{\Delta}.$$

These two points define a straight line and any point on it can be written as

$$X = \alpha + \alpha_1\theta, \qquad Y = \beta + \beta_1\theta, \qquad Z = \gamma + \gamma_1\theta,$$

where θ is a parameter. The points where this line meets the cubic surface $Z^2 = f(X, Y)$ are given by a cubic equation in θ. This has a factor $\theta^2 - \Delta$, and the remaining factor is linear, and determines a rational point. The third root will not be infinite except for a finite number of values of t. For if the coefficient of θ^3 is zero,

$$\alpha_1^3 + \alpha_1\beta_1^2 a + d\beta_1^3 = 0,$$

or
$$(2Pt - Q)^3 + aP^2(2Pt - Q) + dP^3 = 0.$$

On noting the degrees of $2Pt - Q$ and P and the coefficient of t^{12} in the equation, we find $d = 0$. If $2Pt - Q$ is identically zero, $a = e = f = 0$, $b + 9d = 0$, i.e. $b = 0$, and this is the excluded case. If $2Pt - Q$ is not identically zero,

$$(2Pt - Q)^2 + aP^2 = 0.$$

From the coefficient of t^8, $a = 0$, and then $2Pt - Q = 0$, a contradiction.

3. Mordell has proposed the plausible

Conjecture
The cubic equation $F(X, Y, Z, W) = 0$ is solvable if and only if the congruence

$$F(X, Y, Z, W) \equiv 0 \pmod{p^r}, \tag{13}$$

is solvable for all primes p and integers $r > 0$ with $(X, Y, Z, W, p) = 1$.
The conjecture holds in at least two cases:
    I. when the equation takes the form

$$N(X + \theta Y + \theta^2 Z) = mW^3,$$

where N is the norm form in the cubic field $Q(\theta)$.

This can be proved by the theory of algebraic numbers.

II. when the equation takes the form

$$X^3 + aY^3 = b(Z^3 + aW^3).$$

This follows from case I since the relation

$$\frac{X + Y\sqrt[3]{a}}{Z + W\sqrt[3]{a}} = \frac{\xi + \eta\sqrt[3]{a} + \zeta\sqrt[3]{a^2}}{\rho}$$

establishes a 1–1 correspondence between (X, Y, Z, W) and (ξ, η, ζ, ρ). The conjecture, however, is not true for all $F(X, Y, Z, W)$. Thus as shown by Swinnerton-Dyer[7], the equation

$$WX(X + W) = N(X + Y\theta + Z\theta^2),$$

where
$$\theta^3 + 7(\theta + 1)^2 = 0$$

is locally solvable but has no integer solutions.

Other instances have been given by Mordell[8]. The arguments are similar to those of Swinnerton-Dyer. A more interesting counter-example has been given by Cassels and Guy[9].

Theorem 3

The equation

$$5x^3 + 9y^3 + 10z^3 + 12w^3 = 0$$

is solvable everywhere locally but has no rational solutions except $(0, 0, 0, 0)$.

The proof depends upon the application of the cubic fields $k_1 = Q(\sqrt[3]{90})$, $k_2 = Q(\sqrt[3]{30})$ and their composition $K = k_1 k_2$, and requires the theory of relative fields. This seems to be the only known instance of an equation of this form which has been proved impossible otherwise than by simple congruence considerations.

Previously Selmer[10] stated that he has verified the solubility of

$$ax^3 + by^3 + cz^3 + dw^3 = 0$$

in all the relevant cases when $|abcd| \leqslant 500$.

4. Prior to the discovery of Theorem 2, various classes of cubic equations had been shown to have parametric rational solutions. This has been done by Mordell, by combining both quadratic and cubic irrationalities as for equation (10), and by Segre by the use of geometric considerations. Further results by the use of more abstruse geometrical ideas were found by Segre[2]. He developed these in a memoir in which he studied in great detail the configurations arising from the 27 lines on a cubic surface and the sets of 216 doublets, of 720 triplets, of 72 sextuplets, the sets being such that no two lines in a set intersect.

The determination of a set depends upon the solution of an algebraic equation in one variable of degrees 27, 216, 720, 72. The existence of a rational root in one of these equations, say conditions ρ_1, ρ_2, ρ_3, ρ_4, gives results on the existence of rational solutions. Thus, for ρ_1, ρ_2, there is an infinity of solutions, and for ρ_2 all the rational solutions are given as quotients of polynomials of degree 4. He finds numerous results for which his memoir, which contains many references to the literature, should be consulted.

REFERENCES

1. T. Skolem. Einige Bemerkungen über die Auffindung der rationalen Punkte auf gewissen algebraischen Gebilden. *Math. Z.*, **63** (1955), 294–312.
2. B. Segre. On the rational solutions of homogeneous cubic equations in four variables. *Math. Notae* (Rosario Argentina), **11** (1951), 1–68.
3. L. J. Mordell. On Ryley's solution of $x^3 + y^3 + z^3 = n$. *J. Lond. Math. Soc.*, **17** (1942), 139–144.
4. H. W. Richmond. On rational solutions of $x^3 + y^3 + z^3 = R$. *Proc. Edinburgh Math. Soc.*, (2) **2** (1930), 92–100.
5. B. Segre. A parametric solution of the indeterminate cubic equation $z^2 = f(x, y)$. *J. Lond. Math. Soc.*, **18** (1943), 226–233.
6. R. F. Whitehead. A rational parametric solution of the cubic indeterminate equation $z^2 = f(x, y)$. *J. Lond. Math. Soc.*, **19** (1944), 68–71.
7. H. S. P. Swinnerton-Dyer. Two special cubic surfaces. *Mathematika*, **9** (1962), 54–56.
8. L. J. Mordell. On the conjecture for the rational points on a cubic surface. *J. Lond. Math. Soc.*, **40** (1965), 149–158.
9. J. W. S. Cassels and M. J. T. Guy. On the Hasse principle for cubic surfaces. *Mathematika*, **13** (1966), 111–120.
10. E. S. Selmer. Sufficient congruence conditions for the existence of rational points on certain cubic surfaces. *Math. Scand.*, **1** (1953), 113–119.

CHAPTER 12

Rational and Integer Points on Quartic Surfaces

1. Only a few scattered results are known for the rational points on quartic surfaces, and the first now given is due to Euler.

The equation

$$x^4 + y^4 = z^4 + w^4. \tag{1}$$

Put $x = at + c$, $y = bt - d$, $z = at + d$, $w = bt + c$, where a, b, c, d are parameters. A quartic in t arises in which the coefficients of t^4, t^0 are zero. The coefficient of t^3 will also be zero if

$$c(a^3 - b^3) = d(a^3 + b^3).$$

Take $\qquad\qquad c = a^3 + b^3, \qquad d = a^3 - b^3.$

Then $\qquad 3t(a^2 - b^2)(c^2 - d^2) = 2(ad^3 - ac^3 + bc^3 + bd^3).$

This gives, on ignoring the denominators,

$$x = a^7 + a^5b^2 - 2a^3b^4 + 3a^2b^5 + ab^6.$$

$$y = a^6b - 3a^5b^2 - 2a^4b^3 + a^2b^5 + b^7.$$

$$z = a^7 + a^5b^2 - 2a^3b^4 - 3a^2b^5 + ab^6.$$

$$w = a^6b + 3a^5b^2 - 2a^4b^3 + a^2b^5 + b^7.$$

Very little is known about the more general equation

$$ax^4 + by^4 + cz^4 + dw^4 = 0, \quad abcd \neq 0, \tag{2}$$

Richmond[1] has shown that if a rational point $P(x_0, y_0, z_0, w_0)$ is known, others can be found if $abcd$ is a perfect square. His proof depends upon geometrical considerations, but we present the proof rather differently. This condition implies that a rational line can be drawn through P to meet the surface Q in three points at P, and so if the line does not lie on the surface, then Q, the fourth point of intersection, will also be rational.

When $x_0y_0z_0w_0 = 0$, the method does not give a new solution, and Richmond tacitly assumes that $x_0y_0z_0w_0 \neq 0$.

Let the line be

$$\frac{x - x_0}{l} = \frac{y - y_0}{m} = \frac{z - z_0}{n} = \frac{w - w_0}{p} = t. \tag{3}$$

Then

$$a(x_0 + lt)^4 + b(y_0 + mt)^4 + c(z_0 + nt)^4 + d(w_0 + pt)^4 = 0. \qquad (4)$$

This equation will have a triple root $t = 0$ if

$$ax_0^4 + by_0^4 + cz_0^4 + dw_0^4 = 0,$$
$$ax_0^3 l + by_0^3 m + cz_0^3 n + dw_0^3 p = 0, \qquad (5)$$
$$ax_0^2 l^2 + by_0^2 m^2 + cz_0^2 n^2 + dw_0^2 p^2 = 0.$$

Suppose first that $w_0 = 0$, $x_0 y_0 z_0 \neq 0$.
Eliminating a, b, c from equation (5) we have

$$\prod \left(\frac{l}{x_0} - \frac{m}{y_0} \right) = 0.$$

Take $l = x_0$, $m = y_0$, and so from equation (5), $n = z_0$.
Then from equation (4), the line meets the surface where

$$(ax_0^4 + by_0^4 + cz_0^4)(1 + t)^4 + dp^4 t^4 = 0$$

that is, $pt = 0$, and no new solution arises whether $p = 0$ or $p \neq 0$.
Suppose next that $z_0 = 0$, $w_0 = 0$ and so $x_0 y_0 \neq 0$. Now we can take $l = x_0$, $m = y_0$. Then

$$(ax_0^4 + by_0^4)(1 + t)^4 + (cn^4 + dp^4)t^4 = 0.$$

Hence $t = 0$ and no new solution arises unless $cn^4 + dp^4 = 0$.
Then the surface will contain lines of the form

$$x - ry = 0, \qquad z - sw = 0.$$

By a slight change of notation, we can write the equation of the surface (2) in the form

$$a(x^4 - y^4) + c(z^4 - w^4) = 0. \qquad (6)$$

and so (1) is a special case of this. The equation (6) is a particular case of the equation

$$xy(mx^2 + ny^2) = zw(mz^2 + nw^2)$$

dealt with by Euler. A solution rather different from his is given here since the method can be applied to more general equations.

We show that there is a parametric solution, and in general an infinite set of parametric solutions in a variable v.

Write the equation (6) as

$$a(x + y)(x^3 - x^2 y + xy^2 - y^3) + c(z + w)(z^3 - z^2 w + zw^2 - w^3) = 0.$$

Put
$$v(x + y) = z + w,$$

where v is a parameter. The quartic curve in homogeneous coordinates x, y, z so obtained contains the cubic curve

$$a(x^3 - x^2y + xy^2 - y^3) + cv(z^3 - z^2(vx + vy - z) + z(vx + vy - z)^2$$
$$- (vx + vy - z)^3) = 0.$$

This contains the point $x = 1, y = 1, z = v$.

Write $x + y = X, x - y = Y, z = v$. Then

$$f(X, Y) = \tfrac{1}{2}aY(X^2 + Y^2) +$$
$$cv(v^3 - v^2(vX - v) + v(vX - v)^2 - (vX - v)^3) = 0.$$

This curve contains the point $(X, Y) = (2, 0)$. The inflexions on the cubic are given by

$$\frac{\partial^2 f}{\partial X^2} \cdot \frac{\partial^2 f}{\partial Y^2} - \left(\frac{\partial^2 f}{\partial X \partial Y}\right)^2 = 0.$$

Now at $(X, Y) = (2, 0)$,

$$\frac{\partial^2 f}{\partial X^2} = aY + 2cv^4 - 6cv^4(vX - v) = -4cv^4 \qquad \frac{\partial^2 f}{\partial Y^2} = 3aY = 0$$

$$\frac{\partial^2 f}{\partial X \partial Y} = aX = 2a$$

and so no inflexion occurs at $(X, Y) = (2, 0)$. Hence the tangential of this point gives a new solution, and we may expect an infinity of solutions each involving the parameter v in continuing the process.

The method is easily generalized and can be applied to the equation

$$L_1 f_1(x, y, z, w) = L_2 f_2(x, y, z, w), \tag{7}$$

where $L_1 = a_1x + b_1y + c_1z + d_1w$, $L_2 = a_2x + b_2y + c_2z + d_2w$, and f_1, f_2 are cubic polynomials in x, y, z, w. There are of course trivial solutions given by $L_1 = L_2 = 0$.
Put $L_2 = vL_1$, and then

$$f_1\left(x, y, z, \frac{(va_1 - a_2)x + (vb_1 - b_2)y + (vc_1 - c_2)z}{d_2 - vd_1}\right)$$
$$= vf_2\left(x, y, z, \frac{(va_1 - a_2)x + (vb_1 - b_2)y + (vc_1 - c_2)z}{d_2 - vd_1}\right).$$

If we know one solution of this cubic equation, we can proceed as before. Suppose for example that $x = y = z = 1$ is a solution. This will be so if

$$a_1 + b_1 + c_1 + d_1 = 0, \qquad a_2 + b_2 + c_2 + d_2 = 0,$$
$$f_1(1, 1, 1, 1) = vf_2(1, 1, 1, 1).$$

Many examples can be constructed.

We now return to equation (5) when $x_0 y_0 z_0 w_0 \neq 0$.

Put $l = Lx_0 + \dfrac{px_0}{w_0}, \qquad m = My_0 + \dfrac{py_0}{w_0}, \qquad n = Nz_0 + \dfrac{pz_0}{w_0}.$

Then $ax_0^4 L + by_0^4 M + cz_0^4 N = 0,$

$ax_0^4 L^2 + by_0^4 M^2 + cz_0^4 N^2 = 0,$

or, say, $AL + BM + CN = 0,$

$AL^2 + BM^2 + CN^2 = 0.$

Eliminating L,

$$(B^2 + AB)M^2 + 2BCMN + (C^2 + AC)N^2 = 0.$$

The ratio M/N is rational if $-ABC(A + B + C)$ is a perfect square, i.e. if $abcd = k^2$, k rational.

Suppose first that

$$al^4 + bm^4 + cn^4 + dp^4 \neq 0.$$

Then the process gives from equation (4) a value for t and so another solution. This will be the same as x_0, y_0, z_0, w_0 only if either $l/x_0 = m/y_0 = n/z_0 = p/w_0$ which is not so, or if $t = 0$, that is,

$$ax_0 l^3 + by_0 m^3 + cz_0 n^3 + dw_0 p^3 = 0.$$

Eliminating a, b, c, d from this equation and (5), we have

$$\prod \left(\frac{l}{x_0} - \frac{m}{y_0} \right) = 0.$$

But $m/y_0 - n/z_0 = 0$ gives $M - N = 0$ and then

$$(B + C)^2 + A(B + C) = (A + B + C)(B + C) = 0.$$

Clearly $A + B + C \neq 0$ since $w_0 \neq 0$. If $B + C = 0$, then

$$by_0^4 + cz_0^4 = 0, \qquad ax_0^4 + dw_0^4 = 0,$$

and the surface would contain the lines

$$\frac{y}{y_0} = \frac{z}{z_0}, \qquad \frac{x}{x_0} = \frac{w}{w_0}.$$

This case has been dealt with.

Suppose finally that

$$al^4 + bm^4 + cn^4 + dp^4 = 0.$$

On again eliminating a, b, c, d from this equation and (5), we have

$$\left(\frac{l}{x_0} + \frac{m}{y_0} + \frac{n}{z_0} + \frac{p}{w_0} \right) \prod \left(\frac{l}{x_0} - \frac{m}{y_0} \right) = 0.$$

4*

We have already dealt with $l/x_0 - m/y_0 = 0$, etc. and so we have

$$\frac{l}{x_0} + \frac{m}{y_0} + \frac{n}{z_0} + \frac{p}{w_0} = 0.$$

Hence the solution l, m, n, p of equation (2) is different from x_0, y_0, z_0, w_0.

A similar result holds for Segre's[2] equation derived from equation (2) on replacing a, x, etc., by $A_0 + A_1\theta + A_2\theta^2 + A_3\theta^3$, $X + Y\theta + Z\theta^2 + W\theta^3$, etc., where θ is the root of a quartic equation,

$$\theta^4 + p\theta^3 + q\theta^2 + r\theta + s = 0,$$

where all the coefficients are rational numbers. The only difference is that in $abcd = k^2$, k must be a number in the field, reducible or irreducible, defined by θ.

The coefficients of the quartic equation are rational numbers since the coefficients $a_1, b_1, \ldots,$ are now conjugate numbers in the field.

2. A few equations of the form (2) may be noted.

The equation

$$x^4 + y^4 + z^4 = w^4. \tag{8}$$

It has been conjectured by Euler that the equation has no solutions except those with $xyz = 0$. Morgan Ward[3,4] has shown that there are no integer solutions with $w < 10,000$. This is true[5] for $w < 220,000$.

The equation

$$x^4 + y^4 + 4z^4 = 1 \tag{9}$$

has a rational solution given by

$$x = \frac{t^4 - 2}{t^4 + 2}, \qquad y = \frac{2t^3}{t^4 + 2}, \qquad z = \frac{2t}{t^4 + 2},$$

where t is a rational parameter.

This is a particular solution for which

$$x^2 + 2yz = 1.$$

Then $$y^4 + 4z^4 = 1 - x^4 = 1 - (1 - 2yz)^2,$$

and $$(y^2 + 2z^2)^2 = 4yz,$$

$$y^2 + 2z^2 = 2\sqrt{yz}.$$

Put $y = t^2z$. Then

$$(t^4 + 2)z = 2t.$$

Since $$(y^2 - 2z^2)^2 = 4yz(1 - 2yz) = 4yzx^2,$$

$$x = \frac{y^2 - 2z^2}{2\sqrt{yz}} = \frac{t^4 - 2}{2t} \quad z = \frac{t^4 - 2}{t^4 + 2}.$$

The equation

$$x^4 + y^4 + z^4 = 2. \tag{10}$$

Put $z = x + y$, then

$$x^4 + y^4 + (x + y)^4 = 2,$$
$$2(x^2 + xy + y^2)^2 = 2,$$
$$x^2 + xy + y^2 = 1.$$

A parametric solution is given by putting $y = 1 - tx$ giving

$$x(1 - t + t^2) = 2t - 1.$$

The solutions of (9), (10) and (11) below are due to Carmichael[6].

3. *The equation*

$$x^4 + ay^4 + bz^4 = w^2. \tag{11}$$

New solutions can be found in general from a given solution (x_1, y_1, z_1, w_1). The equation is satisfied by the assumption

$$x^2 = X^2 - aY^2 - bZ^2, \qquad y^2 = 2XY, \qquad z^2 = 2XZ,$$
$$w = X^2 + aY^2 + bZ^2.$$

A solution of the first of these is given by

$$X = X_1^2 + aY_1^2 + bZ_1^2, \qquad Y = 2X_1Y_1, \qquad Z = 2X_1Z_1,$$
$$x = X_1^2 - aY_1^2 - bZ_1^2.$$

Then
$$y^2 = 4X_1Y_1(X_1^2 + aY_1^2 + bZ_1^2),$$
$$z^2 = 4X_1Z_1(X_1^2 + aY_1^2 + bZ_1^2).$$

These will be satisfied if we put

$$X_1 = x_1^2, \qquad Y_1 = y_1^2, \qquad Z_1 = z_1^2,$$

and
$$x_1^4 + ay_1^4 + bz_1^4 = w_1^2.$$

The solution of the equation (11) is included in that of finding rational solutions of

$$ax^4 + by^4 + c = z^2, \tag{12}$$

when one (x_0, y_0, z_0) is known.

Put
$$x = x_0 + pt, \qquad y = y_0 + qt,$$

where p and q are parameters. Then the equation (12) becomes a quartic curve in (z, t) with a known rational point $(z_0, 0)$. The classic procedure gives in general another solution in terms of two parameters p, q.

4. Some quartic equations $f(x, y, z) = 0$ which have an infinity of integer solutions, have been given by Mordell[7].

Theorem 1

The equation

$$z^2 = U_1^2 + U_2 U_3, \tag{13}$$

where $U_r = a_r x^2 + h_r xy + b_r y^2 + f_r y + g_r x$ $(r = 1, 2, 3)$, *and the coefficients are integers, has an infinity of integer solutions if* $h_r^2 - 4a_r b_r > 0$ *and is not a perfect square for either* $r = 2$ *or* $r = 3$, *and either* U_2 *or* U_3 *is absolutely irreducible.*

We have from (13)

$$z + U_1 = \frac{p}{q} U_2, \qquad z - U_1 = \frac{q}{p} U_3,$$

where p, q are integers and $(p, q) = 1$. Then

$$2U_1 = \frac{p}{q} U_2 - \frac{q}{p} U_3. \tag{14}$$

For integer solutions of equation (14), $U_2 \equiv 0 \pmod{q}$, $U_3 \equiv 0 \pmod{p}$, and then z is also an integer. Write (14) as

$$P(x, y) = ax^2 + hxy + by^2 + fy + gx = 0, \tag{15}$$

where $a = p^2 a_2 - 2pq a_1 - q^2 a_3,$ $h = p^2 h_2 - 2pq h_1 - q^2 h_3,$

$b = p^2 b_2 - 2pq b_1 - q^2 b_3,$ $f = p^2 f_2 - 2pq f_1 - q^2 f_3,$

$g = p^2 g_2 - 2pq g_1 - q^2 g_3.$

The equation (15) has a solution $x = y = 0$. Hence from Theorem 2, Chapter 9, it follows that (15) will have an infinity of integer solutions if $P(x, y)$ is absolutely irreducible, and $h^2 - 4ab > 0$ and is not a perfect square. The condition for reducibility is

$$2\Delta = \begin{vmatrix} 2a & h & g \\ h & 2b & f \\ g & f & 2c \end{vmatrix} = 0.$$

This is a binary sextic in p, q and is not identically zero since the coefficient of p^6 is obtained by replacing a, b etc. in Δ by a_2, b_2 etc. Hence if either U_2 or U_3 is irreducible, there will be only a finite number of values of p, q for which $P(x, y)$ is reducible.

Next $h^2 - 4ab = (p^2 h_2 - 2pq h_1 - q^2 h_3)^2$

$$- 4(p^2 a_2 - 2pq a_1 - q^2 a_3)(p^2 b_2 - 2pq b_1 - q^2 b_3).$$

If $h_2^2 - 4a_2b_2 > 0$ and is not a perfect square, this holds for $h^2 - 4ab$ if p is large compared with q and for an infinity of p.

There are many special cases not included in the theorem. We need only mention[7]

Theorem 2

The equation

$$z^2 = k^2 + x^2(ax^2 + by^2), \quad abk \neq 0 \tag{16}$$

has an infinity of integer solutions if either $b > 0$, or $b < 0$, $b^2 < 4ak^2$.

We have

$$z + k = \frac{q}{p}(ax^2 + by^2), \qquad z - k = \frac{p}{q}x^2,$$

where p, q are integers and $(p, q) = 1$. Then

$$(aq^2 - p^2)x^2 + bq^2y^2 = 2kpq.$$

This will have the solution $x = 0$, $y = t$, where t is an arbitrary integer if $bqt^2 = 2kp$, and so if $\delta = (b, 2k)$, we can take

$$\lambda p = \frac{b}{\delta}t^2, \qquad \lambda q = \frac{2k}{\delta}, \qquad \lambda = \left(t^2, \frac{2k}{\delta}\right).$$

Hence there will be an infinity of solutions for x, y if $b(p^2 - aq^2) > 0$ and is not a perfect square, i.e. if $b(b^2t^4 - 4ak^2) > 0$ and is not a perfect square. This is possible if $b > 0$ for an infinity of values of t, and also if $b < 0$ and $b^2 < 4ak^2$ for $t = 1$.

The case $b < 0$, $b^2 > 4ak^2$ seems difficult.

Theorem 3[8, 9, 10]

The equation

$$(x^2 + a)(y^2 + a) = (az^2 + b^2)^2, \tag{17}$$

where a and b are integers, has integer solutions given by

$$x = bu + cdv, \qquad y = bu - cdv, \qquad z = u = (x + y)/2b.$$

where c, d are any integers for which

$$a \pm b^2 = c^2d,$$

and the integers u and v satisfy the equation

$$\pm u^2 - dv^2 = 1.$$

The equation with the plus sign has an infinity of solutions if $d > 0$ and is not a perfect square. The equation with the minus sign may have an infinity of solutions if $d < 0$ and $-d$ is not a perfect square, for example if $-d$ is a prime $\equiv 1 \pmod 4$.

Put $x = X + Y, y = X - Y$. Then

$$(X^2 - Y^2)^2 + 2a(X^2 + Y^2) + a^2 = (az^2 + b^2)^2$$

$$(X^2 - Y^2)^2 - 2a(X^2 - Y^2) + a^2 = (az^2 + b^2)^2 - 4aX^2.$$

Take $X = bZ$. Then

$$b^2 Z^2 - Y^2 - a = \pm(aZ^2 - b^2).$$

Hence either

$$Y^2 - (a + b^2)Z^2 = -(a + b^2),$$

or

$$Y^2 + (a - b^2)Z^2 = -(a - b^2).$$

The theorem follows on putting $Y = cdv, Z = u$.

More generally the method applies to a quartic surface $f(x, y, z) = 0$ if its section by a plane consists of two conic sections, for example, if identically,

$$f(x, y, ax + by + c) = g^2(x, y) - h^2(x, y),$$

where $g(x, y), h(x, y)$ are polynomials of the second degree, or its equivalent

$$f(x, y, z) = g^2(x, y) - h^2(x, y) + l(x, y, z)m(x, y, z),$$

where $l(x, y, z), m(x, y, z)$ are linear and cubic polynomials respectively in x, y, z. This remark is due to Mordell.

A quartic equation not without interest is given by

$$\sum_{r,s=0}^{2} a_{rs}x^r y^s = dz^2, \tag{18}$$

where the a's and d are integers (and we may suppose that $d > 0$). It seems difficult to find the integer solutions since no general criterion for solvability exists. However, if $a_{22} < 0$, the term $a_{22}x^2 y^2$ implies that y, say, is bounded and then x and z are given by a quadratic equation. When one integer solution (x_0, y_0, z_0) of (18) is known, an infinity can be found. This leads to solutions $(x_0, y_1, z_1), (x_1, y_1, z_2), (x_1, y_2, z_3), (x_2, y_2, z_4)$, etc. where from a Pellian equation, $y_1, x_1, y_2, x_2, \ldots$ may each have an infinity of values.

For rational values of x, y, z, Mordell has proposed the

Conjecture

There exists in general an infinity of rational values for x, y, z.

Put $x = X/Y, y = P/Q, z = Z/QY$ where X, Y, P, Q, Z are integers and $(X, Y) = 1, (P, Q) = 1$.

Then

$$\sum_{r,s=0}^{2} a_{rs}X^r Y^{2-r} P^s Q^{2-s} = dZ^2,$$

or

$$X^2(a_{22}P^2 + a_{21}PQ + a_{20}Q^2) + XY(a_{12}P^2 + a_{11}PQ + a_{10}Q^2)$$
$$+ Y^2(a_{02}P^2 + a_{01}PQ + a_{00}Q^2) = dZ^2. \qquad (19)$$

Necessary and sufficient conditions can be imposed upon P, Q so that this equation is solvable for X, Y, Z. Suppose for simplicity that $a_{12} = a_{11} = a_{10} = 0$, and write the equation as

$$AX^2 + BY^2 = dZ^2. \qquad (20)$$

The common divisors of A and B are finite in number and can be divided out by applying a linear substitution to P and Q, and replacing Z by kZ. Hence we may suppose that equation (20) is in the normal form, i.e. $(X, Z) = (Y, Z) = (X, Y) = 1$, $(A, B) = 1$, $(A, d) = (B, d) = 1$, and that A, B, d are square free since square factors can be absolved in X^2, Y^2, Z^2. Suppose for simplicity that $(a_{22}, a_{21}, a_{20}) = 1 = (a_{02}, a_{01}, a_{00})$ and that $d = 1$. Then solvability of (20) is possible only if P, Q are such that A and B are not both negative; that (20) is solvable mod 8 i.e. we must exclude $A \equiv B \equiv -1 \pmod 4$; $A \equiv 2 \pmod 4$, $B \equiv 5 \pmod 8$ or $B \equiv A + 1 \pmod 8$, and similarly for $B \equiv 2 \pmod 4$, and that B should be a quadratic residue of every prime factor of A, and similarly for A and the prime factors of B.

These conditions will be simpler if A and B are both primes. It should not be too difficult to prove that they can be satisfied.

REFERENCES

1. H. W. Richmond. On the diophantine equation $F = ax^4 + by^4 + cz^4 + dw^4 = 0$, the product $abcd$ being a square number. *J. Lond. Math. Soc.*, **19** (1944), 193–194.
2. B. Segre. On arithmetical properties of quadratic and quartic surfaces. *J. Lond. Math. Soc.*, **19** (1944), 195–200.
3. Morgan Ward. Euler's three biquadrate problem. *Proc. Nat. Acad. Sci.*, **31** (1945), 125–127.
4. Morgan Ward. Euler's problem on sums of three fourth powers. *Duke Math. J.*, **15** (1948), 827–837.
5. L. J. Lander, T. R. Parkins, and J. L. Selfridge. A survey of equal sums of like powers. *Math. Comp.*, **21** (1967), 446–453.
6. R. D. Carmichael. "Diophantine Analysis." John Wiley & Sons, New York (1915), pp. 44–48.
7. L. J. Mordell. On some ternary quartic diophantine equations. *Elemente der Mathematik.*, **31** (1966), 89–90.
8. H. C. Williams. A note on a diophantine problem. Unpublished.
9. A. Schinzel et W. Sierpinski. Sur l'equation diophantienne $(x^2-1)(y^2-1) = (((y-x)/2)^2-1)^2$. *El. Math.* **22** (1963), 37–38.
10. K. Szymiczek. On a diophantine equation. *El. Math.* **22** (1967), 37–38.

CHAPTER 13

Integer Solutions of Some Cubic Equations
in Three Variables

1. Comparatively little is known about the integer solutions of the equation

$$f(x, y, z) = 0,\tag{1}$$

where $f(x, y, z)$ is the general cubic polynomial with integer coefficients. There are, however, a number of special results, but in general they give some but not all the solutions. Thus a solution may be given in the form

$$x = f_1(t), \qquad y = f_2(t), \qquad z = f_3(t),\tag{2}$$

where f_1, f_2, f_3 are polynomials in an integer parameter t.
A solution may also exist in the form

$$x = f_1(u, v), \qquad y = f_2(u, v), \qquad z = f_3(u, v),\tag{3}$$

where f_1, f_2, f_3 are polynomials in integer parameters and u and v satisfy a Pellian equation.

A particularly interesting equation is

$$x^3 + y^3 + z^3 = n.\tag{4}$$

When $n = a^3$, there are the solutions

$$x = t, \qquad y = -t, \qquad z = a;$$

$$x = 9at^4, \qquad y = 3at - 9at^4, \qquad z = a - 9at^3.$$

When $n = 2a^3$,

$$x = a(1 + 6t^3), \qquad y = a(1 - 6t^3), \qquad z = -6at^2.$$

There are no solutions of equation (4) when $n \equiv \pm 4 \pmod 9$, as is obvious from a congruence (mod 9).

A question arises. If $n \not\equiv \pm 4 \pmod 9$, does the equation (4) have an infinity of integer solutions? When $n = 3$, there are solutions given by

$$(x, y, z) = (1, 1, 1), (4, 4, -5).$$

Excluding these four solutions, there are no others with max $(|x|, |y|, |z|) \leqslant 3164$. This result is due to Miller and Woolett[1] who have given a table of solutions for $0 \leqslant n \leqslant 100$.

These results led to a more extensive table due to V. L. Gardiner, R. B. Lazarus, and P. R. Stein and produced at the Los Alamos Scientific Laboratory of the University of California, Los Alamos, New Mexico.

Write equation (4) in the form

$$x^3 + y^3 = z^3 - d.$$

The range chosen was

$$0 \leqslant x \leqslant y \leqslant 65{,}536, \qquad 0 < z - x \leqslant 65{,}536, \qquad 0 < |d| < 999.$$

No new solution was found for $n = 3$. It would be of great interest to prove there are no other solutions and also if one of the equations for which no solution was found, for example, $n = 30$, could be proved to have no solutions.

It has been shown[2] that the cases $n = a^3$, $2a^3$ are the only ones for which the equation (4) has a parametric solution given by polynomials in t of degree $\leqslant 4$. Segre[3] by geometric considerations has proved the more general

Theorem 1

The equation

$$ax^3 + by^3 + cz^3 + d = 0, \quad abcd \neq 0, \tag{5}$$

where a, b, c, d are integers, has in general no solutions with x, y, z as relatively prime polynomials with rational coefficients of degree $\leqslant 4$, in a parameter t.

There are three essentially distinct exceptions,

$$x^3 + y^3 + cz^3 + c = 0, \tag{6}$$

$$x^3 + y^3 + cz^3 + 2 = 0, \tag{7}$$

$$x^3 + y^3 + 2z^3 + 2 = 0, \tag{8}$$

where $c \neq 2r^3$, r rational.

The solutions of (6) are $x = t$, $y = -t$, $z = -1$, and

$$x = \frac{9}{c} t^4 - 3t, \qquad y = \frac{-9}{c} t^4, \qquad z = \frac{9}{c} t^3 - 1.$$

The solutions of equation (7) are

$$x = \frac{6}{c} t^3 - 1, \qquad y = -\frac{6}{c} t^3 - 1, \qquad z = \frac{6}{c} t^2.$$

The equation (8) has in addition to the three solutions given by $c = 2$, the further solutions

$$x = 4t^2 - 6t - 1, \qquad y = 4t^2 - 2t - 1, \qquad z = -4t^2 + 4t - 1;$$

and

$$27x = 2(4t^4 - 4t^3 - 6t^2 + 17t - 2),$$

$$27y = 4(2t^4 - 8t^3 + 6t^2 + 4t - 13),$$

$$27z = -8t^4 + 20t^3 - 24t^2 - 16t + 37.$$

By putting $t = 1 + 9t_1$, we can reduce the denominators of x, y, z to 3.

An instance of equation (3) is now given.

Theorem 2

The equation

$$ax^3 + ay^3 + bz^3 = bc^3, \quad abc \neq 0, \tag{9}$$

where a, b, c are integers, has an infinity of integer solutions other than the trivial ones $x + y = 0$, $z = c$.

The result is a simple consequence of the existence of the rational generator $x + y = 0$, $z = c$ on the cubic surface defined by the equation (9).

Put
$$z = c + t(x + y),$$

where t is an arbitrary integer parameter. Then dividing out by $x + y$,

$$a(x^2 - xy + y^2) + 3bc^2t + 3bct^2(x + y) + bt^3(x + y)^2 = 0.$$

Put
$$x + y = u, \quad x - y = v.$$

Then
$$\frac{a}{4}(u^2 + 3v^2) + 3bc^2t + 3bct^2u + bt^3u^2 = 0,$$

or
$$-3av^2 = (a + 4bt^3)u^2 + 12bct^2u + 12bc^2t.$$

If an equation

$$Dv^2 = Au^2 + Bu + C,$$

where A, B, C, D are integers, has one integer solution, it will have an infinity if $AD > 0$ and is not a perfect square, and if $B^2 - 4AC \neq 0$. Here a solution will be given by $u = 0$ if $3av^2 = -12bc^2t$, that is, if $t = -abk^2$ where k is an integer. Then $AD = 3a(4a^3b^4k^6 - a) > 0$ for $k \neq 0$, and is not a perfect square for an infinity of values of k.

Also
$$B^2 - 4AC = -48bc^2t(bt^3 + a) = 0$$

only when $t = 0$ or $bt^3 + a = 0$. Hence there are an infinity of integer solutions for u, v. We have now to show that we can find integer values for x, y. The condition for this is $u \equiv v \pmod 2$. Suppose that $a = 2^\alpha a'$, $\alpha \geq 0$, a' odd. Take $t \equiv 0 \pmod{2^\alpha}$. Then the u, v equation gives

$$-3a'v^2 \equiv a'u^2 \pmod 2, \quad \text{or} \quad u \equiv v \pmod 2.$$

In the particular case $x^3 + y^3 + z^3 = 1$, the well known solution $(x, y, z) = (9, -8, -6)$ corresponds to $t = -7$. We have then also solutions

$$(x, y, z) = (-103, 94, 64), (904, -823, -566), (3097, -2820, -1938).$$

Lehmer[5] has dealt in some detail with this equation. He has given recurrence formulae which lead to an infinity of solutions expressed as polynomials in a parameter t.

2. Theorems 2 and 3 are practically the only known results about equations of the form $ax^3 + by^3 + cz^3 = d$. Except for the trivial case $n \equiv \pm 4 \pmod 9$, there are not known any impossible equations,

$$x^3 + y^3 + z^3 = n. \tag{4}$$

However, Hurwitz[6] has shown by considering the number of lattice points and the volume enclosed by the obvious surface, that there are an infinity of values of integers $n \not\equiv \pm 4 \pmod 9$ for which there are no solutions in *positive* integers.

Among the simplest cubic equations are those given by $z^2 = f(x, y)$. There arises the

Conjecture

The equation $z^2 = f(x, y)$, where $f(x, y)$ is a cubic polynomial in x, y with integer coefficients has an infinity of integer solutions if it has one.

We may suppose the solution is given by $x = y = 0$. There are some special cases when the conjecture is true.

Theorem 3

The equation

$$z^2 = p^2 + lx + my + ax^3 + bx^2y + cxy^2 + dy^3, \tag{10}$$

where $(l, m) = 1$, has an infinity of integer solutions.

By making a linear transformation, we may suppose that $l = 1$, $m = 0$.
If $p = 0$, solutions are given by $x = 0$, $z^2 = dy^3$.
If $p \neq 0$, put $x = 4p^2X$, $y = 2pY$, $z = pZ$. Then

$$Z^2 = 1 + 4X + 64ap^4X^3 + 32bp^3X^2Y + 16cp^2XY^2 + 8dpY^3.$$

Put now $Z = 1 + 2X - 2X^2$, $\qquad Z^2 = 1 + 4X - 8X^3 + 4X^4$.

Then $\qquad X^4 = (2 + 16ap^4)X^3 + 8bp^3X^2Y + 4cp^2XY^2 + 2dpY^3$.

Solutions of this are given by putting $Y = tX$, t an integer parameter, since then

$$X = 2dpt^3 + \cdots + 2 + 16ap^4.$$

Similarly we can prove

Theorem 4

The equation

$$z^3 = p^3 + lx + my + ax^2 + bxy + cy^2, \quad (l, m) = 1 \tag{11}$$

has an infinity of solutions.
A parametric solution is given by taking

$$l = 1, \qquad m = 0, \qquad x = 3p^2X, \qquad z = p + X, \qquad y = tX.$$

Theorem[8] 5

The equation

$$z^2 = p^2 + lx + my + ax^2 + bxy + cy^2 + Ax^3 + Bx^2y$$
$$+ Cxy^2 + Dy^3, \quad p \neq 0, \tag{12}$$

has an infinity of integer solutions if $p \mid (l, m)$, and if the equation

$$ax^2 + bxy + cy^2 - (lx + my)^2/4p^2 = \pm 2p,$$

has an infinity of integer solutions.

This will be so if there is one solution, e.g. $x = 0$, $y = 1$, when $m = 0$, $c = \pm 2p$, and if

$$p^2(b^2 - 4ac) + am^2 + cl^2 - blm > 0,$$

and is not a perfect square.

Write the equation as

$$z^2 = p^2 + L_1 + L_2 + L_3,$$

where L_1, L_2, L_3 are the terms of the first, second and third degrees respectively. Put

$$z = p + \frac{L_1}{2p} + S, \qquad 2pS = L_2 - \frac{L_1^2}{4p^2}.$$

Then
$$z^2 = p^2 + L_1 + \frac{L_1^2}{4p^2} + 2pS + \frac{L_1 S}{p} + S^2.$$

Hence x, y satisfy the equation

$$S^2 + \frac{L_1 S}{p} = L_3.$$

Put $x = tX$, $y = tY$ where t is an integer parameter. Then

$$t\left(\frac{L_2(X, Y) - L_1(X, Y)^2/4p^2}{2p}\right)^2$$
$$+ L_1(X, Y)\left(\frac{L_2(X, Y) - L_1(X, Y)^2/4p^2}{2p^2}\right) = L_3(X, Y).$$

By hypothesis there are an infinity of integer values for X, Y for which the coefficient of t is one. Hence the theorem.

3. Even in the simplest case of the equation $z^2 = f(x, y)$, namely,

$$z^2 = ax^3 + by^3 + c, \tag{13}$$

very little is known. In special cases, solutions may be found. Thus if $c = (4abd^3)^2$, a solution is given by

$$x = ap^2, \qquad y = bq^2, \qquad z = a^2p^3 + b^2q^3, \qquad pq = 2d^2,$$

where p, q are integers. This gives a finite number of solutions depending upon the number of factors of d, and so equations can be constructed having at least as many integer solutions as can be desired.

There are some cases where an infinity of integer solutions can be found, as is shown in Chapter 14, for the equation

$$z^2 - (27abc)^2 = ab^2x^3 + y^3. \tag{14}$$

Results may sometimes be found when a solution is known, occasionally rather trivially as, for example, with

$$z^2 = x^3 + y^3 - 1.$$

Put $x = 1 + w$, $y = 1 - w$ and so $z^2 = 6w^2 + 1$.
Hence there are an infinity of integer solutions with $x + y = 2$.

More generally let $(x, y, z) = (p, q, r)$, $r \neq 0$ be a solution of equation (13).
Put $x = p + tX$, $y = q + tY$, where X, Y, t are integers.
Then

$$z^2 = r^2 + 3(ap^2 X + bq^2 Y)t + 3(apX^2 + bqY^2)t^2 + (aX^3 + bY^3)t^3.$$

Put
$$z = r + \frac{3}{2r}(ap^2 X + bq^2 Y)t + kt^2,$$

where k is an integer, and

$$2kr + \frac{9}{4r^2}(ap^2 X + bq^2 Y)^2 = 3(apX^2 + bqY^2), \tag{15}$$

and so
$$k^2 t + \frac{3k}{r}(ap^2 X + bq^2 Y) = aX^3 + bY^3. \tag{16}$$

It may happen that for suitable k, the quadratic equation (15) in X, Y may have an infinity of solutions. Then t is determined by equation (16), and its only possible denominator is a divisor of $k^2 r$. If an integer value of t arises, equation (15) shows that z is an integer.

We apply these results to prove

Theorem[8] 6

The equation

$$z^2 = (6l^2 + 6l - 1)x^3 + (6l^2 - 6l - 1)y^3 + 11 - 12l^2, \tag{17}$$

where l is an integer $\neq 0$, has an infinity of integer solutions.

Take $k = \pm 1$, $r = 3$, in equation (16), then

$$t = aX^3 + bY^3 \mp (ap^2X + bq^2Y)$$

is an integer. Also

$$3(apX^2 + bqY^2) - \tfrac{1}{4}(ap^2X + bq^2Y)^2 = \pm 6.$$

If there is one integer solution in X, Y there will be an infinity if the quadratic in X, Y is indefinite and rationally irreducible. Suppose, for example, that $p = q = 1$, and that $X = 1$, $Y = -1$ is a solution.

Then $\qquad\qquad\qquad 3(a + b) - \tfrac{1}{4}(a - b)^2 = \pm 6.$

Put $\qquad\qquad\qquad a - b = 12l, \qquad a + b = 12l^2 \pm 2,$

and so $\qquad\qquad a = 6l^2 + 6l \pm 1, \qquad b = 6l^2 - 6l \pm 1.$

The discriminant Δ of the quadratic is given by

$$4\Delta = a^2b^2 - (12a - a^2)(12b - b^2),$$
$$= 12ab(a + b - 12).$$

Then $\Delta > 0$ if a and b are positive and $a + b > 12$, or if $ab < 0$ and $a + b < 12$.

The quadratic is irreducible if Δ is not a perfect square. Clearly

$$(a, b) = 1, \qquad (ab, 6) = 1, \qquad (a + b - 12, 3) = 1.$$

Also

$$(a, a + b - 12) = (a, a - b + 12) = (a, 12l + 12) = (a, l + 1) = 1.$$

Hence Δ can be a square only when a, b, $3(a + b - 12)$ are all perfect squares. This is impossible since $(a + b, 3) = 1$. Hence we may take with $l \neq 0$,

$$a = 6l^2 + 6l + 1, \qquad b = 6l^2 - 6l + 1, \quad \text{if } c = 7 - 12l^2,$$

and $\qquad a = 6l^2 + 6l - 1, \qquad b = 6l^2 - 6l - 1, \quad \text{if } c = 11 - 12l^2.$

The discussion of the equation

$$z^3 = ax^2 + by^2 + c \tag{18}$$

requires a simple application of algebraic numbers. This will be given in Chapter 14, with simple conditions for the existence of an infinity of integer solutions.

4. We consider finally the integer solutions of the cubic equation

$$x^2 + y^2 + z^2 - axyz = b. \tag{19}$$

The case $a = 3$, $b = 0$ is classic. Markoff proved that there are an infinity of solutions, and that these were given by a simple algorithm, the so-called Markoff Chain. When $b < 0$, the equation (19) is a particular case of the equation

$$x_1^2 + x_2^2 + \cdots + x_n^2 \ldots - xx_1x_2\ldots x_n = 0 \tag{20}$$

in $n + 1$ positive unknowns $x, x_1, \ldots, x_n$, some of which are equal to one. The equation (20), it will be noted, is related to the equation $z = f(x, y)/g$ (x, y) considered in Chapter 30. Hurwitz[9] made an exhaustive study of the equation (20). An account is given of his ideas as well as of those of Mordell[10] and Schwartz and Muhly[11] as applied to equation (19).

Let (x, y, z) be any solution of equation (19). A trivial solution is one in which two of the unknowns are zero. It can occur only when b is a perfect square. A positive solution is one in which $x > 0, y > 0, z > 0$. From any solution (x, y, z) of (19), other solutions can be derived by the following elementary operations: permuting x, y, z; changing the signs of any two of x, y, z; and what is most important, replacing x by $ayz - x$, or y by $azx - y$, or z by $axy - z$. The last statement is obvious on considering equation (19) as a quadratic in x for given y, z.

There is no loss of generality in supposing that $a > 0$. We show now that we may suppose that the non-trivial solution (x, y, z) is a positive solution and we shall call $x + y + z$ its height. It suffices to assume that $xyz \neq 0$, for if $x = 0$, another solution is (ayz, y, z). If $x > 0, y > 0, z < 0$, the solution $(x, y, axy - z)$ is a positive solution. The solution (x, y, z) is called fundamental if $0 < x \leq y \leq z$, and if no elementary operation produces a positive solution of smaller height. The definition of the height gives at once the

Theorem 7

If a non-trivial solution exists, it can be derived from a fundamental solution by a finite number of elementary operations.

The cases $b > 0$ and $b \leq 0$ must be considered separately. Suppose first that $b > 0$.

Theorem 8

If (x, y, z) is a fundamental solution of equation (19), then $x^2 + y^2 < b$ except when $a = 1, b = 4$, or $a = 2, b = 1$.

For either $axy - z \leq 0$ and then from (19), $x^2 + y^2 \leq b$, or

$$axy - z \geq z, \qquad axy \geq 2z. \tag{21}$$

From (19),

$$3z^2 - axyz \geq b, \qquad z(3z - axy) \geq b, \qquad 3z - axy > 0.$$

Then from (21),

$$\tfrac{1}{3}axy < z \leq \tfrac{1}{2}axy. \tag{22}$$

Write (19) as

$$x^2 + y^2 + (z - \tfrac{1}{2}axy)^2 - (\tfrac{1}{2}axy)^2 = b.$$

Then (22) gives

$$x^2 + y^2 + \tfrac{1}{36} a^2x^2y^2 - \tfrac{1}{4}a^2x^2y^2 \geq b,$$

and since $x \leq y$,

$$2y^2 \left(1 - \frac{a^2x^2}{9}\right) \geq b. \tag{23}$$

Hence $ax < 3$ and so $a = 1$, $x = 1, 2$, or $a = 2$, $x = 1$.
When $a = 1$, $x = 1$, and then equation (21) gives $y \geq 2z$ whereas $y \leq z$. Hence the only possible fundamental solutions are those with $x^2 + y^2 \leq b$. When $z = 1$, $x = 2$, equation (21) gives $2y \geq 2z$ and so $y = z$. Now equation (19) becomes $(y - z)^2 = b - 4$ and so $b = 4$. Then all the solutions $(2, y, y)$, $y \geq 2$ are fundamental since their heights cannot be decreased. These are the only possible fundamental solutions with $x^2 + y^2 > 4$. When $y = 1$, the solution $(2, 1, 1)$ is a permutation of the fundamental solution $(1, 1, 2)$. This and $(2, y, y)$, $y \geq 2$ are the only fundamental solutions of $x^2 + y^2 + z^2 - xyz = 4$. When $a = 2$, $x = 1$, equation (19) becomes $(y - z)^2 = b - 1$. Also $2y \geq 2z$ and so $y = z$, and $b = 1$. The solutions $(1, y, y)$, $y \geq 1$ are fundamental.

Theorem 9

If a non-trivial solution exists, there will be an infinity of solutions except when $a = 1$, $b = 2$.

For the special cases $a = 1$, $b = 2$, i.e. $x^2 + y^2 + z^2 - xyz = 2$, there exists only one fundamental solution, namely $(1, 1, 1)$, since only for this is $x^2 + y^2 \leq 2$. The elementary operations produce only the further solutions such as $(\pm 1, \pm 1, 0)$, $(1, -1, 0)$, $(1, -1, -1)$.

We shall now show that a solution can be found with a height greater than that of a given solution. We consider in order the cases $a > 2$; $a = 2$, $b = 1$; $a = 2$, $b > 1$; $a = 1$, $b > 2$.

$a > 2$

If a non-trivial solution exists, there will be a solution (x, y, z) with $x \leq y \leq z$. Then $(y, z, ayz - x)$ is a solution of greater height since $ayz - x > x$ from $yz > x$.

The infinity of solutions is also obvious from a Pell equation in two of the variables.

$a = 2$, $b = 1$

There are solutions $(1, y, y)$ with infinitely many fundamental solutions.

$a = 2$, $b > 1$

Since $(1, 1, 1)$ is not a solution, at least one of x, y, z exceeds 1, say $z \geq 2$. Then $ayz - x > x$ as before since $yz \geq 2x$.

$a = 1, b > 2$

Since $(1, 1, 1)$ is not a solution, we may suppose that $z \geq 2$ in a fundamental solution (x, y, z). The cases $(1, 1, 2)$, $(1, 2, 2)$, $(2, 2, 2)$ are the only possible ones with $z \leq 2$. If either $(1, 1, 2)$ or $(2, 2, 2)$ is a fundamental solution, $b = 4$, and it has been shown that then there are an infinity of solutions. For the solution $(1, 2, 2)$, and those with $z > 2$, we have as before $ayz - x > x$ etc.

Trial of the possible fundamental solutions of equation (19) seems to be the only method for determining whether (19) is solvable. A necessary condition is that if $b \equiv 3 \pmod 4$, then $a \equiv 0 \pmod 4$. This follows from the congruence

$$x^2 + y^2 + z^2 - axyz \equiv 3 \pmod 4.$$

This is impossible if any of the x, y, z are even. Hence

$$x \equiv y \equiv z \equiv 1 \pmod 2, \qquad axyz \equiv 0 \pmod 4, \qquad a \equiv 0 \pmod 4.$$

Suppose next that $b \leq 0$, say $b = -c$. Then from equation (19)

$$z(axy - 3z) \leq c.$$

Two cases arise according as $axy - 3z > 0$ and then $x \leq y \leq z \leq c$, and such values can be found by trial, or $axy - 3z \leq 0$.
   Then from equation (21),

$$\tfrac{1}{3}axy \leq z \leq \tfrac{1}{2}axy,$$
$$2y^2(1 - \tfrac{1}{9}a^2x^2) \geq -c. \tag{23}$$

Suppose first $x < 3/a$ and so $a = 1, x = 1, 2$ or $a = 2, x = 1$. These values are impossible since they make the left-hand side of equation (19) positive. Hence

$$x \geq 3/a, \qquad 2y^2(\tfrac{1}{9}a^2x^2 - 1) \leq c,$$

and so if $c \neq 0$, x, y, z are bounded and the fundamental solutions are easily found by trial.
   If $c = 0$, then $x = 3/a$ and so $a = 3$ or 1.
If $a = 3, x = 1$ and then $y \leq z \leq \tfrac{3}{2}y$. But

$$0 = 1 + y^2 + z^2 - 3yz \leq 1 + y^2 + \tfrac{9}{4}y^2 - 3y^2.$$

The only solutions are $y = 0, 1$ and so we have a fundamental solution $(1, 1, 1)$ for Markoff's equation[12,13].
   If $a = 1, x = 3$ and then $3y \leq z \leq 3y/2$, and now

$$0 = 9 + y^2 + z^2 - 3yz.$$

We have $y = 3, z = 3$ and the fundamental solution $(3, 3, 3)$.

We note that when $c = 0$ and $a > 0$, solutions occur only when $a = 1, 3$. The more general equation

$$ax^2 + by^2 + cz^2 + dxyz = e \qquad (24)$$

is not easily amenable to treatment.

A simple result is given by

Theorem 10

If $a \equiv b \equiv c \equiv -d \not\equiv 0$ (mod 3), $e \equiv \pm 3$ *(mod 9), the equation* (24) *has no integer solutions.*

Obviously $x \equiv y \equiv z \equiv 0$ (mod 3) is impossible.

From (24),

$$x^2 + y^2 + z^2 - xyz \equiv 0 \,(\text{mod } 3).$$

Then $x \not\equiv 0$ (mod 3) since otherwise $y \equiv z \equiv 0$ (mod 3).

Also $xyz \equiv \pm 1$ (mod 3) gives $1 \equiv 0$ (mod 3), and can so be ruled out.

REFERENCES

1. J. C. P. Miller and M. F. C. Woolett. Solutions of the diophantine equation $x^3 + y^3 + z^3 = k$. *J. Lond. Math. Soc.*, **28** (1955), 500–510.
2. L. J. Mordell. On sums of three cubes. *J. Lond. Math. Soc.*, **17** (1942), 139–144.
3. B. Segre. On the rational solutions of homogeneous cubic equations in four variables. *Mathematicae Notae* (Rosario, Argentina), **11** (1951), 1–68.
4. L. J. Mordell. On the infinity of integer solutions of $ax^3 + ay^3 + bz^3 = bc^3$. *J. Lond. Math. Soc.*, **30** (1955), 111–113.
5. D. H. Lehmer. On the diophantine equation $x^3 + y^3 + z^3 = 1$. *J. Lond. Math. Soc.*, **31** (1956), 275–280.
6. A. Hurwitz. Über die Darstellung der ganzen Zahlen als Summen von n^{ten} Potenzen ganzer Zahlen. *Math. Annalen.*, **65** (1908), 424–427; also in *Math. Werke* (Birkhäuser-Cie, Basel), **2** (1933), 421–426.
7. L. J. Mordell. On cubic equations $z^2 = f(x, y)$ with an infinity of integer solutions. *Proc. Am. Math. Soc.*, **3** (1952), 210–217.
8. L. J. Mordell. Note on cubic diophantine equations $z^2 = f(x, y)$ with an infinity of integer solutions. *J. Lond. Math. Soc.*, **17** (1942), 199–203.
9. A. Hurwitz. Über eine Aufgabe der unbestimmten Analysis. *Archiv der Math. und Phys.*, 3 (14) (1907), 185–196; also *Math. Werke* (Birkhäuser-Cie, Basel), **2** (1933), 410–421.
10. L. J. Mordell. On integer solutions of the equation $x^2 + y^2 + z^2 + 2xyz = n$. *J. Lond. Math. Soc.*, **28** (1953), 500–510.
11. H. Schwartz and H. T. Muhly. On a class of cubic diophantine equations. *J. Lond. Math. Soc.*, **32** (1957), 379–383.
12. A. A. Markoff. Sur les formes quadratiques binaires indéfinies. *Math. Ann.*, **15** (1879), 381–409.
13. J. W. S. Cassels. "An Introduction to Diophantine Approximation". Cambridge University Press (1957).

CHAPTER 14

Simple Algebraic Considerations

1. Some results require only the definition of an algebraic number, namely, that θ is an algebraic number if it is the root of an equation, reducible or irreducible, over the rational field Q,

$$\theta^n + a_1\theta^{n-1} + a_2\theta^{n-2} + \cdots + a_n = 0,$$

where the a are rational numbers. Many of these results are classical and are due to Euler and Lagrange.

The equation

$$ax^2 + by^2 = cz^n, \tag{1}$$

where a, b, and c are integers.

Suppose first that n is odd. Consider the classical case when $c = 1$. Some integer solutions may be found by putting

$$z = ap^2 + bq^2,$$

where p and q are arbitrary integers, and taking

$$x\sqrt{a} + y\sqrt{-b} = (p\sqrt{a} + q\sqrt{-b})^n,$$
$$x\sqrt{a} - y\sqrt{-b} = (p\sqrt{a} - q\sqrt{-b})^n.$$

Then x, y are expressed as polynomials in p and q.

Occasionally as will be seen in Chapter 15 all the integer solutions may be obtained in this way. The proof requires arithmetic theory.

Suppose next that $n = 2m$ is even. Then unless $a = 1$ when a solution is given above for all n, the question becomes more difficult. From Chapter 7, it is seen that now the problem is to find integer solutions for X, Y of the equation

$$z^m = AX^2 + BXY + CY^2$$

for a finite set of integer values of A and B.

These can be reduced to the form (1). Then if $c = c_1^2 + abc_2^2$ or $c = ac_1^2 + bc_2^2$ solutions may be found as before by factorizing c.

The equation

$$w^n = \prod_\theta (x + y\theta + z\theta^2), \tag{2}$$

where $\theta = \theta_1, \theta_2, \theta_3$ are roots of the equation

$$t^3 + at^2 + bt + c = 0,$$

where a, b, c are integers.

A partial integer solution is given by

$$x + y\theta_1 + z\theta_1^2 = (p + q\theta_1 + r\theta_1^2)^n,$$

$$x + y\theta_2 + z\theta_2^2 = (p + q\theta_2 + r\theta_2^2)^n,$$

$$x + y\theta_3 + z\theta_3^2 = (p + q\theta_3 + r\theta_3^2)^n,$$

$$w = \prod_\theta (p + q\theta + r\theta^2),$$

where p, q, r are arbitrary integers and n runs through the integers.

The general solution depends upon the theory of algebraic numbers and is connected with the units in an algebraic number field.

The equation

$$z^2 = ax^3 + bx^2 y + cxy^2 + dy^3, \tag{3}$$

where a, b, c, d are rational numbers.

All the rational solutions are given at once by putting $x = pz$, $y = qz$ where p and q are arbitrary rational numbers. Finding the integer solutions is a different matter. However, as shown by Lagrange, some integer solutions are found without much difficulty when a, b, c, d are integers and $a = 1$. Let $\theta = \theta_1, \theta_2, \theta_3$ be roots of the equation, reducible or irreducible,

$$t^3 + bt^2 + ct + d = 0.$$

Write

$$z^2 = (x - \theta_1 y)(x - \theta_2 y)(x - \theta_3 y),$$

and

$$x - ty = (p + qt + rt^2)^2, \quad t = \theta_1, \theta_2, \theta_3,$$

where p, q, r are integers. This implies that when we replace t^3 by $-bt^2 - ct - d$ and t^4 by

$$-bt^3 - ct^2 - dt = -b(-bt^2 - ct - d) - ct^2 - dt,$$

the coefficients of t^2 in the above must be zero.

Hence

$$q^2 + 2pr - 2qrb + r^2(b^2 - c) = 0.$$

This gives an integer value for p if $r(b^2 - c)$ is even and $2r \mid q^2$. These conditions are easily satisfied, for example, by $r = 2r_1$, $q = 2r_1 q_1$. Clearly then x, y and $z = N(p + q\theta + r\theta^2)$ are integers.

The complete integer solution requires arithmetic theory and is given in Chapter 25.

2. The application of both quadratic and cubic irrationalities is sometimes useful. This introduces many parameters satisfying a few equations, and so it is not difficult sometimes to find particular solutions. A simple instance[1] is given by

Theorem 1

The equation

$$y^2 - ax^2 = z^3 + bz + c, \tag{4}$$

where $a \neq 0$, and b, c are rational, has a two parameter rational solution.
Let $\theta = \theta_1, \theta_2, \theta_3$ be the roots of the equation

$$t^3 + bt + c = 0.$$

Put $\qquad y \pm x\sqrt{a} = \prod_{\theta} (p + q\theta^2 \pm (r + s\theta)\sqrt{a}),$

where p, q, r, s are rational parameters. Clearly these two equations define x, y as rational numbers and

$$y^2 - ax^2 = \prod_{\theta} ((p + q\theta^2)^2 - a(r + s\theta)^2).$$

Hence equation (4) is satisfied if

$$z - t = (p + qt^2)^2 - a(r + st)^2,$$

for $t = \theta_1, \theta_2, \theta_3$, since

$$z^3 + bz + c = \prod_{t=\theta} (z - t).$$

Multiply out, put $t^4 = -bt^2 - ct$ and equate coefficients of t^0, t, t^2 on both sides. Then

$$z = p^2 - ar^2, \qquad -1 = -cq^2 - 2ars, \qquad 0 = 2pq - bq^2 - as^2.$$

These give

$$p = \frac{bq^2 + as^2}{2q}, \qquad r = \frac{1 - cq^2}{2as},$$

i.e. a two parameter solution.
Another application[2] is to the

Theorem 2

The equation

$$z^3 = ax^2 + by^2 + c \tag{5}$$

has an infinity of integer solutions if a, b, c are odd integers, $(a, b) = 1$, and if when $a \equiv 0 \pmod 7$, $c \not\equiv b^3 \pmod 7$, or when $b \equiv 0 \pmod 7$, $c \not\equiv a^3 \pmod 7$ and so if $ab \equiv 0 \pmod 7$, it suffices if $c \not\equiv \pm 1 \pmod 7$.

Denote the three roots of $t^3 = c$ by $\theta = \theta_1, \theta_2, \theta_3$. Then, say,

$$ax^2 + by^2 = (z - \theta_1)(z - \theta_2)(z - \theta_3) = f(z),$$

Put

$$z - \theta = a(l + m\theta + n\theta^2)^2 + b(p + q\theta + r\theta^2)^2 = aX^2 + bY^2, \quad (6)$$

say, where l, m, n, p, q, r are rational integers. Then $f(z)$ can be expressed in the form

$$f(z) = (aX_1^2 + bY_1^2)(aX_2^2 + bY_2^2)(aX_3^2 + bY_3^2),$$

and so we can take

$$x\sqrt{a} + y\sqrt{-b} = \prod_{r=1}^{3} (X_r\sqrt{a} + Y_r\sqrt{-b}).$$

Then

$$x = aX_1X_2X_3 - bX_1Y_2Y_3 - bX_2Y_3Y_1 - bX_3Y_1Y_2,$$

$$y = -bY_1Y_2Y_3 + aX_1X_2Y_3 + aX_2X_3Y_1 + aX_3X_1Y_2,$$

and so x, y are rational integers.

Expanding equation (6) and equating coefficients of θ, θ^2 on both sides, we have the two equations,

$$2mal + 2qbp = -1 - an^2c - br^2c,$$
$$2nal + 2rbp = -am^2 - bq^2. \qquad (7)$$

These are linear in l, p and we have four variables in m, n, q, r at our disposal to ensure that l and p are integers. The right-hand sides of equations (7) will be even numbers if

$$m \equiv q \equiv 1 \ (\text{mod } 2), \qquad n + r \equiv 1 \ (\text{mod } 2).$$

We impose the condition $mr - qn = \pm 1$. Then l, p will be integers if

$$bq^3 - r - bcr^3 \equiv 0 \ (\text{mod } a), \qquad -am^3 + n + acn^3 \equiv 0 \ (\text{mod } b).$$

Solutions are shown to exist for these congruences from the result in Chapter 6 on the solvability of

$$y^2 \equiv x^3 + k \ (\text{mod } a).$$

No difficulties arise in the proof which now is straightforward.

When $a = b = 1$, a solution is given in terms of an integer parameter t, by

$$x + iy = \prod_\theta (1 + t\theta - \tfrac{1}{2}(t^2 + 1)\theta^2 + i(t + \theta)),$$

$$z = 1 - ct(t^2 + 1) + \frac{1}{4}\left(1 + 2t + \frac{c}{4}(t^2 + 1)^2\right),$$

where $i^2 = -1$, $\theta^3 = c$.

A particular case[3] of the equation

$$z^2 = ax^3 + by^3 + c$$

is given by

Theorem 3
  The equation

$$z^2 - (27abd)^2 = ab^2x^3 + y^3, \quad ab \neq 0, \tag{8}$$

where a, b, d are integers, has an infinity of integer solutions.
  Consider the equation

$$z^2 - k^2 = ab(x^3 + cy^3), \quad abc \neq 0, \tag{9}$$

Denote by $\theta = \theta_1, \theta_2, \theta_3$ the roots of $t^3 = c$. Take

$$z + k = a \prod_\theta (p + q\theta + r\theta^2), \tag{10}$$

$$z - k = b \prod_\theta (p_1 + q_1\theta + r_1\theta^2), \tag{11}$$

where the p, p_1, etc. are integers.
Then

$$z^2 - k^2 = ab \prod_\theta (P + Q\theta + R\theta^2) = ab(P^3 + cQ^3 + c^2R^3 - 3cPQR),$$

and we take

$$P = pp_1 + c(qr_1 + q_1r) = x,$$
$$Q = pq_1 + p_1q + crr_1 = y, \tag{12}$$
$$R = pr_1 + p_1r + qq_1 = 0.$$

From equations (10) and (11),

$$2k = a(p^3 + cq^3 + c^2r^3 - 3cpqr) - b(p_1^3 + cq_1^3 + c^2r_1^3 - 3cp_1q_1r_1). \tag{13}$$

The six variables p, q, r, p_1, q_1, r_1 satisfy the two equations (12) and (13) and particular solutions may be found without difficulty.
  Take $p_1 = q, q_1 = -r, r_1 = 0$. Then equation (13) is satisfied.
Also $x = pq - cr^2, \qquad y = -pr + q^2, \qquad z - k = b(q^3 - cr^3),$ (14)

$$2k = a(p^3 + cq^3 + c^2r^3 - 3cpqr) - b(q^3 - cr^3). \tag{15}$$

Take now $c = b/a$. Then equation (15) becomes

$$2k = ap^3 + 2b^2r^3/a - 3bpqr, \tag{16}$$

and equation (9) becomes

$$z^2 - k^2 = abx^3 + b^2y^3. \tag{17}$$

Also in equation (14), x and z will be integers if br^2/a and b^2r^3/a are integers. Take now $p = 3bX$, $q = Y$, $r = 3aZ$, $k = 27ab^2d$. Then x and z are integers and $x \equiv 0 \pmod{b}$, $z \equiv 0 \pmod{b}$.

Replacing x and z by bx, bz, equation (17) becomes

$$z^2 - (27abd)^2 = ab^2x^3 + y^3. \tag{18}$$

Also equation (16) becomes

$$2d = bX^3 + 2aZ^3 - XYZ.$$

This equation is of the first degree in Y and has an infinity of integer solutions as will be noted in Chapter 30.

3. Simple algebraic considerations sometimes suffice to find the solutions of an equation in a given algebraic number field K. Consider the equation $f(x,y) = 0$ in the field $K = Q(t)$ defined by an irreducible equation $F(t) = 0$ of degree n.

Then
$$x = x_0 + x_1t + \cdots + x_{n-1}t^{n-1} = x(t),$$
$$y = y_0 + y_1t + \cdots + y_{n-1}t^{n-1} = y(t),$$

where the x_0, y_0 etc. are rational numbers.

Since $f(x(t), y(t))$ must be divisible by $F(t)$, we have an identity in a variable z given by

$$f(x(z)), y(z)) = F(z)G(z),$$

where $G(z)$ is a polynomial in z. In some instances, $G(z)$ is linear and so the left-hand side must vanish for a rational value of z. If the equation $f(x, y) = 0$ has only a finite number of rational solutions, for example, when $f(x, y) = x^4 + y^4 - 1$, some progress may be expected. In this way, we can prove results due to Aigner[5] and Fadeev[6] respectively.

Theorem 4

When K is a quadratic field, the only non-rational solutions of the equation $x^4 + y^4 = 1$ are given by

$$K = Q(i), \quad x = \pm i, \quad y = 0, \quad x = 0, \quad y = \pm i,$$
$$K = Q(\sqrt{-7}), \quad x = \varepsilon_1\left(\frac{1 + \varepsilon\sqrt{-7}}{2}\right), \quad y = \varepsilon_2\left(\frac{1 - \varepsilon\sqrt{-7}}{2}\right), \tag{19}$$
$$\varepsilon^2 = \varepsilon_1^2 = \varepsilon_2^2 = 1.$$

When K is a cubic field, then the only solutions, except for rational ones, are given by

$$y = \pm 1 + tx, \quad x^4 + (\pm 1 + tx)^4 = 1,$$
$$or \quad x = \pm 1 + ty, \quad y^4 + (\pm 1 + ty)^4 = 1. \tag{20}$$

where t is a rational parameter.

For the first part, on putting $1 - x^2 = ty^2$, we obtain the parametric solution,

$$x^2 = \frac{1 - t^2}{1 + t^2}, \qquad y^2 = \frac{2t}{1 + t^2},$$

and so t is in K. Write

$$X = (1 + t^2)xy, \qquad Y = (1 + t^2)y.$$

Then

$$X^2 = 2t(1 - t^2), \qquad Y^2 = 2t(1 + t^2),$$

and it is known that the only rational solutions of the first equation are $t = 0, \pm 1$, and of the second, $t = 0, 1$. If t is rational, then since either X^2/Y^2 or Y^2/X^2 is rational, K can only be the quadratic field $Q(i)$ arising from $t = -1$ or ∞. Suppose then that t is not rational.

We can put

$$X = a + bt, \qquad Y = a_1 + b_1 t,$$

where a, b, a_1, b_1 are rational.
Then we have the two identities in z,

$$(a + bz)^2 - 2z(1 - z^2) = F(z)(P + Qz),$$

$$(a_1 + b_1 z)^2 - 2z(1 + z^2) = F(z)(P_1 + Q_1 z).$$

Hence the first left-hand side must vanish for $z = 0, \pm 1$ and the second for $z = 0, 1$, and so there are six possibilities for the pairs $P + Qz, P_1 + Q_1 z$.

Thus if these are $1 + z, 1 - z$, then $a = b$, and we may take $a_1 + b_1 = 2$, and on dividing out by $1 + z, 1 - z$, respectively,

$$a^2(1 + z) - 2z(1 - z) = PF(z),$$

$$(2 - b_1)^2 + (2 - b_1^2)z + 2z^2 = P_1 F(z).$$

Hence

$$a^2 = (2 - b_1)^2, \qquad a^2 + b_1^2 = 4,$$

and so $a = 0, b_1 = 2$ which must be rejected, and

$$a = \pm 2 = b, \qquad a_1 = 2, \qquad b_1 = 0.$$

These give

$$F(z) = z^2 + z + 2, \qquad t = \frac{-1 + \sqrt{-7}}{2} \qquad K = Q(\sqrt{-7}),$$

and then the values for x, y.

It is easily shown that the other five possibilities do not lead to a solution. Similar considerations apply to the proof of the results for a cubic field.

5+

Another application is given by

Theorem 5

Let, a, b, c be rational integers where $(b, c) = (c, a) = (a, b) = 1$, and a and b are square free.

Then the integer solutions of the equation

$$ax^2 + by^2 + c = 0 \tag{21}$$

can exist in a quadratic field $Q(t)$ if and only if there exist rational integers p, q, d, d_1 such that

$$ap^2 + bq^2 = d, \quad (ap, bq) = d_1, \tag{22}$$

and either (A), d is some divisor of abc, and t satisfies the equation

$$t^2 + abk^2/d_1 + c/d = 0, \tag{23}$$

and k is a rational integer such that $abk^2/d_1 + c/d$ is an integer. Then

$$x = pt + bqk/d_1, \quad y = qt - apk/d_1; \tag{24}$$

or (B), $d \equiv 0 \pmod{2}$, d is some divisor of $2abc$, and t satisfies the equation

$$t^2 + t + \tfrac{1}{4}(1 + abk/d_1^2) + c/d = 0, \tag{25}$$

where k is an integer such that

$$(1 + abk/d_1^2)/4 + c/d$$

is an integer. Then

$$x = pt + \tfrac{1}{2}(p + bqk/d_1), \quad y = qt + \tfrac{1}{2}(q - apk/d_1). \tag{26}$$

We can put

$$x = pt + p_1, \quad y = qt + q_1, \tag{27}$$

where p, q, p_1, q_1 are rational integers. There is no loss of generality in supposing that $(p, q) = 1$, and so t is an integer. Then since $(a, b) = 1$, from (22), $d_1 \mid ab$.

On substituting in (21) for x, y from (27), t becomes a root of the equation

$$(ap^2 + bq^2)t^2 + 2(app_1 + bqq_1)t + ap_1^2 + bq_1^2 + c = 0. \tag{28}$$

From (22), since t is an algebraic integer,

$$2(app_1 + bqq_1) \equiv 0 \pmod{d}, \tag{29}$$

$$ap_1^2 + bq_1^2 + c \equiv 0 \pmod{d}. \tag{30}$$

The solution of (29) for p_1, q_1 can be written as

$$2p_1 = pl + bqk/d_1, \quad 2q_1 = ql - apk/d_1, \tag{31}$$

since it is easily verified that these equations give integer values for l, k in terms of p_1, q_1.

Substituting from (31) in (28), we have

$$(ap^2 + bq^2) t^2 + l(ap^2 + bq^2)t + \tfrac{1}{4}((ap^2 + bq^2)l^2 + abk^2(ap^2 + bq^2)/d_1^2) + c = 0,$$

or

$$t^2 + lt + \tfrac{1}{4}(l^2 + abk^2/d_1^2) + c/d = 0, \tag{32}$$

where k is an integer such that

$$L = \tfrac{1}{4}(l^2 + abk^2/d_1^2) + c/d \tag{33}$$

is an integer.

On writing $t - t_0$ for t in (32), we need only consider the values $l = 0, 1$. Suppose first that $l = 0$ giving case (A). Then from (31),

$$2p_1 = bqk/d_1, \quad 2q_1 = -apk/d_1.$$

Since $(bq/d_1, ap/d_1) = 1$, k is even. Replacing k by $2k$,

$$p_1 = bqk/d_1, \quad q_1 = -apk/d_1.$$

and (33) becomes $L = abk^2/d_1^2 + c/d.$

Since abL and ab/d_1 are integers, $d \mid abc$. Then we have (23) and (24).

Suppose next that $l = 1$ giving case (B). Then from (33),

$$L = \tfrac{1}{4}(1 + abk^2/d_1^2) + c/d.$$

From (31), on multiplying the equations by ap, bp and adding, $d \equiv 0 \pmod 2$. Suppose first that $d_1 \equiv 0 \pmod 2$. Then since ap and bq are both even and $(a, b) = (p, q) = 1$, we have, say,

$$a \equiv 0 \pmod 2, b \equiv 1 \pmod 2, p \equiv 1 \pmod 2, q \equiv 0 \pmod 2,$$

and so $a/2$, and $d/2$ are both odd. Hence $\tfrac{1}{2}(1 + abk^2/d_1^2)$ must not have a denominator divisible by 2 but this is impossible since abk^2/d_1^2 will have a 2 in the numerator. Hence $d_1 \equiv 1 \pmod 2$, and then three possibilities arise of which two are typified by $ap \equiv 0 \pmod 2$, $bq \equiv 1 \pmod 2$, and from (22), produce the contradiction $d \equiv 1 \pmod 2$. Hence $ap \equiv bq \equiv 1 \pmod 2$, and then from (31), k is odd.
Now

$$2Lab = \tfrac{1}{2}(ab + \left(\frac{ab}{d_1}\right)^2 k) + \frac{2abc}{d}.$$

The first term on the right is an integer and so $d \mid 2abc$. We now have (25) and (26).

This finishes the proof.

Finally, we notice some results by Fjellstedt[8] on the solvability in a quadratic field $Q(\sqrt{-m})$, $m > 0$ of equations of the form $x^2 - \alpha y^2 = \beta$ where α, β are integers in the field $Q(\sqrt{-m})$. He discusses the cases $\beta = \pm 1$ by methods due to Nagell but his paper contains many misprints. He gives many references.

REFERENCES

1. L. J. Mordell. A rational parametric solution of $z^2 - k = ax^3 + bx^2y + cxy^2 + dy^3$. *J. Lond. Math. Soc.*, **18** (1943), 222–226.
2. L. J. Mordell. Note on cubic equations in three variables with an infinity of integer solutions. *Ann. Mat. Pura Appl.*, IV., **29** (1949), 301–305.
3. L. J. Mordell. The congruence $ax^3 + by^3 + c \equiv 0 \pmod{xy}$, and integer solutions of cubic equations in three variables. *Acta Mathematica*, **88** (1952), 77–83.
4. L. J. Mordell. The diophantine equation $x^4 + y^4 = 1$ in algebraic number fields. *Acta Arith.*, **14** (1968), 347–355.
5. A. Aigner. Über die Möglichkeit von $x^4 + y^4 = z^4$ in quadratische Körper. *Jahresbericht der deutschen Math. Verein.*, **43** (1934), 226–228
6. D. K. Fadeev. Group of divisor classes on the curve defined by the equation $x^4 + y^4 = 1$. *American Math. Soc. Trans. Soviet Maths. Dokl.*, **1** (1960), 1149–1151.
7. L. J. Mordell. The integer solutions of the equation $ax^2 + by^2 + c = 0$ in quadratic fields. *Bull. Lond. Math. Soc.*, **1** (1969), 43–44.
8. L. Fjellstedt. On a class of diophantine equations of the second degree in imaginary quadratic fields. *Ark. Mat.*, **2** (1954), 435–461.

CHAPTER 15

Applications of Algebraic Number Theory

1. A great many results have been found by applying this theory, and many of the most important results in Diophantine analysis have been proved in this way. Let $K = Q(\theta)$ be an algebraic number field defined by a number θ given as a root of an irreducible equation of degree n with rational integer coefficients and leading coefficient unity. Then every integer ω in K can be expressed in the form

$$\omega = x_1\omega_1 + \cdots + x_n\omega_n,$$

where the x are rational integers and the ω are a basis of the integers. The integers of the form

$$\omega = x_0 + x_1\theta + \cdots + x_{n-1}\theta^{n-1}$$

form a ring $Z[\theta]$, say.

A unit η in K or $Z[\theta]$ is an integer divisor of unity and so $N(\eta) = \pm 1$. All the units are given by Dirichlet's

Theorem 1

Suppose that K has r_1 real conjugate fields and r_2 pairs of conjugate imaginary fields. Write $r = r_1 + r_2 - 1$. Then every unit η in the field K can be expressed in the form

$$\eta = \eta_0^{t_0}\, \eta_1^{t_1} \ldots \eta_r^{t_r},$$

where η_0 is a root of unity in the field, $\eta_1, \eta_2, \ldots, \eta_r$ are the so called fundamental units, and the t take all integer values, positive, negative or zero.

An obvious consequence is that if l is a given integer, all the units can be expressed in the form

$$\eta = \zeta_0\zeta^l,$$

where ζ_0, ζ are units and ζ_0 belongs to a finite set.

Similar results hold for the units in the ring $Z[\theta]$. This Theorem 1 and the next are of the greatest importance in the applications.

Theorem 2

The number h of ideal classes in K is finite. If a is any ideal in K, then

$$a^h = (\beta),$$

where β is an integer in K. If a^l is a principal ideal and $(l, h) = 1$, then a is a principal ideal (α).

These theorems are easily applied. There are others which require more detailed arithmetical knowledge, such as the properties of K considered as an extension of a field k, and in particular a study of the relative discriminant. Sometimes the application of the reciprocity laws in the fields proves useful. The proof of theorems often depends upon intricate numerical calculations.

We recall the results when K is a quadratic field, say $K = Q(\sqrt{d})$, where d is a square free integer.

Two cases arise:

I. $d \equiv 2, 3 \pmod 4$. Then the integers are given by $x = x_1 + x_2\sqrt{d}$, where x_1, x_2 are rational integers. Also x is a unit if $x_1^2 - dx_2^2 = \pm 1$, and this is the Pell equation.

II. $d \equiv 1 \pmod 4$. The integers are given by $x = x_1 + x_2(1 + \sqrt{d})/2$, and x is a unit if

$$x_1^2 + x_1 x_2 + \tfrac{1}{4}(1 - d)x_2^2 = \pm 1.$$

Then all units η are given by $\eta = \pm \zeta^n$ where ζ is a fundamental unit and n takes all integer values.

If $d < 0$, the only units are ± 1, except that when $d = -1$, there are four units given by i^n, $n = 0, 1, 2, 3$, i.e. ± 1, $\pm i$, and that when $d = -3$, there are six units $\pm \rho^n$, $n = 0, 1, 2$, where $\rho = (-1 + \sqrt{-3})/2$, i.e.

$$\pm 1, \ \pm(-1 + \sqrt{-3})/2, \ \pm(-1 - \sqrt{-3})/2.$$

2. Many important Diophantine equations are particular cases of the equation

$$XY = cZ^l,$$

where X, Y, Z are integers in K and c is a given integer in K. The solution of this depends upon ideal theory. Denote by h the number of classes of ideals. We commence with the case $h = 1$, and then and only then does unique factorization exist for the integers in K. We suppose that the common divisors of X, Y belong to a finite set, and then there is no loss of generality in supposing that $(X, Y) = 1$. We have now

$$X = \zeta_1 c_1 P^l, \qquad Y = \zeta_2 c_2 Q^l, \qquad Z = \zeta_3 c_3 PQ,$$

where
$$\zeta_1 \zeta_2 = \zeta_3^l, \qquad c_1 c_2 = cc_3^l.$$

Here $\zeta_1, \zeta_2, \zeta_3$ are units, c_1, c_2, c_3 are algebraic integers, each trio being taken from a finite set, and P, Q are arbitrary algebraic integers with $(P, Q) = 1$.

We consider some applications in the simpler Euclidean fields, namely $Q(i), Q(\sqrt{-2}), Q(\sqrt{-3})$.

The field $Q(i)$

The equation

$$x^2 + y^2 = z^l, \quad l > 1,$$

where x, y are rational integers, $(x, y) = 1$ and $z > 0$.

Here
$$(x + iy)(x - iy) = z^l.$$

Write $d = (x + iy, x - iy)$. Then $d \mid (2x, 2y)$ and so $d \mid 2$, and $d = 1, 1 + i, 2$. If $d = 2$, $x \equiv y \equiv 0 \pmod 2$. If $d = 1 + i$,

$$\frac{x + iy}{1 + i} = \frac{x + y + i(-x + y)}{2},$$

is an integer and so $x \equiv y \pmod 2$; but then $z^l \equiv 2 \pmod 4$, and this is impossible. Hence $d = 1$ and so

$$x + iy = i^r (a + ib)^l, \qquad x - iy = (-i)^r(a - ib)^l, \quad r = 0, 1, 2, 3,$$

$$z = a^2 + b^2,$$

where a, b are rational integers.

In particular, for the equation

$$1 + y^2 = z^l,$$

a and b must satisfy the equation

$$\pm 2 = i^r(a + ib)^l + (-i)^r(a - ib)^l.$$

We prove that when $l = 3$, the only solution is $y = 0$. Since $i = (-i)^3$, the i^r can be absorbed in $(a + ib)^3$, hence

$$\pm 1 = a^3 - 3ab^2 = a(a^2 - 3b^2),$$

and so $a = \pm 1, b = 0, z = 1, y = 0$.

We prove that when $l = 4$, the only solution is $y = 0$.

Here
$$1 + iy = \pm(a + ib)^4 \quad \text{or} \quad \pm i(a + ib)^4,$$

The first gives

$$\pm 1 = a^4 - 6a^2b^2 + b^4 = (a^2 - b^2 + 2ab)(a^2 - b^2 - 2ab),$$

and so

$$a^2 - b^2 + 2ab = \pm 1, \qquad a^2 - b^2 - 2ab = \pm 1, \mp 1,$$

giving $a = \pm 1, b = 0$ or $a = 0, b = \pm 1$.
The second gives

$$\pm 1 = 4a^3b - 4ab^3,$$

and is impossible.

It will be shown in Chapter 30 that, for all l, the only solution is $y = 0$.

The equation

$$y^2 + 4 = z^3,$$

has only the solutions $z = 2, 5$.

If y is odd, we have

$$2 + iy = (a + ib)^3,$$

$$2 = a(a^2 - 3b^2),$$

giving $a = 2, b = 1, z = 5$; or $a = -1, b = 1, z = 2$, and an even value for y.
If y is even, put $y = 2Y, z = 2Z$, and so

$$Y^2 + 1 = 2Z^3.$$

Then Y is odd and since $(Y + i, Y - i) = 1 + i$,

then $1 + iY = (1 + i)(a + ib)^3,$

and $1 = a^3 - 3a^2b - 3ab^2 + b^3,$

$$= (a + b)(a^2 - 4ab + b^2).$$

Hence $a + b = \pm 1, \qquad a^2 - 4ab + b^2 = \pm 1,$

and so $a = \pm 1, b = 0 \quad \text{or} \quad a = 0, b = \pm 1,$

and $Z = 1, \qquad z = 2.$

The result is due to Fermat.

The field $Q(\sqrt{-2})$

The equation $y^2 + 2 = x^3$ has only the integer solutions $x = 3, y = \pm 2$.
Clearly $x \not\equiv 0 \pmod 2$, and so

$$y + \sqrt{-2} = (a + b\sqrt{-2})^3, \qquad x = a^2 + 2b^2,$$

where a, b are integers. Hence

$$1 = b(3a^2 - 2b^2),$$

and so $b = 1, a = \pm 1, x = 3$.
The result is due to Fermat.

The field $Q(\sqrt{-3})$

The application of this field, say $Q(\rho)$, where $\rho^2 + \rho + 1 = 0$, is of great importance in the discussion of many cubic equations, and in particular of equations of the form

$$x^3 + y^3 = az^3.$$

This equation has attracted the attention of many mathematicians over a period of years as can be seen from the second volume of Dickson's "History of the Theory of Numbers".

We give a brief résumé, sufficient for our applications, of the arithmetical properties of the field, and for which one may consult Bachmann[1] and Marshall Hall, Jr.[2]

The integers in the field are given by $a + b\rho$ where a and b are rational integers and the units by $\pm \rho^n$, $n = 0, 1, 2$. The primes are:

I.   the rational primes $q \equiv -1 \pmod 3$,
II. the factors $\pi = a + b\rho$, $\pi_1 = a + b\rho^2$ of $p = \pi\pi_1 = a^2 - ab + b^2$, where p is a prime $\equiv 1 \pmod 3$.
III. the prime $\lambda = 1 - \rho$ where $\lambda^2 = -3\rho$.

We define a primary integer $x + \rho y$ as one with $x \equiv 1$, $y \equiv 0 \pmod 3$, and then each integer $a + b\rho$ has a unique primary associate $x + y\rho$ given by $a + b\rho = \pm \rho^n(x + y\rho)$, $n = 0, 1, 2$. The primary integers form a subgroup.

We require some results on cubic residues. There are $N(\pi) = p$ residues mod π, and so these can be taken as $0, 1, \ldots, p - 1$. If α is any integer $\not\equiv 0 \pmod \pi$ in $Q(\rho)$, then

$$\alpha^{N(\pi) - 1} \equiv 1 \pmod \pi,$$

and so
$$\alpha^{(p-1)/3} \equiv \rho^t \pmod \pi, \quad t = 0, 1, 2.$$

Then the cubic character of $\alpha \pmod \pi$ is defined by

$$\left(\frac{\alpha}{\pi}\right)_3 = \rho^t.$$

The cubic law of reciprocity states that if π, π' are two primary primes, then

$$\left(\frac{\pi}{\pi'}\right)_3 = \left(\frac{\pi'}{\pi}\right)_3.$$

This also holds when $\pi' = -q$. There is the supplementary law,

$$\left(\frac{3}{\pi}\right)_3 = \rho^{b/3}.$$

The cubic character has the usual properties, i.e.

$$\left(\frac{\alpha\beta}{\pi}\right)_3 = \left(\frac{\alpha}{\pi}\right)_3 \left(\frac{\beta}{\pi}\right)_3.$$

We give criteria for the cubic characters of 2 and 3. When $\pi' = -2$,

$$\left(\frac{\pi}{-2}\right)_3 = \left(\frac{-2}{\pi}\right)_3 = \left(\frac{2}{\pi}\right)_3.$$

Now $\left(\frac{\pi}{2}\right)_3 = 1$ if and only if $b \equiv 0 \pmod 2$. For

$$(x + y\rho)^3 \equiv a + b\rho \pmod 2,$$

gives $x^2 y - xy^2 \equiv b \pmod 2$, and so $b \equiv 0 \pmod 2$, and then we can take $x \equiv a$, $y \equiv 0 \pmod 2$. Also $b \equiv 0 \pmod 3$, and so $\left(\frac{2}{\pi}\right)_3 = 1$ if and only if $b = 6b_1$, and

$$p = a^2 - 6ab_1 + 36b_1^2 = (a - 3b_1)^2 + 27b_1^2.$$

5*

If $x^3 \equiv 2 \pmod{\pi}$, then, since we can take x to be a rational integer, $x^3 \equiv 2 \pmod{p}$ is solvable if and only if

$$p = X^2 + 3Y^2, \quad \text{with } Y \equiv 0 \pmod{3}.$$

Further 3 is a cubic residue of p, i.e. $x^3 \equiv 3 \pmod{p}$ is solvable, if and only if

$$4p = X^2 + 3Y^2, \quad \text{with } Y \equiv 0 \pmod{9}.$$

The condition for this is $b \equiv 0 \pmod{9}$. For

$$4p = (2a - b)^2 + 3b^2.$$

For immediate application, we require the

Lemma

If q is a prime $\equiv 2, 5 \pmod{9}$, then ρ is not a cubic residue of q, i.e. $x^3 \equiv \rho \pmod{q}$ is not solvable.

Write $q = 3r + 2$, and suppose $x^3 \equiv \rho \pmod{q}$ is solvable. Then

$$x^{N(q)-1} \equiv 1, \qquad x^{q^2-1} \equiv 1, \qquad x^{(3r+1)(3r+3)} \equiv 1 \pmod{q},$$

and so $\rho^{(3r+1)(r+1)} \equiv 1, \qquad \rho^{r+1} \equiv 1 \pmod{q}, \qquad \rho^{r+1} = 1.$

This is impossible since $r \not\equiv -1 \pmod{3}$.

Theorem 3

Let $a = p$ or p^2, where $p \equiv 2, 5 \pmod{9}$ is a prime, and let ε be a unit in $Q(\rho)$. Then the equation

$$x^3 + y^3 + \varepsilon a z^3 = 0,$$

has no solutions (x, y, z, ε) in the field $Q(\rho)$ except

$$z = 0, \qquad x = -y, \, -\rho y, \, -\rho^2 y,$$

unless $a = 2$, when there are also the solutions

$$x^3 = y^3 = -\varepsilon z^3, \qquad \varepsilon = \pm 1.$$

We may suppose that x, y, z are integers in $Q(\rho)$, that $xyz \neq 0$, $(x, y) = 1$, $(y, z) = 1$, $(z, x) = 1$. Let (x, y, z, ε) be a solution for which $N(xyz)$ is a minimum, where N denotes the norm in the field. Write

$$\alpha = x + y, \qquad \beta = \rho x + \rho^2 y, \qquad \gamma = \rho^2 x + \rho y.$$

Then $\delta = (\alpha, \beta, \gamma) = 1$ or $1 - \rho$ or $1 - \rho^2.$

Also $\alpha + \beta + \gamma = 0, \qquad \dfrac{\alpha}{\delta} \cdot \dfrac{\beta}{\delta} \cdot \dfrac{\gamma}{\delta} + \varepsilon a \left(\dfrac{z}{\delta}\right)^3 = 0.$

Here α/δ, β/δ, γ/δ are relatively prime in pairs since their sum is zero. Hence if a is a factor, say, of γ/δ,

$$\frac{\alpha}{\delta} = \varepsilon_1 x_1^3, \qquad \frac{\beta}{\delta} = \varepsilon_2 y_1^3, \qquad \frac{\gamma}{\delta} = a\varepsilon_3 z_1^3,$$

where $\varepsilon_1, \varepsilon_2, \varepsilon_3$ are units and x_1, y_1, z_1 are integers in $Q(\rho)$. Also $x_1 y_1 z_1 \neq 0$ as otherwise $z = 0$. Hence

$$\varepsilon_1 x_1^3 + \varepsilon_2 y_1^3 + \varepsilon_3 a z_1^3 = 0,$$

or say,

$$x_1^3 + \eta_2 y_1^3 + \eta_3 a z_1^3 = 0,$$

where η_2, η_3 are units. Now y_1 is prime to a as otherwise $x_1 \equiv 0 \pmod{p}$. Hence η_2 is a cubic residue of p and so $\eta_2 = \pm 1$. Then

$$x_1^3 \pm y_1^3 + \eta_3 a z_1^3 = 0,$$

i.e. an equation of the same type as the original one.

Also

$$N(xyz)^3 \leqslant N(x_1 y_1 z_1)^3 = N\left(\frac{\alpha\beta\gamma}{\delta^3 a}\right) = N\left(\frac{z}{\delta}\right)^3.$$

hence,

$$1 \geqslant N(\delta xy),$$

and so x, y, δ are units and $x^3 = \pm 1$, $y^3 = \pm 1$.
If $a > 2$, then $z = 0$ and the only solutions are those with $xyz = 0$. If $a = 2$ there is now also a solution $x^3 = y^3 = -\varepsilon z^3$, $\varepsilon = \pm 1$. These and $x^3 + y^3 = 0$, $z = 0$ are the only solutions.

It has also been long known that there are a number of other values of a for which the equation

$$x^3 + y^3 = az^3$$

has no rational solutions except $x + y = 0$, $z = 0$. Let $p \equiv 5 \pmod{18}$, $q \equiv 11 \pmod{18}$ be primes, and so p and q are primes in $Q(\rho)$. Then there are no rational solutions except $z = 0$ when

$$a = p, 2p, 9p, p^2, 9p^2, 4p^2, pq, p_1 p_2^2,$$

and also when

$$a = q, 4q, 9q, 2q^2, q^2, 9q^2, q_1 q_2^2, p^2 q^2.$$

We prove the result when $a = 9p$. We may suppose x, y, z are rational integers, $z \neq 0$, and $|z|$ has its least value and that $(x, y) = 1$. Since

$$(x + y)(x + y\rho)(x + y\rho^2) = 9pz^3,$$

and

$$(x + y, x + y\rho) = 1 \text{ or } 1 - \rho, \text{ etc.,}$$

we have

$$x + y = 3pw^3,$$

$$x + y\rho = \rho^\lambda(1 - \rho)(u + v\rho)^3, \quad x + y\rho^2 = \rho^{2\lambda}(1 - \rho^2)(u + v\rho^2)^3, \quad \lambda = 0, 1, 2,$$

where $u, v, w \neq 0$ are rational integers and $(u, v) = 1$.

Suppose first that $\lambda = 0$.

The last two equations give

$$x = u^3 + 3u^2v - 6uv^2 + v^3, \qquad y = -u^3 + 6u^2v - 3uv^2 - v^3,$$

and so
$$x + y = 9uv(u - v) = 3pw^3,$$

whence $w \equiv 0 \pmod{3}$, $w = 3w_1 \neq 0$. Then

$$uv(u - v) = 9pw_1^3.$$

Hence we have five possibilities with $(x_1, y_1) = 1$.

I. $u = x_1^3$, $v = y_1^3$, $u - v = 9pz_1^3$, $x_1 y_1 z_1 = w_1$.

This gives $x_1^3 - y_1^3 = 9pz_1^3$, where

$$|x_1 y_1 z_1| = |w_1| = \tfrac{1}{3}|w| \leqslant \tfrac{1}{3}\sqrt[3]{3}|z|,$$

since
$$9p|z|^3 = 3p|w|^3(x^2 - xy + y^2) \geqslant 3p|w|^3.$$

Hence $|z_1| \leqslant w_1 \leqslant \tfrac{1}{3}\sqrt[3]{3}|z|$, a contradiction.

II. $u = x_1^3$, $v = 9y_1^3$, $u - v = pz_1^3$,

and so
$$x_1^3 - 9y_1^3 = pz_1^3.$$

Clearly $z_1 \not\equiv 0 \pmod{3}$, and so $z_1^3 \equiv \pm 1 \pmod 9$, $x_1^3 \equiv \pm 5 \pmod 9$, and this is impossible.

III. $u = x_1^3$, $v = py_1^3$, $u - v = 9z_1^3$.

Here
$$x_1^3 - py_1^3 = 9z_1^3.$$

This is the same as II.

IV. $u = x_1^3$, $v = 9py_1^3$, $u - v = z_1^3$.

Since $x_1^3 - 9py_1^3 = z_1^3$, this is really the same as I.

V. $u = 9x_1^3$, $v = py_1^3$, $u - v = z_1^3$.

Here
$$9x_1^3 - py_1^3 = z_1^3.$$

This is the same as II.

Suppose next that $\lambda = 1, 2$. Then by addition

$$3pw^3 + \rho^{\lambda+1}(1 - \rho)(u + v\rho)^3 + \rho^{2\lambda+2}(1 - \rho^2)(u + v\rho^2)^3 = 0,$$

or
$$(1 - \rho^2)pw^3 + \rho^{\lambda+1}(u + v\rho)^3 - \rho^{2\lambda+4}(u + v\rho^2)^3 = 0.$$

This is impossible since it implies that ρ is a cubic residue of p.

Example
 A solution of

$$x^3 + y^3 = az^3$$

can be deduced from any solution of

$$AX^3 + BY^3 + CZ^3 = 0, \quad where \ ABC = a.$$

For the substitution

$$x = u^3 + 3u^2v - 6uv^2 + v^3, \quad y = -u^3 + 6u^2v - 3uv^2 - v^3,$$

gives
$$9uv(u - v)3(u^2 - uv + v^2)^3 = az^3.$$

This is satisfied if we take now

$$u = AX^3, \quad v = -BY^3, \quad u - v = -CZ^3.$$

Then
$$z = 3XYZ(u^2 - uv + v^2).$$

We now take the case $a = 1$ and prove the

Theorem 4

The equation $x^3 + y^3 + z^3 = 0$ has no solutions in $Q(\rho)$ except those given by $xyz = 0$.

We may suppose that x, y, z are integers and $(x, y) = 1$, etc. Write $\lambda = 1 - \rho$ so that λ is a prime and

$$3 = (1 - \rho)(1 - \rho^2) = \lambda^2(1 + \rho) = -\lambda^2\rho^2, \text{ and } \lambda^2 = -3\rho.$$

We prove first that $xyz \equiv 0 \pmod{\lambda}$. For suppose that $xyz \not\equiv 0 \pmod{\lambda}$. Put with rational integers a and b,

$$x = a + b\rho = a + b(1 - \lambda) \equiv a + b \pmod{\lambda}.$$

Since $x \not\equiv 0 \pmod{\lambda}$, $a + b \equiv \pm 1 \pmod{3}$, $x^3 \equiv \pm 1 \pmod{3\lambda}$. Then

$$x^3 + y^3 + z^3 = \pm 1, \pm 3 \pmod{3\lambda} \not\equiv 0 \pmod{3\lambda}.$$

Hence we may assume that $z \equiv 0 \pmod{\lambda}$.
 We prove the more general result that the equation

$$x^3 + y^3 = \eta\lambda^{3n}z^3,$$

where η is any unit, $n > 0$, $z \neq 0$, $(z, \lambda) = 1$, $(x, y) = 1$ and so $(x, \lambda) = 1$, has no solutions.
 We show first that if x, y are any integers in $Q(\rho)$ and $(x, y) = 1$, $(x, y, \lambda) = 1$ and $x^3 + y^3 \equiv 0 \pmod{\lambda^3}$, then $x^3 + y^3 \equiv 0 \pmod{\lambda^4}$.

For
$$(x + y)((x + y)^2 - 3xy) \equiv 0 \pmod{\lambda^3}.$$

Then
$$x + y \equiv 0 \pmod{\lambda}, \quad x = -y + \lambda t, \quad \text{say.}$$

Then
$$x^3 + y^3 = \lambda^3 t^3 - 3\lambda^2 t^2 y + 3\lambda t y^2$$
$$\equiv \lambda^3 t(t^2 - \rho^2 y^2) \pmod{\lambda^4}$$
$$\equiv 0 \pmod{\lambda^4},$$

since $y^2 \equiv 1$, $\rho \pmod \lambda$ and $t \equiv 0, \pm 1 \pmod \lambda$.

The next stage is to show that if the equation is solvable for an exponent n it is also solvable for $n - 1$, and so for $n = 1$. Since $z \not\equiv 0 \pmod \lambda$, this contradicts $x^3 + y^3 \equiv 0 \pmod{\lambda^4}$.

Write
$$(x + y)(x + \rho y)(x + \rho^2 y) = \eta \lambda^{3n} z^3.$$

Then one and so all of the three factors must be divisible by λ, since $x + y = x + \rho y + \lambda y$ etc. Also only one of them can be divisible by a power of λ greater than one. On writing y for ρy or $\rho^2 y$, if need be, we may suppose that

$$x + y = \eta_1 \lambda^{3n-2} z_1^3, \qquad x + \rho y = \eta_2 \lambda y_1^3, \qquad x + \rho^2 y = \eta_3 \lambda x_1^3,$$

where η_1, η_2, η_3 are units, $(x_1 y_1, \lambda) = 1$, $(x_1, y_1, z_1) = 1$, $x_1 y_1 z_1 = z \neq 0$. Multiply by $\rho, \rho^2, 1$ and add. Then

$$\rho \eta_1 \lambda^{3n-2} z_1^3 + \rho^2 \eta_2 \lambda y_1^3 + \eta_3 \lambda x_1^3 = 0,$$

or
$$x_1^3 + \zeta_1 y_1^3 = \zeta \lambda^{3n-3} z_1^3,$$

where ζ, ζ_1 are units. Then as $n > 1$,

$$x_1^3 + \zeta_1 y_1^3 \equiv 0 \pmod{\lambda^3}.$$

Since $(x_1 y_1, \lambda) = 1$, $x_1^3 \equiv \pm 1 \pmod{\lambda^2}$, $y_1^3 \equiv \pm 1 \pmod{\lambda^2}$,

and so $\zeta_1 \equiv \pm 1 \pmod{\lambda^2}$,   and $\zeta_1 = \pm 1$.

Hence we have a similar equation with $n - 1$ in place of n. This concludes the proof.

There are applications of the field $Q(\sqrt{-3})$ to some equations of the form

$$ax^3 + by^3 + cz^3 - dxyz = 0 \quad (x, y, z) = 1. \tag{1}$$

Such equations also occur in the discussion of the integer solutions of the simultaneous equations

$$X + Y + Z = dW, \tag{2}$$
$$XYZ = eW^3, \tag{3}$$

Thus equation (3) leads to

$$X = ax^3, \qquad Y = by^3, \qquad Z = cz^3, \qquad W = xyz,$$

where $abc = e$ is some factorization of e and so (1) follows from (2).

It is very difficult to prove the non-existence of integer solutions of the general equation (1). Sometimes progress can be made with the special case $a = b$, and in particular with

$$x^3 + y^3 + cz^3 - dxyz = 0, \quad (x, y, z) = 1. \tag{4}$$

The question now is whether there exist integer solutions other than the trivial ones given by $xyz = 0$ which we exclude hereafter. Suppose for simplicity that c is not divisible by the cube of any prime divisor of d. Then obviously $(x, y, d) = 1$. Also $(x, z) = (y, z) = 1$. Write $2\rho = -1 \pm \sqrt{-3}$. In equation (4), put

$$X = p\rho x + p\rho^2 y + qz, \qquad Y = p\rho^2 x + p\rho y + qz, \tag{5}$$

$$Z = px + py + qz.$$

Then if

$$pd - 3q = 0, \tag{6}$$

$$XYZ = p^3(x^3 + y^3) + q^3 z^3 - 3p^2 qxyz$$

$$= p^3(-cz^3 + dxyz) + q^3 z^3 - 3p^2 qxyz$$

$$= (q^3 - cp^3)z^3.$$

Suppose first that $d \equiv 0 \pmod 3$. Then we take $p = 3$, $q = d$, and

$$X = 3(\rho x + \rho^2 y) + dz, \qquad Y = 3(\rho^2 x + \rho y) + dz,$$

$$Z = 3(x + y) + dz. \tag{7}$$

Then

$$X + Y + Z = 3dz, \tag{8}$$

$$XYZ = \Delta z^3, \tag{9}$$

where

$$\Delta = d^3 - 27c.$$

Here X, Y are integers in $Q(\sqrt{-3})$, and Z is a rational integer $\neq 0$ from equation (9). Write $\delta = (X, Y, Z)$. Then from equation (7), since $\delta \mid \rho^2 X + \rho Y + Z$ etc.

$$\delta \mid 9x, 9y, 3dz,$$

and so we may take $\delta = 1, \sqrt{-3}, 3$. We cannot have $\delta = \sqrt{-3}$.

For then $\quad z \equiv 0 \pmod{\sqrt{-3}}, \quad z \equiv 0 \pmod 3$ and $3 \mid \delta$.

On replacing X by $3^\alpha X$ etc., z by $3^\alpha z$, $\alpha = 0, 1$, we may suppose that equations (8), (9) hold and that $(X, Y, Z) = 1$. This is obvious when $\alpha = 0$. When $\alpha = 1$, equation (7) becomes

$$X = \rho x + \rho^2 y + dz, \qquad Y = \rho^2 x + \rho y + dz, \qquad Z = x + y + dz.$$

Now $(X, Y) = 1$, for if $(X, Y) \neq 1$, $\sqrt{-3} \mid (X, Y)$ and $X + Y + Z = 3dz$ shows that $(X, Y, Z) \neq 1$. Similarly $(Y, Z) = (Z, X) = 1$. Also $z \not\equiv 0 \pmod 3$ since $X \equiv Y \equiv Z \pmod{\sqrt{-3}}$ and equation (9) would give $X \equiv Y \equiv Z \equiv 0 \pmod{\sqrt{-3}}$.

The equations (8), (9) are of the forms (2) and (3) but now X, Y are conjugate integers in $Q(\sqrt{-3})$. Further progress depends upon the residues mod 3 of the prime factors of Δ.

Suppose first that Δ is divisible only by rational primes $\pi \equiv 2 \pmod 3$. Then either X and Y are both divisible by π or neither is. If Δ is square free, the first alternative is impossible since it would give $z \equiv Z \equiv 0 \pmod \pi$ from equations (8) and (9). Hence with $\beta = 0, 1, 2$,

$$X = \rho^\beta x_1^3, \qquad Y = \rho^{2\beta} y_1^3, \qquad Z = \Delta z_1^3, \qquad z = x_1 y_1 z_1,$$

where x_1, y_1 are conjugate integers in $Q(\sqrt{-3})$, and $z_1 \neq 0$. Then

$$\rho^\beta x_1^3 + \rho^{2\beta} y_1^3 + \Delta z_1^3 = 3dx_1 y_1 z_1. \tag{10}$$

We show now that $\beta = 0$ and so equation (10) takes the form (4). Since $(z, 3) = 1$, x_1, y_1, z_1 are all prime to $\sqrt{-3}$. Hence

$$x_1^3 \equiv \pm 1 \pmod{3\sqrt{-3}}, \quad y_1^3 \equiv \pm 1 \pmod{3\sqrt{-3}}, \quad z_1^3 \equiv \pm 1 \pmod 9.$$

Hence since $\Delta \equiv \pm 1 \pmod 9$,

$$\frac{\pm \rho^\beta \pm \rho^{2\beta} \pm 1}{3} \not\equiv 0 \pmod{\sqrt{-3}}.$$

This occurs only when $\beta = 0$.

We now apply to equation (10) the transformation used for (4). We take $p = 1$, $q = d$, and then

$$X_1 = \rho x_1 + \rho^2 y_1 + dz_1, \qquad Y_1 = \rho^2 x_1 + \rho y_1 + dz_1, \tag{11}$$

$$Z_1 = x_1 + y_1 + dz_1,$$

and so X_1, Y_1, Z_1 are all rational integers. Also

$$X_1 Y_1 Z_1 = (d^3 - \Delta)z_1^3 = 27cz_1^3, \tag{12}$$

$$X_1 + Y_1 + Z_1 = 3dz_1. \tag{13}$$

One of X_1, Y_1, Z_1 is $\equiv 0 \pmod 3$ and since from equation (11) $X_1 \equiv Y_1 \equiv Z \pmod{\sqrt{-3}}$, $X_1 \equiv Y_1 \equiv Z_1 \equiv 0 \pmod 3$. Hence we can dispense with the factors 27 and 3. Also $Z_1 \neq 0$.

Now account must be taken of the factorization of c. If c is a prime, we deduce the same equation (4). Hence the method of infinite descent applies. Then there may be either no solution at all, or a finite number from which all the solutions can be deduced by rational processes.

An illustration is given by Ward's[3] result that the equation

$$x^3 + y^3 + 5z^3 - 5xyz = 0 \tag{14}$$

has only the solution $x + y = 0$, $z = 0$.
Here $c = 5$, $d = 5$, $\Delta = -10$ and no other solution arises.
The equation (14) arises from the equation

$$\sum x^3 + \sum x^2 y + xyz = 0$$

on writing $X = x + 2y + 2z$ etc., and so the only solutions are $x + y = 0$, $z = 0$, etc.

Suppose next that Δ is divisible by rational primes $\pi \equiv 1 \pmod 3$. Now $\pi = \pi_1 \pi_2$ where π_1, π_2 are conjugate primes in $Q(\sqrt{-3})$. This implies that from equations (8) and (9), we may deduce a relation of the form

$$Ax_1^3 + By_1^3 + Cz_1^3 = 3dx_1 y_1 z_1,$$

where A, B, C are conjugate. It is problematic if this equation reduces to the form (4).

Cassels and Sansone[4] show that this occurs for the equation

$$x^3 + y^3 + z^3 - xyz = 0,$$

which has only the solutions $x + y = 0$, $z = 0$ etc.

Here
$$XYZ = -26z^3, \tag{15}$$

$$X + Y + Z = 3z.$$

Clearly we may suppose $z \not\equiv 0 \pmod 3$. Hence we have two possibilities. The first is

$$X = \rho^\gamma x_1^3, \qquad Y = \rho^{2\gamma} y_1^3, \qquad Z = -26z_1^3, \qquad z = x_1 y_1 z_1,$$

and so
$$\rho^\gamma x_1^3 + \rho^{2\gamma} y_1^3 - 26z_1^3 = 3x_1 y_1 z_1.$$

Since $x_1 y_1 z_1 \not\equiv 0 \pmod 3$, we have as before $\gamma = 0$ and so

$$x_1^3 + y_1^3 - 26z_1^3 = 3x_1 y_1 z_1. \tag{16}$$

This leads to
$$X_1 Y_1 Z_1 = (3z_1)^3,$$

$$X_1 + Y_1 + Z_1 = 3z_1,$$

and as before, X_1, Y_1, Z_1 are all divisible by 3. Hence the method of infinite descent applies and no non-trivial solution emerges.

The second possibility, since $13 = (3\rho - 1)(3\rho^2 - 1)$, is given by

$$X = \rho^\delta(3\rho - 1)x_1^3, \quad Y = \rho^{2\delta}(3\rho^2 - 1)y_1^3, \quad Z = -2z_1^3, \quad z = x_1 y_1 z_1,$$

and so
$$\rho^\delta(3\rho - 1)x_1^3 + \rho^{2\delta}(3\rho^2 - 1)y_1^3 - 2z_1^3 = 3x_1 y_1 z_1. \tag{17}$$

As before, since $x_1 y_1 z_1 \not\equiv 0 \pmod 3$, $\delta = 0$ and so

$$(3\rho - 1)x_1^3 + (3\rho^2 - 1)y_1^3 - 2z_1^3 = 3x_1 y_1 z_1.$$

Now we apply the substitution

$$X_1 = \rho x_1 + \rho^2 y_1 + z_1, \qquad Y_1 = \rho^2 x_1 + \rho y_1 + z_1,$$

$$Z_1 = x_1 + y_1 + z_1.$$

and so $\quad 3x_1 = \rho^2 X_1 + \rho Y_1 + Z_1, \qquad 3y_1 = \rho^2 X_1 + \rho Y_1 + Z_1,$

$$3z_1 = X_1 + Y_1 + Z_1.$$

Then $\qquad\qquad x_1 y_1^2 + y_1 z_1^2 + z_1 x_1^2 = x_1 y_1 z_1.$ (18)

We show that this gives

$$x_1 = y_2^2 z_2, \qquad y_1 = z_2^2 x_2, \qquad z_1 = x_2^2 y_2,$$

and $\qquad\qquad\qquad x_2^3 + y_2^3 + z_2^3 = x_2 y_2 z_2.$ (19)

Hence the method of infinite descent applies. For let $x_2 = (y_1, z_1)$ etc. and then

$$x_1 = p y_2 z_2, \qquad y_1 = q z_2 x_2, \qquad z_1 = r x_2 y_2,$$

where

$$(p, q) = 1, \qquad (x_2, y_2) = 1 \text{ etc. and } (x_2, p) = (y_2, q) = (z_2, r) = 1.$$

Then $\qquad\qquad pq^2 x_2 z_2^2 + qr^2 y_2 x_2^2 + rp^2 z_2 y_2^2 = pqr x_2 y_2 z_2.$

On dividing by y_2, we see that since $(q x_2 z_2, y_2) = 1$, we can put

$$p = P y_2, \qquad q = Q z_2, \qquad r = R x_2,$$

and so $\qquad\qquad PQ^2 z_2^3 + QR^2 x_2^3 + RP^2 y_2^3 = PQR x_2 y_2 z_2.$

Dividing by R shows that $R = 1 = P = Q$ and so we have equation (19). No solutions emerge from the descent.

3. We can now consider some results when unique factorization is not assumed to hold in K. We consider the equation

$$XY = cZ^l,$$

where l is prime to h, the number of classes of ideals in K. For simplicity, we suppose that $(X, Y) = 1$ and that all the factors of c in K are principal ideals. We have now the ideal equations

$$(X) = (c_1)\mathfrak{a}^l, \qquad (Y) = (c_2)\mathfrak{b}^l,$$

where c_1, c_2 refer to all possible factorizations.

Now $c = c_1 c_2$, $(c_1, c_2) = 1$. Hence a^l, ℓ^l are principal ideals, and since $(l, h) = 1$, a, ℓ are principal ideals. Then we have as before,

$$X = c_1 \zeta_1 P^l, \qquad Y = c_2 \zeta_2 Q^l, \qquad Z = \zeta_3 PQ,$$

where c_1, c_2 are a finite set of integers in K with $c_1 c_2 = c$, $(c_1, c_2) = 1$, and $\zeta_1, \zeta_2, \zeta_3$ belong to a finite set of units with $\zeta_1 \zeta_2 = \zeta_3^l$. Also the algebraic integers P, Q satisfy the condition $(c_1 P, c_2 Q) = 1$.

The simplest application is to the equation

$$y^2 = x^3 + k.$$

and full details are given in Chapter 26. A simple case may be given here. We suppose that $h(Q(\sqrt{k})) \not\equiv 0 \pmod 3$, $d \equiv 2, 3 \pmod 4$ and is square free. Then $x \not\equiv 0 \pmod 2$, and from

$$(y + \sqrt{k})(y - \sqrt{k}) = x^3.$$

we deduce with rational integers a, b,

$$y + \sqrt{k} = \varepsilon(a + b\sqrt{k})^3,$$

where $\varepsilon = 1, \eta, \eta^{-1}$ where η is the fundamental unit in the field, i.e.

$$\eta = T + U\sqrt{k}, \qquad T^2 - kU^2 = \pm 1.$$

We now have binary cubics in a, b which require further discussion. The real difficulty with the equation

$$XY = cZ^l, \qquad (X, Y) = 1,$$

arises when h is not prime to l. Suppose for simplicity that $h \mid l$. Then

$$(X) = c_1 a_1^l, \qquad (Y) = c_2 a_2^l,$$

where
$$(c) = c_1 c_2, \qquad (c_1, c_2) = 1,$$

refers to all the ideal factorizations of c. Since (X) and a_1^l are principal ideals, c_1, c_2 must be principal ideals. Hence solutions can occur only for factorizations of c not involving ideal factors. It may happen that only $(c) = c_1$ need be considered. This also arises sometimes when $(X, Y) \neq 1$. We may then deduce an equation $(X) = d_1 a_1^l$ where a_1 is an ideal and if $l = h$ the equation is impossible if d_1 is not a principal ideal.

An application is given in Chapter 26 to the equation

$$y^2 = x^3 + k$$

when $k \equiv 1 \pmod 8$, $k < 0$, $k \neq -7$, $h(Q(\sqrt{k})) = 3$, e.g., when $k = -31$.

We now give an application to a cubic field.

Theorem 5

   The equation $x^3 + dy^3 = 3z^3$, where d is square free, $d \equiv \pm 2, \pm 4 \pmod 9$, and $h(Q(\sqrt[3]{d})) = 3$, has no rational solutions if $3 = c^3$ and the ideal c is not principal.

   We require some results on the cubic field $Q(\theta)$ where $\theta^3 = d$. The integers have the form $a + b\theta + c\theta^2$ where a, b, c are rational integers. Also $(3) = c^3$ is given by $(3) = (3, \sqrt[3]{d} \pm 1)^3$ or $(3, \sqrt[3]{d} \mp 1)^3$ according as $d \equiv \pm 2$ or $\pm 4 \pmod 9$.

   We may suppose that x, y, z are integers and that $(x, y) = 1$ and so $(y, z) = 1$. We prove that $(z, 3) = 1$.

If $3 \mid z$, $$x^3 + dy^3 \equiv 0 \pmod 9.$$

Since $3 \nmid y$, $y^3 \equiv \pm 1 \pmod 9$, and $x^3 \pm d \equiv 0 \pmod 9$, which is impossible.

Write $$(x + \theta y)(x^2 - \theta xy + \theta^2 y^2) = 3z^3.$$

Since $$x^2 - \theta xy + \theta^2 y^2 = (x + \theta y)^2 - 3\theta xy,$$

3 cannot be a common divisor of the two left-hand factors. Clearly $x + \theta y \equiv 0 \pmod c$ but not $\pmod{c^2}$. Hence

$$(x + \theta y) = ca^3, \qquad (x^2 - \theta xy + \theta^2 y^2) = c^2 b^3.$$

Since a^3 is a principal ideal, so is c, a contradiction.

An illustration is given by $d = 22$. This is of special interest since the congruence $x^3 + 22y^3 - 3z^3 \equiv 0 \pmod M$ is solvable for all M.

4. When no restrictions are placed on the class number h, we have the fundamental

Theorem 6

   The solution of $XY = cZ^l$, where $(X, Y) \mid \delta$ where δ is a given ideal, has the form

$$X = \lambda \zeta_1 P^l, \qquad Y = \mu \zeta_2 Q^l, \qquad Z = \nu \zeta_3 PQ,$$

where P, Q are arbitrary integers in K, and $\zeta_1, \zeta_2, \zeta_3$ are units, λ, μ, ν are numbers in K not necessarily integers, all six being taken from a finite set and such that

$$\lambda \mu \zeta_1 \zeta_2 = c\nu^l \zeta_3^l.$$

   For now we have the ideal equation

$$(X) = \delta_1 c_1 a^l, \qquad (Y) = \delta_2 c_2 b^l,$$

where δ_1, δ_2 are elements of a finite set of ideals all of whose prime ideal divisors divide δ and where $(c) = c_1 c_2$ is an ideal factorization of c.

   There are only a finite number of classes of ideals, say those typified by $a_1, a_2, \ldots, a_n$. Let the inverse class of a be typified by a^{-l}. Then $aa^{-l} = (P)$

where P is an integer. Hence $a^{-l}(X) = \delta_1 c_1 (P)^l$ and so $\delta_1 c_1 / a^{-l} = (\lambda)$ is a principal ideal. Hence

$$(X) = (\lambda)(P)^l, \qquad X = \lambda \zeta P^l,$$

where ζ is a unit. Since $\zeta = \zeta_1 \zeta_0^l$ where ζ_1 takes only a finite number of values, we have the theorem. Also λ is one of a finite set of numbers in K.

An application to the equation $y^2 = x^3 + k$ will be given in Chapter 26.

There are obvious extensions to the solution of the more general equation

$$X_1 X_2 \ldots X_n = CZ^l,$$

where we suppose now that

$$(X_r, X_s) \mid \delta_{r,s} \quad (r, s = 1, 2, \ldots, n, \ r \neq s.)$$

where $\delta_{r,s}$ is an ideal of a finite set.

The most important application is to Fermat's last theorem, namely, that if $l > 2$, the only solutions in rational integers of the equation

$$x^l + y^l = z^l$$

are given by $xyz = 0$. This will be investigated in Chapter 28.

For some equations reducing to the form $XY = cZ^l$, it may prove convenient to consider solutions in a field K' containing K as a subfield, and so the relative units must be studied. Often considerable numerical detail may be involved.

REFERENCES

1. P. Bachmann. "Die Lehre von der Kreistheilung". B. G. Teubner, Leipzig (1872), pp. 185–199 and 220–224.
2. Marshall Hall, Jr. Some equations $y^2 = x^3 - k$ without integer solutions. *J. Lond. Math. Soc.*, 38 (1953), 381.
3. M. Ward. The vanishing of the homogeneous product sum of the roots of a cubic. *Duke Math. J.*, 26 (1952), 553–562.
4. G. Sansone and J. W. S. Cassels. Sur le problème de M. Werner Mnich. *Acta Arith.*, 7 (1962), 187–190.

CHAPTER 16

Finite Basis Theorem for the Rational Points on a Cubic Curve $f(x,y,z) = 0$ of Genus One

1. Theorem 1

All the rational points of a cubic curve $f(x, y, z) = 0$ of genus one, can be found from a finite number by the chord and tangent process.

A sketch is given of the original proof by Mordell[1]. It may be supposed that there are an infinity of solutions, as otherwise there is nothing to prove. We show first that the problem is equivalent to that of finding the integer solutions in x, y, z of an equation with integer coefficients.

$$ax^4 + bx^3y + cx^2y^2 + dxy^3 + ey^4 = z^2. \tag{1}$$

Let (x', y', z') be a rational solution of $f(x, y, z) = 0$; a solution with $z' = 0$ may be considered trivial, and so we may suppose $z' \neq 0$. Put

$$x = x'Z + X, \qquad y = y'Z + Y, \qquad z = z'Z.$$

Then $$S_1Z^2 + S_2Z + S_3 = 0, \tag{2}$$

where S_1, S_2, S_3 are homogeneous functions in X, Y of degrees one, two, three. Since the curve is of genus one, $S_1 \neq 0$. Hence

$$2S_1Z = -S_2 \pm (S_2^2 - 4S_1S_3)^{1/2}.$$

Here $S_2^2 - 4S_1S_3$ is a homogeneous binary quartic in X, Y which becomes a perfect square for values of X, Y given by $S_1 = 0$. This square cannot be zero for then $S_2 = 0$, $S_3 = 0$, and so a linear factor would divide out in equation (2). Hence by a linear transformation on X, Y, we are led to an equation (1) in which a is a perfect square $\neq 0$. By a further transformation, we have now the problem of finding the solution in integers x, y, z where $(x, y) = 1$ of an equation, say,

$$x^4 + bx^3y + cx^2y^2 + dxy^3 + ey^4 = fz^2, \tag{3}$$

where b, c, d, e, f are integers.

Let the algebraic integer θ be defined by

$$\theta^4 + b\theta^3 + c\theta^2 + d\theta + e = 0. \tag{4}$$

Write equation (3) as

$$(x - \theta y)(x^3 + (\theta + b)x^2y + \cdots) = fz^2.$$

The common ideal factors of the two factors on the left-hand side are finite in number. Hence from the general result of Theorem 4, Chapter 15,

$$x - \theta y = \mu T^2/m, \tag{5}$$

where μ is one of a finite set of integers in $Q(\theta)$, and m is one of a finite set of rational integers, and

$$T = p + q\theta + r\theta^2 + s\theta^3,$$

where p, q, r, s are rational integers. Since there are an infinity of solutions for x, y, the same μ, m must also occur for a particular solution, say (x', y').

Then
$$m^2(x - \theta y)(x' - \theta y') = (P + Q\theta + R\theta^2 + S\theta^3)^2, \tag{6}$$

where P, Q, R, S are rational integers.

If the quartic for θ is irreducible, equation (6) will also hold for all the conjugates of θ. This will still be true if the quartic is reducible. On making a linear transformation on x, y, we may suppose that $x' = 1$, $y' = 0$. On multiplying out equation (6) and replacing θ^6, θ^5, θ^4 in terms of θ^3, θ^2, θ from (4), and equating to zero the coefficients of θ^3, θ^2, we have two equations in P, Q, R, S. On solving for two of the unknowns in terms of the others, we find that another solution (x_1, y_1) of equation (3) can be expressed linearly in terms of P, Q, R, S. Hence from equation (6),

$$max(|x_1|, |y_1|) \leqslant k \, max(|x|, |y|)^{1/2},$$

where k is a constant. But from a sequence $s_n > 0$, where $s_{n+1} \leqslant k s_n^{1/2}$, s_n is bounded, and if any of the s have $s > k$, then after a certain stage we arrive at an n such that $s_n \leqslant k$. This proves that the infinity of solutions can be expressed in terms of a finite number by rational processes.

The geometrical meaning of the process is that if a rational point P is known on the quartic (3), another rational point is found from the intersection with the quartic of a parabola $z^2 = gx^2 + hx + j$ having three point contact with the quartic at P. The connection with the chord tangent process follows from the 1–1 correspondence between the points of the quartic

$$y^2 = x^4 + 6cx^2 + 4dx + e,$$

and the cubic

$$t^2 = 4s^3 - g_2 s - g_3$$

given by

$$2x(s + c) = t - d, \qquad y = 2s - x^2 - c,$$

where g_2, g_3 are the invariants of the quartic.

2. We now prove by Weil's[2] method the finite basis theorem.

Theorem 2

There exists a finite set S of rational points $P_1, P_2, \ldots, P_r$ on the cubic curve

$$y^2 = 4x^3 - g_2 x - g_3, \tag{7}$$

such that all the rational points on the curve can be derived from the P by rational processes.

This is given by taking the point $P_{1,1}$ where the tangent at P_1 meets the curve again, and the point $P_{1,2}$ where the line joining P_1, P_2 meets the curve again, adding these points to the set S, and then proceeding similarly with all the points of the enlarged set.

On replacing x, y by $x/4$, $y/4$, the equation (7) takes the form

$$y^2 = x^3 - h_2 x - h_3. \tag{8}$$

We may suppose that h_2 and h_3 are integers, for if $h_2 = H_2/H$, $h_3 = H_3/H$, it suffices to replace x, y by x/H^2, y/H^3.

Since the curve is of genus one, the equation

$$x^3 - h_2 x - h_3 = (x - e_1)(x - e_2)(x - e_3) = 0$$

does not have equal roots. The equation can be considered as defining cubic fields $K = Q(e)$, $(e = e_1, e_2, e_3)$, reducible or irreducible.

We require the coordinates of the points $P_{1,2}, P_{1,1}$. Let e denote any of e_1, e_2, e_3. We prove that $P_{1,2}$ is given by

$$x_{1,2} - e = \frac{1}{(x_1 - e)(x_2 - e)} \left(\frac{y_1(x_2 - e) - y_2(x_1 - e)}{x_2 - x_1} \right)^2. \tag{9}$$

The equation of the line joining P_1 and P_2 is

$$y - y_1 = \frac{y_2 - y_1}{x_2 - x_1} (x - x_1).$$

Hence

$$x^3 - h_2 x - h_3 = \left(y_1 + \frac{y_2 - y_1}{x_2 - x_1} (x - x_1) \right)^2. \tag{10}$$

Two roots are x_1, x_2 and the third is $x_{1,2}$.

Put $x = e + X$, $x_1 = e + X_1$, $x_2 = e + X_2$. Then, say,

$$X^3 + H_1 X^2 + H_2 X = \left(y_1 + \frac{y_2 - y_1}{X_2 - X_1} (X - X_1) \right)^2. \tag{11}$$

The product of the three values of X gives

$$(x_{12} - e)(x_1 - e)(x_2 - e) = \left(\frac{y_1(x_2 - e) - y_2(x_1 - e)}{x_1 - x_2} \right)^2. \tag{12}$$

Another form for x_{12} follows from equation (10). This gives

$$x_{12} + x_1 + x_2 = \left(\frac{y_2 - y_1}{x_2 - x_1} \right)^2.$$

This can be written as

$$X_{12} = \frac{(x_1 x_2 - h_2)(x_1 + x_2) - 2h_3 - 2y_1 y_2}{(x_1 - x_2)^2} \tag{13}$$

on putting $y_1^2 = x_1^3 - h_2 x_1 - h_3$, etc.

We now deal with $P_{1,1}$. The equation (11) takes the form

$$X^3 + H_1 X^2 + H_2 X = \left(y_1 + \frac{3x_1^2 - h_2}{2y_1}(X - X_1) \right)^2$$

on replacing $(y_2 - y_1)/(x_2 - x_1)$ by dy_1/dx_1. Now the product of the roots gives

$$(x_{11} - e)(x_1 - e)^2 = \left(y_1 - \frac{(3x_1^2 - h_2)}{2y_1}(x_1 - e) \right)^2$$

$$= \left(\frac{2y_1^2 - (3x_1^2 - h_2)(x_1 - e)}{2y_1} \right)^2,$$

$$x_{11} - e = \left(\frac{2(x_1^2 + ex_1 + e^2 - h_2) - 3x_1^2 + h_2}{2y_1} \right)^2$$

$$= \left(\frac{x_1^2 + h_2 - 2ex_1 - 2e^2}{2y_1} \right)^2. \tag{14}$$

We write equation (7) as

$$y^2 = (x - e_1)(x - e_2)(x - e_3) = N(x - e).$$

We use the term norm for $N(x - e)$ even when the cubic is reducible. Here e stands for each of the numbers e_1, e_2, e_3. Our problem is to find in $K_e = Q(e)$ those numbers of the form $x - e$, where x is a rational number, whose norm is the square of a rational number, and this is to hold for $e = e_1$, e_2, e_3.

These numbers are included in the set $S(e)$ of numbers $x_0 + x_1 e + x_2 e^2$, x_0, x_1, x_2, rational, whose norm is a perfect square. Clearly $S(e)$ includes the squares of the numbers of K. We divide $S(e)$ into classes putting into a class C, say, all those numbers of $S(e)$ which differ from an element of C by a squared factor of a number of K. There are infinitely many classes.

Two classes C_1 and C_2 can be multiplied together since any element of C_1 multiplied by any element of C_2 belongs to a uniquely defined class, say $C_1 C_2$. The principal class is formed by those numbers of K which are perfect squares and plays the role of a unit class E in the multiplication.

If C is any class, clearly $C^2 = E$. The classes form an infinite Abelian group in which every element is of order 2.

We prove now the fundamental.

Theorem 3

The numbers of the form $x - e$ ($e = e_1$, e_2, e_3), whose norms are rational squares, belong to only a finite number of classes.

In $y^2 = N(x - e)$, put $x = U/W_1$ where U and W_1 are rational integers and $(U, W_1) = 1$. Then

$$(yW_1^2)^2 = W_1 N(U - eW_1),$$

and since $(W_1, U) = 1$, W_1 is prime to $N(U - eW_1)$, and so $W_1 = W^2$. Then $y = V/W^3$ and $(V, W) = 1$. Hence

$$V^2 = N(U - eW^2)$$
$$= (U - e_1 W^2)(U - e_2 W^2)(U - e_3 W^2).$$

In the field $Q(e_1)$, $U - e_1 W^2$ and $(U - e_2 W^2)(U - e_3 W^2)$, which is also a number in $Q(e_1)$, have only a finite number of common ideal factors $\not{p}$ since if $U - e_1 W^2 \equiv 0 \pmod{\not{p}}$, then $(e_1 - e_2)(e_1 - e_3) \equiv 0 \pmod{\not{p}}$. Hence by the general theory

$$U - e_1 W^2 = \mu \beta^2,$$

where μ is one of a finite set of numbers in $Q(e_1)$ and β is an integer in $Q(e_1)$. Hence on dividing by W^2, we have, say,

$$x - e_1 = \mu_1 \alpha_1^2,$$

where μ_1 is one of a finite set and α_1 is a number in $Q(e_1)$. A similar result holds if e_1 is replaced by e_2 or e_3, This proves the theorem.

The numbers $x - e$ do not form a multiplication group since the product of two such numbers need not be of the same form.

An addition process can be defined for the rational points giving them a group structure.

Thus we define $P_1 + P_2$, the sum of two rational points, as the image of P_{12} in the x axis and write $P_3 = P_1 + P_2$.

We can say that the rational point $P(x, y)$ is associated with the number $x - e$ and that P belongs to the class C if $x - e$ does.

Theorem 4

If P_1, P_2 belong to the classes C_1, C_2, then $P_1 + P_2$ belongs to the class $C_1 C_2$. This is obvious from equation (9).

Theorem 5

The point $P_2 = 2P_1$ belongs to the principal class, i.e. $x_2 - e = v^2$, where v is in $Q(e)$.

This is obvious from equation (14).

The converse of this theorem is given by

Theorem 6

If P_2 belongs to the principal class, there exists a rational point P_1 such that $P_2 = 2P_1$.

Let
$$x_2 - e = (A + Be + Ce^2)^2, \tag{15}$$

where A, B, C are rational numbers. This holds for $e = e_1, e_2, e_3$. On multiplying out, replacing e^3 by $h_2e + h_3$, and e^4 by $h_2e^2 + h_3e$, and equating coefficients of 1, e, e^2 on both sides,

$$A^2 + 2BCh_3 = x_2,$$

$$2AB + 2BCh_2 + C^2h_3 = -1, \tag{16}$$

$$B^2 + 2AC + C^2h_2 = 0.$$

On eliminating A from the second and third equations,

we have $$B^3 - h_2BC^2 - h_3C^3 = C,$$

or as $C \neq 0$, $$\frac{1}{C^2} = \left(\frac{B}{C}\right)^3 - h_2\left(\frac{B}{C}\right) - h_3.$$

Write $1/C = y_1$, $B/C = x_1$. Then x_1, y_1 is a rational solution of

$$y_1^2 = x_1^3 - h_2x - h_3. \tag{17}$$

The third equation in (16) gives $2Ay_1 + x_1^2 + h_2 = 0$. Then substituting for A, B, C,

$$A + Be + Ce^2 = \frac{-x_1^2 - h_2}{2y_1} + \frac{x_1}{y_1}e + \frac{e^2}{y_1},$$

and so from equations (15), (14), $x_2 = x_1$, and so $P_2 = 2P_1$.

Theorem 7

If P_1, P_2 belong to the same class, then

$$P_1 + P_2 = 2P_3,$$

where P_3 is also a rational point.

This is obvious from Theorems 4 and 6, since $P_1 + P_2$ belongs to the principal class.

Theorem 8

All the rational points on the curve $y^2 = x^3 - h_2x - h_3$ can be obtained from a finite number by the addition process.

We distribute all the rational points into classes putting in the same class all those points for which $x - e$ belongs to a given class as previously defined. From Theorem 3, the rational points then fall into a finite number of classes, and these may be represented by the points

$$A_1(x_1, y_1), A_2(x_2, y_2), \ldots, A_n(x_n, y_n).$$

We now apply the following reduction process to a rational point $P(x, y)$. We take the point $A = A_j$, say, belonging to the same class as P. Then from Theorem 7,

$$P + A_j = 2P_1, \tag{18}$$

with a rational point P_1. Similarly

$$P_1 + A_{j,1} = 2P_2,$$

where $A_{j,1}$ is one of the A's and P_2 is rational.

$$\dot{P}_s + \dot{A}_{j,s} = 2\dot{P}_{s+1},$$

where the P's are all rational points. Hence P is expressed linearly in terms of the A and P_{s+1}. Thus eliminating $P_1, P_2, \ldots, P_s$, we have

$$P + A_j + 2A_{j,1} + \cdots + 2^s A_{j,s} = 2^{s+1} P_{s+1}. \tag{19}$$

We prove now that the process leads after a finite number of steps to a point P_{s+1} also belonging to a finite set.

We change our notation slightly, i.e. write $(x/z^2, y/z^3)$ for (x, y) and now $(x, z) = (y, z) = 1$, and equation (7) in the form

$$y^2 z = x^3 - h_2 x z^4 - h_3 z^6,$$

so that the homogeneous coordinates of the point P are now (xz, y, z^3). We suppose that x, y, z are integers and that $(x, z) = 1$.

We turn now to equation (18) and consider the relation

$$P + A = 2P_1$$

connecting any three rational points P, A, P_1. Suppose that the coordinates of $P, A, P_1, 2P_1$ are $(x, y, z), (a, b, c), (x_1, y_1, z_1)$, and (X, Y, Z) respectively. Write $\mu = \max(|x|, z^2)$, $\alpha = \max(|a|, c^2)$, $\mu_1 = \max(|x_1|, z_1^2)$, $M = \max(|X|, Z^2)$.

Clearly $|y| = O(\mu^{3/2})$ where the constant in O (and hereafter) depends upon h_2, h_3. Here it can be taken as $(1 + |h_2| + |h_3|)^{1/2}$.

We require the abscissa of $P + A$. From equation (13), on using the homogeneous coordinates, we have

$$\frac{X}{Z^2} = \frac{(ax - h_2 c^2 z^2)(c^2 x + az^2) - 2h_3 c^4 z^2 - 2bcyz}{(c^2 x - az^2)^2}.$$

Since $(X, Z) = 1$, $|X|, |Z|$ are respectively less than the moduli of the numerator and denominator of the right-hand side. Hence

$$M = O(\mu^2).$$

We now prove that $\mu_1 = O(M^{1/4})$. The formula (14) gives

$$(X - eZ^2)^{1/2} = \frac{Z}{2y_1 z_1} (x_1^2 + h_2 z_1^4 - 2ex_1 z_1^2 - 2e^2 z_1^4)$$

$$= p + qe + re^2, \tag{20}$$

say. Since $(X - eZ^2)^{1/2}$ is an integer in K, so is $p + qe + re^2$. Hence if Δ is the discriminant of the e equation, $\Delta p, \Delta q, \Delta r$ are rational integers. So also are the numbers

$$\Delta(2p + h_2 r) = \frac{\Delta Z x_1^2}{y_1 z_1}, \quad \text{and} \quad -\Delta r = \frac{\Delta Z}{y_1 z_1} z_1^4.$$

Since $(x_1, z_1) = 1$, $\Delta Z / y_1 z_1$ is also an integer. Hence

$$x_1^2 \mid \Delta(2p + hr), \qquad z_1^4 \mid \Delta r.$$

But $\Delta(2p + h_2 r)$ and Δr can be expressed linearly in terms of $(X - eZ^2)^{1/2}$ with $e = e_1, e_2, e_3$, and so they are $O(\sqrt{M})$. Hence $x_1^2 = O(\sqrt{M})$, $z_1^4 = O(\sqrt{M})$, and so $\mu_1 = O(M^{1/4})$, and then $\mu_1 = O(\mu^{1/2})$.

Applying the same process to the equations similar to (18), and denoting the corresponding μ by $\mu_1, \mu_2, \ldots$, we have $\mu_{r+1} = O(\mu_r^{1/2})$. Such a sequence is bounded and so we come to a stage P_{s+1}, a point with bounded coordinates and so only with a finite number of possibilities for P_{s+1}. The theorem now follows from equation (19).

There is a simple analytical interpretation of these arithmetical results. The coordinates (x, y) of any point P on the curve

$$y^2 = x^3 - h_2 x - h_3$$

can be expressed in terms of an elliptic parameter u by means of

$$x = \wp(u), \qquad 2y = \wp'(u),$$

where $\wp(u)$ is the Weierstrass elliptic function with invariants $4h_2, 4h_3$ and periods ω_1, ω_2, say. Then there is a 1–1 correspondence between the elliptic parameter $u \bmod(\omega_1, \omega_2)$ and the points $P = P(u)$, say. Clearly the point $P(-u)$ is the image of $P(u)$ in the x axis.

The addition theorem for the elliptic function $\wp(u)$ shows that the three points with parameters u_1, u_2, u_3 are collinear if

$$u_1 + u_2 + u_3 \equiv 0 \pmod{\omega_1, \omega_2}.$$

We now define the sum $P_1 + P_2$ of two points $P_1(u_1)$ and $P_2(u_2)$ as the point with parameter $u_1 + u_2 = -u_3$. Hence the sum is the image in the x axis of $P_{1,2}$, the third point of intersection of the line P_1, P_2 with the cubic.

The finite basis theorem can now be stated in the form:

Theorem 9

All the rational points on the cubic (7) *are given parametrically by*

$$u = m_1 u_1 + \cdots + m_r u_r,$$

where $u_1, \ldots, u_r$ *are a fixed finite set and the m take all integer values.*

An infinity of rational points can be derived from a given one u unless there exists an integer n such that nu equals a period of the elliptic function and then u is of finite order and is called an exceptional point. The parameters u of the exceptional points form a finite Abelian group of the cubic.

The minimum number g of generators of infinite order of the basis is called the rank of the curve.

We have Nagell's

Theorem 10

If (x_1, y_1) is an exceptional point not at infinity of the curve

$$y^2 = x^3 - Ax - B,$$ (21)

where A, B are integers, then x_1, y_1 are integers and either $y_1 = 0$ or y_1^2 is a divisor of the discriminant $D = 4A^3 - 27B^2$.

It is an open question whether curves exist with an assigned number N of exceptional points. There exist a number of nonequivalent cubics with $N = 1, 2, 3, 4$ (cyclic or non-cyclic group), 5, 6, 7, 8 (cyclic or not), 9 (cyclic) 10, 12, 16 (non-cyclic), but none with N divisible by 11, 14, 15, 16 (cyclic) 20, 24, 32. For proofs and references, see Lind[6] and Nagell[10].

Estimates have been given by Billing[4] for g, the number of generators of infinite order for the rational points on a cubic curve in his comprehensive and valuable memoir. He has also found all the generators for $0 < |A|, |B| \leqslant 3$. Birch and Swinnerton-Dyer[5] have given g for most of the sets $0 < |A| \leqslant 20$, $0 < |B| \leqslant 30$, $|A| \leqslant 200$, $B = 0$.

3. Two particular cases of the equation (21) are of special interest and have been discussed by many writers, namely, the equation $y^2 = x^3 + k$ which will be discussed in Chapter 26, and the equation

$$y^2 = x^3 - Ax$$ (22)

which we deal with here. Many results have been found by Billing[4], Birch and Swinnerton-Dyer[5], and Lind[6]. The equation (22) is associated with the equation

$$Y^2 = X^3 + 4AX$$ (23)

by the relation

$$X = \frac{x^2 - A}{x}, \qquad Y = \frac{y(x^2 + A)}{x^2},$$ (24)

and so a solution of equation (23) can be derived from one of (22). Conversely on applying the transformation (24) to (23), a solution of (22) can be deduced from one of (23).

Further equation (22) is birationally related to the equation

$$X^4 + 4A = Z^2$$ (25)

by the relation

$$2x = X^2 - Z, \qquad y = Xx.$$

Billing[4] gives the basis points for equation (22) for $|A| \leq 50$ with, however, an error for $A = 33$. The range has been extended by Birch and Swinnerton-Dyer[5].

Lind[6] has dealt exhaustively with the question of finding values of A for which equations (22) and (23) have only exceptional solutions. His results depend upon the study of the equation (25) already considered in Chapter 4. He gives, *inter alia*, the instances

$$A = p, \qquad p \equiv \pm 3, -5 \text{ (mod 16)},$$

$$A = -p, \qquad p \equiv -5, 7 \text{ (mod 16)},$$

$$p \equiv 1 \text{ (mod 8)}, \quad \left(\frac{2}{p}\right)_4 = -1,$$

the symbol being a biquadratic character,

$$A = -2p, \quad p \equiv \pm 3 \text{ (mod 8)}.$$

He gives also results for $A = \pm pq, 2pq$, e.g. $A = pq, p \equiv 3 \text{ (mod 16)}$, $q \equiv -5 \text{ (mod 16)}$. Here p and q are either primes or cubes of primes.

4. Recently Birch and Swinnerton-Dyer[7] have found interesting results and conjectures for the number of generators of infinite order. These depend on the association of a curve with a congruence zeta-function of a complex variable s. This takes a comparatively simple form for the cubic curve.

$$y^2 = x^3 - Ax - B.$$

Let p be a prime and denote by $N_p - 1$ the number of solutions of the congruence

$$y^2 \equiv x^3 - Ax - B \text{ (mod } p).$$

Then

$$|N_p - p - 1| < 2\sqrt{p},$$

and excluding a finite number of exceptional values of p, the zeta function takes the form

$$f(s) = \prod_p (1 + (N_p - p - 1)p^{-s} + p^{1-2s}),$$

where the exceptional primes are excluded from the product. The product converges absolutely for $R(s) > 3/2$, and it has been conjectured by Hasse that $f(s)$ can be continued meromorphically over the whole plane. Then there is the

Conjecture
  The function $f(s)$ has at $s = 1$ a pole whose order is the number of generators of the rational points of infinite order.

They have given a great deal of numerical evidence in support of this remarkable conjecture for special cubics, for example, those with $AB = 0$. Confirmation[8] is also available for the equation

$$x^3 + y^3 = az^3.$$

Now N_p, where p is a prime, is the number of solutions of the congruence

$$x^3 + y^3 \equiv az^3 \pmod{p}.$$

The zeta function associated with the curve turns out to be

$$\zeta(s)\zeta(s - 1)/L_a(s),$$

where $\zeta(s)$ is the Riemann zeta-function, and $L_a(s)$ is a Hecke L series.

As above, the behaviour of $L_a(s)$ at $s = 1$ leads to the conjectures for the number g of generators of the rational solutions, i.e. $L_a(s)$ has a zero at $s = 1$ of order precisely g. This was verified for special values of cube-free $a = 2^r 3^s M$, $r, s = 0, 1$, when the product of the prime divisors $\neq 2, 3$ of M is < 100. There were 262 instances with $g = 0$, 297 with $g = 1$, 56 with $g = 2$, and 2 with $g = 3$.

It may be noted that Wiman[11,12,13] has constructed an infinity of non-equivalent cubics with $g = 4, 5$, and a number with $g = 6$.

As can be seen from Cassels'[9] exhaustive survey article, the question of the rational points on a cubic curve has of late engaged the attention of many mathematicians. No criterion, however, has actually been proved for determining whether such points exist. The recent work of Birch and Swinnerton-Dyer[7] leads to very useful empirical methods which are frequently successful in finding solutions.

The two last papers contain many references.

REFERENCES

1. L. J. Mordell. On the rational solutions of the indeterminate equations of the 3rd and 4th degrees. *Proc. Camb. Phil. Soc.*, **21** (1922), 179–192.
2. A. Weil. Sur un théorème de Mordell. *Bull. Sci. Math.*, (2) **54** (1930), 182–191.
3. T. Nagell. Solution de quelques problèmes dans la théorie arithmétique des cubiques planes du premier genre. *Vid. Akad. Skrifter Oslo*, I (1935), Nr 1.
4. G. Billing. Beiträge zur arithmetischen Theorie der ebenen kubischen Kurven vom Geschlecht Eins. *Nova Acta. Reg. Soc. Scient. Upsaliensis.*, ser IV. **11** (1938), Chapter IV.
5. B. Birch and H. P. F. Swinnerton-Dyer. Notes on elliptic curves I. *J. reine angew Math.*, **212** (1963), 7–25.
6. C. E. Lind. Untersuchungen uber die rationalen Punkte der ebenen kubischen Kurven vom Geschlecht Eins. *Dissertation, Uppsala* (1940).
7. B. Birch and H. P. F. Swinnerton-Dyer. Notes on elliptic curves II. *J. reine angew Math.*, **218** (1965), 79–108.
8. N. M. Stephens. Conjectures concerning elliptic curves. *Bull. Am. Math. Soc.*, **73** (1967), 160–163.

9. J. W.ʳ.S. Cassels. Diophantine equations with special reference to elliptic curves. *J. Lond. Math. Soc.*, **41** (1966), 193–291.

10. T. Nagell. Recherches sur l'arithmétique des cubiques planes du premier genre dans un domaine de rationalité quelconque. *Nova Acta Reg. Soc. Scient. Upsaliensis, Ser.* IV **15**, Nr 6, 1952.

11. A. Wiman. Über den Rang von den Kurven $y^2 = x(x + a)(x + b)$. *Acta Math.*, **76** (1944), 225–251.

12. A. Wiman. Über rationale Punkte auf den Kurven $y^2 = x(x^2 - a^2)$. *Acta Math.*, **77** (1945), 281–320.

13. A. Wiman. Über rationale Punkte auf Kurven dritter Ordnung vom Geschlechte Eins. *Acta Math.*, **80** (1948), 223–257.

CHAPTER 17

Rational Points on Curves of Genus $g = 0$ or 1 and $g > 1$

1. Let $f(x, y, z) = 0$ be the equation in homogeneous coordinates x, y, z of an irreducible curve of the nth degree where f is a homogeneous polynomial of degree n with rational coefficients. Such polynomials or curves will be called rational. The general polynomial of degree n contains $\frac{1}{2}(n + 1)(n + 2)$ terms.

A curve of degree n is in general uniquely defined by $\frac{1}{2}n(n + 3)$ linearly-independent linear conditions on its coefficients, for example, if it is to pass through $\frac{1}{2}n(n + 3)$ points. This, however, is not always so. Thus a cubic curve is in general determined by nine points, but an infinity of cubics $S_1 + kS_2 = 0$, where k is an arbitrary parameter, pass through the nine points of intersection of the cubics $S_1 = 0$, $S_2 = 0$.

Definition

A point on the curve $f = f(x, y, z) = 0$ which also satisfies the equations

$$\frac{\partial f}{\partial x} = 0, \qquad \frac{\partial f}{\partial y} = 0, \qquad \frac{\partial f}{\partial z} = 0, \tag{1}$$

is called a singular point.

Such a point is called a double point if it does not also satisfy all of the six equations typified by $\partial^2 f/\partial x^2 = 0$, $\partial^2 f/\partial x \partial y = 0$. We shall consider only curves all of whose singular points, say N in number, are double points. Then each such point is counted at least twice in the number of intersections of $f = 0$ with another curve. The singular points of a rational curve are determined by rational equations, and so all the symmetric functions of the co-ordinates of these N points are rational numbers. A set of n points with such a property will be called a rational n set.

Theorem 1

$$N \leqslant \tfrac{1}{2}(n - 1)(n - 2). \tag{2}$$

For if $N > \frac{1}{2}(n - 1)(n - 2)$, a curve of degree $n - 2$ can be drawn through $\frac{1}{2}(n - 1)(n - 2) + 1$ of the double points, and any other $n - 3$ points of the curve $f = 0$ of degree n, since

$$\tfrac{1}{2}(n - 2)(n + 1) = \tfrac{1}{2}(n - 1)(n - 2) + 1 + n - 3.$$

These two curves would intersect in at least

$$n - 3 + (n - 1)(n - 2) + 2 = n^2 - 2n + 1 > n^2 - 2n$$

points. This is impossible by Bezout's theorem.

Hence an integer $p > 0$, called the genus of the curve, is defined by

$$N = \tfrac{1}{2}(n - 1)(n - 2) - p. \tag{3}$$

Definition

A curve passing through the N double points of the curve $f = 0$ is called an adjoint curve of f.

When the double points form a rational set, the conditions on the adjoint curve can be expressed linearly with rational coefficients in terms of the coefficients of the adjoint curve, which are supposed hereafter to be rational numbers.

We recall that two curves $f(x, y, z) = 0$, $F(X, Y, Z) = 0$ can be birationally transformed into each other if their points, except for a finite number, are connected by a relation of the form,

$$x = A(X, Y, Z), \qquad y = B(X, Y, Z), \qquad z = C(X, Y, Z),$$
$$X = a(x, y, z), \qquad Y = b(x, y, z), \qquad Z = c(x, y, z),$$

where A's etc. are polynomials in the arguments X, Y, Z, etc. This is a 1–1 correspondence, except for the singular points. Such curves have the same genus. When rational, they are called equivalent if the polynomials A, a, etc. have rational coefficients.

It is well known that a curve with singularities of order greater than two can be transformed by a birational transformation into a curve with only double points.

2. A fundamental result due to Hilbert and Hurwitz[1] is given by

Theorem 2

Every rational curve C of degree n and genus zero is equivalent to a rational curve of degree $n - 2$ and genus zero.

An adjoint curve of degree $n - 2$ can be made to pass through $n - 2$ further points, for example, arbitrary rational points, or a rational $n - 2$ point set, since

$$\tfrac{1}{2}(n - 2)(n + 1) = \tfrac{1}{2}(n - 1)(n - 2) + n - 2.$$

Hence a family of adjoint curves of degree $n - 2$ is given by

$$\lambda_1 \phi_1 + \lambda_2 \phi_2 + \cdots + \lambda_{n-1} \phi_{n-1} = 0,$$

where the λ are arbitrary constants, and the ϕ are rational polynomials in x, y, z of degree $n - 2$. By the choice of the $n - 2$ points defining the ϕ, we may suppose that the ϕ are irreducible and linearly independent.

Define a curve C_1 by

$$\frac{\xi_1}{\phi_1} = \frac{\xi_2}{\phi_2} = \cdots = \frac{\xi_{n-1}}{\phi_{n-1}},$$

where the ξ are homogeneous coordinates in $n - 2$ dimensional space. Then C_1 is of degree $n - 2$. For it meets an arbitrary hyperplane

$$\lambda_1 \xi_1 + \cdots + \lambda_{n-1} \xi_{n-1} = 0$$

in points determined by the intersection of

$$\lambda_1 \phi_1 + \cdots + \lambda_{n-1} \phi_{n-1} = 0,$$

a curve of degree $n - 2$, and $f(x, y, z) = 0$, a curve of degree n. Of these $n(n - 2)$ intersections, $(n - 1)(n - 2)$ are given by the double points leaving $n - 2$ variable intersections depending on the λ and forming a rational set. Thus if we take any two of the equations, say

$$\frac{\xi_1}{\phi_1} = \frac{\xi_2}{\phi_2} = \frac{\xi_3}{\phi_3},$$

we have, on eliminating x, y, z, a curve of degree $n - 2$

$$g(\xi_1, \xi_2, \xi_3) = 0.$$

The transformation is birational in the ξ and x, y, z.

It follows that a rational curve of odd degree and genus zero has an infinity of rational points since it is equivalent to a line.

A rational curve C of even degree and genus zero is equivalent to a conic. If the conic has one rational point, it has an infinity of rational points and so does C. If the conic has no rational points, the only possible rational points on C are the singular points, since these have been excluded in the birational transformation.

It may be remarked that the conic, and so also the curve C, have an infinity of rational 2 sets, i.e. points (x_1, y_1) and (x_2, y_2) for which $x_1 + x_2, x_1 x_2,$ $y_1 + y_2, y_1 y_2$ are all rational. This is obvious from the intersection of a conic $f(x, y) = 0$ and an arbitrary line $lx + my + n = 0$. It becomes a difficult question if the solutions are required to be in a given quadratic field.

A quartic curve of genus zero whose only possible rational points are its singular points is easily[1] constructed.

Let F, F_1, F_2, F_3 be four homogeneous rational quadratic forms, and L a linear rational form, in x, y, z. Suppose that $F = 0$ has no rational points, that $F_1 = 0$ and $F_2 = 0$ each pass through the intersection of $F = 0, L = 0$, that F, F_1, F_2 are linearly independent, and that $F_3 = 0$ does not pass through either point of intersection.

The quartic is given by

$$F(X, Y, Z) = 0, \quad X = F_1(x, y, z), \quad Y = F_2(x, y, z), \quad Z = F_3(x, y, z).$$

The curve is of genus zero since X, Y, Z, and so x, y, z, can be expressed in terms of a variable t but with algebraic coefficients. The two intersections of $F(x, y, z) = 0$ and $L(x, y, z) = 0$ both give $X = Y = Z = 0$ and so this must be a double point on $F(X, Y, Z) = 0$. Rational points on $F(X, Y, Z) = 0$ other than the singular points would lead to rational points on $F(x, y, z) = 0$.

3. Results for curves of genus >0 have been given by Poincaré[2].

Theorem 3

Every rational curve C of genus one and degree $n > 3$, which has a rational point P, is equivalent to a cubic curve.

The curve has $\tfrac{1}{2}n(n - 3)$ double points since

$$1 = \tfrac{1}{2}(n - 1)(n - 2) - \tfrac{1}{2}n(n - 3).$$

Draw an adjoint curve of degree $n - 2$ which meets the curve C in three points at P. Its equation contains $n - 4$ arbitrary constants since

$$\tfrac{1}{2}(n - 2)(n + 1) - \tfrac{1}{2}n(n - 3) - 3 = n - 4.$$

The adjoint meets C in a rational $n - 3$ set since

$$n(n - 2) - n(n - 3) - 3 = n - 3.$$

We now draw another adjoint curve of degree $n - 2$ through the rational $n - 3$ set. This family of adjoint curves involves two arbitrary parameters since

$$\tfrac{1}{2}(n - 2)(n + 1) - \tfrac{1}{2}n(n - 3) - (n - 3) = 2,$$

and so takes the form

$$\lambda_1\phi_1 + \lambda_2\phi_2 + \lambda_3\phi_3 = 0,$$

where the λ are rational. These adjoints intersect C in a rational 3 set since

$$n(n - 2) - n(n - 3) - (n - 3) = 3.$$

Then
$$\xi_1:\xi_2:\xi_3 = \phi_1:\phi_2:\phi_3$$

is a birational transformation with rational coefficients which changes C into a cubic curve.

4. Very little is known about the rational points on curves of genus >1. It may be that some curves of genus two or three are more amenable to attack, and so two well known relevant results in algebraic function theory may be mentioned.

Theorem 4

A rational curve of genus two is equivalent to a curve

$$y^2 = a_0x^6 + a_1x^5 + \cdots + a_6.$$

Theorem 5

The quartic curve

$$ax^4 + by^4 + cz^4 + 2fy^2z^2 + 2gz^2x^2 + 2hx^2y^2 = 0$$

is in general of genus three.

Mordell put forward in 1922, the

Conjecture

There are only a finite number of rational points on a curve of genus > 1.

Much attention has been given to this in recent years but it is still unproved. There are not known many non-trivial instances of this conjecture apart from those given by Fermat's last theorem. The known results for the quartic above are found by replacing z^2 by z and so reducing the problem to that of rational points on a curve of genus 1.

In Chapter 4 a quartic curve of genus three was given which has no rational points except trivial ones.

Some curves of genus two which have no rational points have been found by Mordell[3]. The equations may be written in the form

$$z^2 = (a_1x^2 + b_1y^2)(a_2x^2 + b_2y^2)(a_3x^2 + b_3y^2),$$

where the a and b are integers and are all positive, except that in one pair, a and b may have opposite signs.

Theorem 6

The equation (4) *has no integer solutions except* $(0, 0, 0)$ *if all the following conditions are satisfied:*

(i) $a_1 + a_2 + a_3 \equiv -1 \pmod 4$, $b_1 + b_2 + b_3 \equiv 0 \pmod 4$,

(ii) *only one b is even,*

(iii) *none of the sets* $a_1, a_2, a_3,$ *or* $a_1 + b_1, a_2 + b_2, a_3 + b_3,$ *are congruent* mod 4 *to* 1, 1, 1, *or to a permutation of* $(0, 1, 2)$.

(iv) $a_2b_3 - a_3b_2, a_3b_1 - a_1b_3, a_1b_2 - a_2b_1$ *have no common divisor, and all their odd factors are* $\equiv 1 \pmod 4$.

The equations so found are of special interest since they may be everywhere locally solvable.

Suppose that $(x, y) = 1$. Then we easily deduce that

$$a_1x^2 + b_1y^2 = d_2d_3z_1^2,$$
$$a_2x^2 + b_2y^2 = d_3d_1z_2^2,$$
$$a_3x^2 + b_3z^2 = d_1d_2z_3^2,$$

where $d_1 \,|\, a_2b_3 - a_3b_2$, etc.

Two cases arise according as all or only two of the d are odd.

In the first case,

$$z_1^2 \equiv a_1 x^2 + b_1 y^2,$$
$$z_2^2 \equiv a_2 x^2 + b_2 y^2, \quad (\mathrm{mod}\ 4)$$
$$z_3^2 \equiv a_3 x^2 + b_3 y^2.$$

By addition

$$z_1^2 + z_2^2 + z_3^2 + x^2 \equiv 0\ (\mathrm{mod}\ 4).$$

Either $z_1 \equiv z_2 \equiv z_3 \equiv x \equiv 0\ (\mathrm{mod}\ 2)$, and since at least one b is odd, $y \equiv 0\ (\mathrm{mod}\ 2)$ and so $(x, y) \neq 1$; or $z_1 \equiv z_2 \equiv x_3 \equiv x \equiv 1\ (\mathrm{mod}\ 2)$. Then according as y is odd or even,

$$a_1 + b_1 \equiv a_2 + b_2 \equiv a_3 + b_3 \equiv 1\ (\mathrm{mod}\ 4),$$

or

$$a_1 \equiv a_2 \equiv a_3 \equiv 1\ (\mathrm{mod}\ 4),$$

and these have been excluded by (iii).

The case when, say d_3, is even can be dealt with similarly. A simple numerical illustration is given by

$$(a_1, a_2, a_3) = (4a + 1, 3, 4b + 3), \quad (b_1, b_2, b_3) = (2, 1, 1).$$

Then the only condition to be satisfied is that the odd factors of $5 - 4a$, $8b - 4a + 5$ should be $\equiv 1\ (\mathrm{mod}\ 4)$. Some instances are given by $(a, b) = (0, 1), (1, 2), (-2, 2)$.

These equations are everywhere locally solvable, that is, as a congruence mod p^r, p a prime. On giving x or y a fixed value, the curve has genus two, and it is easily shown by Weil's theorem, that the congruences are solvable for $p > 17$. The smaller values of p must be considered separately.

New results[4,5,6] of considerable interest have been found very recently concerning rational points on some curves of genus greater than one. Moreover the methods suffice to determine the points and these are also shown to be finite in number.

Let $f(x, y) = 0$ be a curve Γ with coefficients and variables defined in an algebraic number field K or in a finite extension of K. Let a rational mapping ϕ, defined over K of Γ into a curve Γ_1 of genus one be given by

$$\phi : \{u, v\} = \{M_1(x, y), M_2(x, y)\}.$$

The mappings when $M_1(x, y)$, $M_2(x, y)$ are constant, form a subgroup G of the group Φ of the mappings, and this is the group of the rational points of Γ_1. The mappings are called independent if their images in Γ_1 are linearly independent from the view point of the group law of addition of the points of Γ_1. Then if the rank of the quotient group Φ/G is greater than the rank of the generators of G_1, there are only a finite number of points in K on Γ and these can be effectively determined.

Illustrations are given by

$$\Gamma: x^4 + y^4 = A, \qquad \Gamma_1: u^4 + v^2 = A,$$

with the two independent mappings.

$$\phi_1: \{u, v\} = \{x, y^2\}, \qquad \phi_2: \{u, v\} = \{y, x^2\}$$

if G has at most one generator,
and by

$$\Gamma: x^6 + y^6 = A, \quad G: u^3 + v^2 = A, \quad \text{or} \quad u^3 + 1 = Av^2 \quad \text{or} \quad v^2 + 1 = Au^3,$$

with the respective mappings,

$$\{u, v\} = \{x^2, y^3\}, \{x^2/y^2, 1/y^3\}, \{x^3/y^3, 1/y^2\}$$

if any of the G have at most two generators.

A simplified version has just been given by Cassels[7].

REFERENCES

1. D. Hilbert and A. Hurwitz. Über die diophantischen Gleichungen von Geschlecht Null. *Acta. Math.*, **14** (1890), 217–224.
2. H. Poincaré. Sur les propriétés arithmétiques des courbes algébriques. *J. Math.* (3), **7** (1901), 161–233.
3. L. J. Mordell. On some sextic diophantine equations of genus two. *Proc. Amer. Math. Soc.*, 1969–1970.
4. V. A. Demjanenko. Rational points on some classes of algebraic curves. (Russian) *Izvestija Akad. Nauk.* (*ser. Mat.*), **30** (1966), 1373–1396.
5. J. I. Manin. The Tate height of points on an Abelian variety, its variants and applications. (Russian) *Izvestija Akad. Nauk.* (*ser. Mat.*), **28** (1964), 1363–1390.
6. V. A. Demjanenko. Rational points on some curves of higher genus. (Russian) *Acta. Arith.*, **12** (1967), 333–354.
7. J. W. S. Cassels. On a theorem of Demjanenko. *J. Lond. Math. Soc.*, **43** (1968), 61–66.

CHAPTER 18

Representation of Numbers by Homogeneous Forms in Two Variables

1. Problem

Let
$$f(x, y) = a_0 x^n + a_1 x^{n-1} y + \cdots + a_n y^n, \tag{1}$$

where the a are integers, and $(a_0, a_1, \ldots, a_n) = 1$. To solve in integers x, y,
$$f(x, y) = m, \tag{2}$$

where m is any given integer.

If $m = 0$, the only solution is $x = y = 0$ unless $f(x, y)$ has a rational linear factor and then the solution is obvious. We suppose hereafter that $m \neq 0$.

The solution of $f(x, y) = m$ is equivalent to the solution of any other equation $F(X, Y) = m$ if we can establish a 1–1 correspondence between integer sets (x, y) and (X, Y). Such a one is given by the substitution

$$S\begin{pmatrix} \alpha, \beta \\ \gamma, \delta \end{pmatrix}, \quad x = \alpha X + \beta Y, \quad y = \gamma X + \delta Y, \text{ i.e. } \begin{pmatrix} x \\ y \end{pmatrix} = \begin{pmatrix} \alpha, \beta \\ \gamma, \delta \end{pmatrix} \begin{pmatrix} X \\ Y \end{pmatrix}, \tag{3}$$

if $\alpha, \beta, \gamma, \delta$ are integers and

$$\Delta = \alpha\delta - \beta\gamma = \pm 1.$$

These conditions are necessary and sufficient. For on putting $(X, Y) = (1, 0)$ and $(0, 1)$, then $\alpha, \beta, \gamma, \delta$ are integers. On putting $(x, y) = (1, 0)$ and $(0, 1)$, then $\alpha/\Delta, \beta/\Delta, \gamma/\Delta, \delta/\Delta$ and so $(\alpha\delta - \beta\gamma)/\Delta^2 = \pm 1/\Delta$ are integers. Hence $\Delta = \pm 1$.

It suffices to consider only the case $\Delta = 1$. Then the forms $f(x, y)$ and $F(X, Y) = f(\alpha X + \beta Y, \gamma X + \delta Y)$ are called equivalent. We write

$$f(x, y) \sim F(x, y),$$

and say that all the forms equivalent to a given form define a class of forms. The concept $\sim$ of equivalence satisfies the usual equivalence axioms.

We need only consider solutions with $(x, y) = 1$. For if $(x, y) = d$, $x = dX, y = dY$ then

$$f(X, Y) = m/d^n,$$

and so only a finite number of values of d arise.

6*

We show that the solution of equation (2) can be reduced to the case when $m = 1$. We may suppose that $(a_0, m) = 1$ by means of a unimodular substitution if need be. We may also suppose that $(y, m) = 1$ on writing dy for y when $(y, m) = d$. For any such solution (x_0, y_0), we can find l so that $x_0 \equiv ly_0 \pmod{m}$ and $f(l, 1) \equiv 0 \pmod{m}$. Then the substitution

$$x = lX + mY, \qquad y = X,$$

gives an equation (2) in which m divides out. There are as many such equations as there are roots of the congruence $f(l, 1) \equiv 0 \pmod{m}$.

Invariants

When $f(x, y) \sim F(x, y)$, algebraic theory shows that certain functions of the coefficients of $f(x, y)$, say, $I(f)$, are unaltered by the substitutions of determinant unity.

Thus if $I_1(f) = I_1(F), \quad I_2(f) = I_2(F), \quad \ldots,$

then $I_1, I_2, \ldots$, are called invariants of $f(x, y)$.

There are also certain functions of the coefficients and the variables, say $J(x, y, f)$, which are unaltered by the substitution. Thus if

$$J(x, y, f) = J(X, Y, F),$$

J is called a covariant of $f(x, y)$.

If, however, $f(x, y)$, $F(x, y)$ have the same invariants and covariants, it does not necessarily follow that $f(x, y) \sim F(x, y)$. There arises the following

Problem

To construct all the forms with a given set of invariants and covariants, and then to separate these into classes of non-equivalent forms.

This is facilitated by picking out a suitable representative of each class of equivalent forms, say a reduced form, and preferably in such a way that, firstly, its coefficients are bounded in terms of the invariants, and secondly that there is only one reduced form in each class.

This leads to other questions:

I. the discussion of the minimum value of $|f(x, y)|$ for integer values of x, y not both zero.

   This question is a particular case of a general problem in the Geometry of Numbers or in Diophantine Approximation.

II. to investigate whether the number of classes is finite.

III. to find all the substitutions S changing $f(x, y)$ into an equivalent form $F(X, Y)$.

Those substitutions, say A, for which $f(x, y) = f(X, Y)$, are called the automorphs of $f(x, y)$. Then all the S are given by

$$S = AS_1,$$

where S_1 is any particular substitution changing $f(x, y)$ into $F(X, Y)$.

We now come back to

$$f(x, y) = m, \quad (x, y) = 1.$$

Suppose that a particular solution is given by $(x, y) = (\alpha, \gamma)$. Take any two integers β, δ such that $\alpha\delta - \beta\gamma = 1$. As before, denote by S the substitution

$$x = \alpha X + \beta Y, \qquad y = \gamma X + \delta Y.$$

Then

$$f(x, y) = F(X, Y). \tag{4}$$

say, and the coefficient of the highest power of X in $F(X, Y)$ is m. Hence we must now construct the forms $F(X, Y)$ whose leading coefficient is mX^n and which has the same invariants and covariants as $f(x, y)$. We must then find those of the $F(X, Y)$ which are equivalent to $f(x, y)$. If S above is the corresponding substitution, then $(x, y) = (\alpha, \gamma)$ gives a representation of m by $f(x, y)$.

We have the same representation independently of the choice of β, δ. All the solutions β', δ' of $\alpha\delta - \beta\gamma = 1$ are given by $\beta' = \beta + t\alpha$, $\delta' = \delta + t\gamma$, where β, δ is a fixed solution, and t is any integer. We have now the substitution

$$x = \alpha(X + tY) + \beta Y, \qquad y = \gamma(X + tY) + \delta Y,$$

and so

$$f(x, y) = F(X + tY, Y) \sim F(X, Y).$$

Hence the same solution (α, γ) arises from $F(X, Y)$ and $F(X + tY, Y)$.

2. We give now a brief résumé of the results for the binary quadratic form

$$f(x, y) = ax^2 + bxy + cy^2. \tag{5}$$

These are given in the usual textbooks.

There is a single invariant

$$d = b^2 - 4ac. \tag{6}$$

If $d < 0$, the form is definite and it suffices to consider only the case $a > 0$, i.e. a positive definite form. The reduced form satisfies

$$c \geqslant a \geqslant |b|, \quad \text{whence} \quad a \leqslant \sqrt{(-d/3)}, \tag{7}$$

and so the number of classes of forms of discriminant d is finite. These conditions define a unique reduced form except when $c = a$ or $b = \pm a$. We then have a unique reduced form if we impose the supplementary condition $b > 0$.

It suffices to consider primitive forms, i.e. those with $(a, b, c) = 1$.

The automorphs are easily found.

When $d < -4$, these are

$$\begin{pmatrix} \pm 1 & 0 \\ 0 & \pm 1 \end{pmatrix}.$$

When $d = -4$, there are also two further ones

$$\begin{pmatrix} 0, & \pm 1 \\ \pm 1, & 0 \end{pmatrix}.$$

When $d = -3$, there are the four further ones

$$\begin{pmatrix} 0, & \mp 1 \\ \pm 1, & \pm 1 \end{pmatrix}, \qquad \begin{pmatrix} \pm 1, & \pm 1 \\ \mp 1, & 0 \end{pmatrix}.$$

When $d > 0$, the form is indefinite. Write

$$f = \frac{-b + \sqrt{d}}{2a}, \qquad s = \frac{-b - \sqrt{d}}{2a}. \tag{8}$$

The form $f(x, y)$ is called reduced if $|f| < 1, |s| > 1, fs < 0$. These conditions are equivalent to

$$0 < \sqrt{d} - b < 2|a| < \sqrt{d} + b. \tag{9}$$

This implies $b < \sqrt{d}$, and so the number of classes of forms of discriminant d is finite. Now there is not a unique reduced form but a chain of reduced forms, and two forms are equivalent if and only if their reduced forms occur in the same chain.

The automorphs of a primitive form are given by

$$A = \begin{pmatrix} \alpha, & \beta \\ \gamma, & \delta \end{pmatrix}$$

where $\alpha = \frac{1}{2}(t - bu)$, $\beta = -cu$, $\gamma = \delta u$, $\delta = \frac{1}{2}(t + bu)$,

where t, u run through the integer solutions of $X^2 - dY^2 = 4$. Denote by T, U that solution with least positive X and Y. Then

$$\frac{t + u\sqrt{d}}{2} = \pm\left(\frac{T + U\sqrt{d}}{2}\right)^n, \quad n = 0, \pm 1, \pm 2, \ldots \tag{10}$$

gives all the solutions for t, u.

We remark that in the quadratic field $R(\sqrt{d})$, where d has no squared factors, the units, i.e. the algebraic integers ε satisfying $N(\varepsilon) = \pm 1$, are given by $\varepsilon = \pm\eta^n$, $n = 0, \pm 1, \pm 2, \ldots$, where η is the fundamental unit. When

$d \equiv 1 \pmod 4$, $\quad \varepsilon = x + y\left(\dfrac{1 + \sqrt{d}}{2}\right)$, $\quad x^2 + xy + y^2\left(\dfrac{1 - d}{4}\right) = \pm 1$,

$d \equiv 2, 3 \pmod 4$, $\quad \varepsilon = x + y\sqrt{d}$, $\qquad\qquad x^2 - dy^2 = \pm 1$,

where x, y are integers and the minus sign is taken if the corresponding equation is solvable.

The solution of $f(x, y) = m$, where m is square free, requires the construction of forms

$$F(x, y) = mx^2 + Bxy + Cy^2$$

equivalent to $f(x, y)$. Since

$$B^2 - 4mC = d, \qquad \frac{B^2 - d}{4m} = C,$$

a necessary condition for the representation is that there exist integers B for which C is an integer. In particular, d must be a quadratic residue of every odd prime factor p of m, i.e. $(d/p) = 1$. No other conditions arise when m is odd since $d \equiv 0, 1 \pmod 4$.

Two simple illustrations may suffice:

$$d = -4, \qquad \frac{B^2 + 4}{4m} = C.$$

If m is odd, every prime factor p of m must satisfy $(-1/p) = 1$, i.e. $p \equiv 1 \pmod 4$. Since there is only one class of forms when $d = -4$, typified by $x^2 + y^2$, every such odd number m can be represented as $x^2 + y^2 = m$.

$$d = 8, \qquad \frac{B^2 - 8}{4m} = C.$$

If m is odd, every prime factor p of m must satisfy $(2/p) = 1$, i.e. $p \equiv \pm 1 \pmod 8$. Since there is only one class of forms when $d = 8$, every such m can be represented as $x^2 - 2y^2 = m$.

If the number of classes of forms with discriminant d is greater than 1, it is in general a very difficult problem to determine which of the classes represents m.

3. We shall now give Hermite's[1,2] method of reducing the general binary form. Considerable numerical work may be required in applying it except perhaps for the binary cubic which will be dealt with separately further on.

Theorem 1

The binary forms with integer coefficients,

$$f(x, y) = a_0 x^n + a_1 x^{n-1} + \cdots + a_n y^n, \tag{11}$$

with given invariants, can be arranged in a finite number of classes.

We may suppose that $a_0 \neq 0$. Suppose that $f(x, y)$ has λ real linear factors $x + \alpha_i y$, and μ pairs of conjugate imaginary factors $x + \beta_j y$, $x + \gamma_j y$. Consider the quadratic form

$$g(x, y) = \sum_{i=1}^{\lambda} t_i^2 (x + \alpha_i y)^2 + 2 \sum_{j=1}^{\mu} u_j^2 (x + \beta_j y)(x + \gamma_j y), \tag{12}$$

where the t and u are real positive variables. Let the unimodular integral substitutions;

$$x = pX + qY, \qquad y = rX + sY,$$

change $f(x, y)$ into the equivalent form

$$F(X, Y) = A_0 X^n + A_1 X^{n-1} Y + \cdots + A_n Y^n.$$

Then
$$A_0 = a_0 \prod_{i=1}^{\lambda} (p + \alpha_i r) \prod_{j=1}^{\mu} (p + \beta_j r)(p + \gamma_j r).$$

Let S change $g(x, y)$ into, say,

$$G(X, Y) = \sum_{i=1}^{\lambda} T_i^2 (X + \alpha_i' Y)^2 + 2 \sum_{j=1}^{\mu} U_j^2 (X + \beta_j' Y)(X + \gamma_j' Y), \qquad (13)$$

$$= PX^2 + QXY + RY^2, \qquad (14)$$

of discriminant D.

We note that the set of forms $g(x, y)$ corresponding to real t, u, is the same as the set of forms $G(X, Y)$ corresponding to real T, U. For

$$x + \alpha y = (p + \alpha r)X + (q + \alpha s)Y,$$

and so we need only write

$$t_i(p + \alpha_i r) = T_i, \qquad u_j^2(p + \beta_j r)(p + \gamma_j r) = U_j^2. \qquad (15)$$

Then, say,

$$\frac{A_0}{T_1 \ldots T_\lambda U_1^2 \ldots U_\mu^2} = \frac{a_0}{t_1 \ldots t_\lambda u_1^2 \ldots u_\mu^2} = \frac{a_0}{h(t, u)}. \qquad (16)$$

We shall now show that the coefficients t, u can be chosen so that $g(x, y)$ is a real quadratic covariant of $f(x, y)$. We then call $F(X, Y)$ reduced if the quadratic form $G(X, Y)$ is reduced. We show that in this case the coefficients $A_0, A_1, \ldots, A_n$ are bounded in terms of the invariants of $f(x, y)$.

From equation (13),

$$P = T_1^2 + \cdots + T_\lambda^2 + 2U_1^2 + \cdots + 2U_\mu^2,$$

$$R = \alpha_1'^2 T_1^2 + \cdots + \alpha_\lambda'^2 T_\lambda^2 + 2\beta_1' \gamma_1' U_1^2 + \cdots + 2\beta_\mu' \gamma_\mu' U_\mu^2.$$

Put $T_1 = \xi_1 \sqrt{P}, \qquad U_1 = \eta_1 \sqrt{P}$, etc.

$$\alpha' T_1 = \phi \sqrt{R}, \qquad \beta' U_1 = \psi_1 \sqrt{R} \, e^{iw}, \qquad \gamma' Y_1 = \psi_1 \sqrt{R} \, e^{-iw},$$

etc., where ψ, etc. are real. Then

$$\xi_1^2 + \cdots + \xi_\lambda^2 + 2\eta_1^2 + \cdots + 2\eta_\mu^2 = 1, \qquad (17)$$

$$\phi_1^2 + \cdots + \phi_\lambda^2 + 2\psi_1^2 + \cdots + 2\psi_\mu^2 = 1. \qquad (18)$$

Here the ξ, η, ϕ, ψ are positive variables.

Now

$$T_1 \ldots T_\lambda U_1^2 \ldots U_\mu^2 F(X, Y)$$

$$= A_0 \prod_{i=1}^{\lambda} (T_i X + \alpha_1' T_i Y) \prod_{j=1}^{\mu} (U_j X + \beta_j' U_j Y)(U_j X + \gamma_j' U_j Y),$$

or

$$F(X, Y) = \frac{A_0}{h(T, U)} \prod_{i=1}^{\lambda} (\xi_i \sqrt{P}\, X + \phi_i \sqrt{R}\, Y) \times$$

$$\prod_{j=1}^{\mu} (\eta_j \sqrt{P}\, X + e^{iw_j}\psi_j \sqrt{R}\, Y)(\eta_j \sqrt{P}\, X + e^{-iw_j}\psi_j \sqrt{R}\, Y).$$

Hence we can write for $0 \leqslant m \leqslant n$,

$$A_m A_{n-m} = \frac{A_0^2 (PR)^{n/2}}{h(T, U)^2} \, \Omega(\xi, \eta, \phi, \psi, w),$$

where Ω is a real polynomial in ξ, η, ϕ, ψ. Then as seen from equations (17) and (18), Ω has an attained maximum value Ω_0 depending only on n.

Suppose now that $G(X, Y)$ is reduced. Then $PR \leqslant \frac{1}{3}D$, and so

$$|A_m A_{n-m}| \leqslant \left(\frac{1}{3}\right)^{n/2} \Omega_0 \frac{A_0^2 D^{n/2}}{h(T, U)^2}.$$

The discriminant D involves only the T, U and so we take for T, U such values as make

$$E = D^{n/2} A_0^2 / h(T, U)^2$$

a minimum. This process defines a quadratic covariant of $f(x, y)$.

It does not follow at once that the inequality above establishes bounds for A_m since A_{n-m} may be zero. This difficulty was noted by Julia [3] who produced a satisfactory treatment based upon the principles given in Hermite's first paper.

REFERENCES

1. C. Hermite. Note sur la réduction des fonctions homogènes à coefficients entiers et à deux indéterminées. *Oeuvres*, **1** (1905), 84–93.
2. C. Hermite. Sur l'introduction des variables continues dans la théorie des nombres. *Oeuvres*, **1** (1905), 173–178.
3. G. Julia. Étude sur les formes binaires non quadratiques. *Mem. Acad. Sci. l'Inst. France*, **55** (1917), 1–293.

CHAPTER 19

Representation of Numbers by Special Binary Quadratic and Quaternary Quadratic Forms

1. We deal here with the representation of numbers by special quadratic forms in 2 and 4 variables. Such questions are included in the general theory of the representation of numbers by quadratic forms which is discussed in Chapters 18 and 20. Many results however can be found very simply without using the general theory, and this had been long known when $a = b = 1$. The method now expounded is due to Thue, who applied it in a few instances, as did also Nagell, but it is capable of wider application.

The equation

$$ax^2 + by^2 = m.$$

We suppose that $m > 0$ and that $(ab, m) = 1$.

Write
$$f(x, y) = ax^2 + by^2 = m, \tag{1}$$

We shall suppose that $(x, y) = 1$ and so $(xy, m) = 1$.

Solvability of equation (1), if $(x, y) = 1$, implies the existence of an integer k such that

$$ak^2 + b \equiv 0 \ (\text{mod } m). \tag{2}$$

This imposes conditions on a and b. Thus if m is odd, the Legendre symbol $(-ab/p) = 1$ for every prime p dividing m. We first prove the [1,2]

Theorem 1

If the congruence

$$ak^2 + b \equiv 0 \ (\text{mod } m)$$

is solvable, integers x, y, not both zero, exist such that

$$ax^2 + by^2 = Mm \tag{3}$$

for some integer M with $M < 2\sqrt{ab}$ if $a > 0, b > 0$, and $|M| < \sqrt{|ab|}$ if $ab < 0$.

Put $x = kX + mY, y = X$. Then by Minkowski's theorem on linear forms in Chapter 5, there exist integers $(X, Y) \neq (0, 0)$ such that

$$|x| < l\sqrt{m}, \qquad |y| \leqslant l^{-1}\sqrt{m},$$

where l is any positive constant.

Hence if $a > 0$, $b > 0$,

$$f(x, y) < (al^2 + b/l^2)m < 2\sqrt{ab}\, m,$$

if we take $l^2 = \sqrt{b/a}$.

If $ab < 0$,

$$|f(x, y)| < \max(|a|l^2 m, |b|l^2 m) < \sqrt{|ab|}\, m,$$

if we take $l^2 = \sqrt{|b/a|}$.

Further

$$f(x, y) = a(kX + mY)^2 + bX^2$$

$$= (ak^2 + b)X^2 + 2akmXY + am^2Y^2 \equiv 0 \pmod{m}$$

$$= Mm.$$

The problem now is to determine whether $M = 1$ is possible. Many of the possibilities for M can be eliminated by congruence considerations. Suppose that m is odd.

I. congruences mod 4 or mod 8. Thus all to mod 4, $a \equiv 1$, $b \equiv -1$ excludes $M \equiv 2 \pmod 4$ since then x and y are odd and $x^2 - y^2 \equiv 0 \pmod 4$. If $a \equiv 1$, $b \equiv 1, 2$, then solvability for $M \equiv 0 \pmod 4$ implies solvability for $M/4$ since now $x \equiv y \equiv 0 \pmod 2$.

II. congruences mod q, $q = 3, 5, 7, \ldots$, a prime. If $(-ab/q) = -1$, then $M \not\equiv 0 \pmod q$.

III. sometimes it may be shown that if $M = M_1$, say, is possible, then $M = M_2$ is also possible and conversely. For this we use the results,

if $\qquad ax^2 + by^2 = m, \qquad ax_1^2 + by_1^2 = m_1,$

then $\qquad (axx_1 + byy_1)^2 + ab(xy_1 - x_1y)^2 = mm_1; \qquad (4)$

and if $\qquad x^2 + aby^2 = m, \qquad ax_1^2 + by_1^2 = m_1,$

then $\qquad a(xx_1 + byy_1)^2 + b(xy_1 - ayx_1)^2 = mm_1. \qquad (5)$

IV. If $(m, ab) = 1$, and a is square free, then solvability of $ax^2 + by^2 = am$ implies that of $x^2 + aby^2 = m$ and conversely.

We suppose for simplicity that m is an odd prime p since solvability when m is composite follows easily from the identities in III. Let us now consider the detailed results.

We begin with the case $a > 0$, $b > 0$. We take $a = 1$ and then

$$x^2 + by^2 = Mp, \qquad M < 2\sqrt{b},$$

and $(-b/p) = 1$ is the necessary condition for solvability. We write this in a slightly different form, for example, if $b \equiv 1 \pmod 4$, then $(-1/p)(p/b) = 1$, and if $b \equiv 3 \pmod 4$, then $(p/b) = 1$. If $\frac{1}{2}b = r \equiv 3 \pmod 4$, then $(2/p)(p/r) = 1$, but if $\frac{1}{2}b = r \equiv 1 \pmod 4$, then $(-2/p)(p/r) = 1$.

2. It will suffice if we give the results for square free $b < 20$ and give details for a few values of b.

$M = 1$ *if* $b = 1, 2, 3, 7$ *and* $(-b/p) = 1$

Take for example $b = 7$ and so $M < \sqrt{28} = 1, 2, 3, 4, 5$. We can exclude $M = 2, 4$ since then $x \equiv y \equiv 1 \pmod 2$ and $x^2 + 7y^2 \equiv 0 \pmod 8$. We can exclude $M = 3, 5$ since $(-7/3) = -1 = (-7/5)$.

$M = 1$ *if* $b = 5$ provided that $(-1/p) = (p/5) = 1$. If $(-1/p) = (p/5) = -1$, then $M = 2$ or 3 and either value implies the other. The condition $(-5/p) = 1$ gives $(-1/p) = (p/5)$. Here $M < \sqrt{20} = 1, 2, 3, 4$. If $M = 4$, then $x \equiv y \equiv 0 \pmod 2$ and implies $M = 1$. For this, $(p/5) = 1$ and so $(-1/p) = 1$. Then $M = 2$ or 3 can arise only when $(2p/5) = 1$ or $(3p/5) = 1$, i.e. $(p/5) = -1$.

Suppose now $x^2 + 5y^2 = 2p$. Multiply by $1^2 + 5.1^2 = 6$. Then from equation (4),

$$X^2 + 5Y^2 = 3p,$$

where $\qquad\qquad x + 5y = 2X, \qquad x - y = 2Y,$

and so $\qquad\qquad 3x = X + 5Y, \qquad 3y = X - Y.$

If x and y are given, $x \equiv y \pmod 2$ and so X, Y are integers. If X and Y are given, we can choose Y so that $X \equiv Y \pmod 3$, and then x, y are integers.

$M = 1$ *if* $b = 6$ provided that $(2/p) = (p/3) = 1$ but if $(2/p) = (p/3) = -1$, then $2x^2 + 3y^2 = p$.

$M = 1$ *if* $b = 10$ provided that $(-2/p) = (p/5) = 1$ but if $(-2/p) = (p/5) = -1$, then $2x^2 + 5y^2 = p$.

$M = 1$ *or* 4 *if* $b = 11$ *or* 19, but we cannot remove the ambiguity. The solvability of $x^2 + by^2 = Mp$ means that

$$x^2 + xy + 3y^2 = p, \qquad x^2 + xy + 5y^2 = p$$

are both solvable.

$M = 1$ *if* $b = 13$ provided that $(-1/p) = (p/13) = 1$ but if $(-1/p) = (p/13) = -1$, then $M = 2$ or 7 and $M = 2 \leftrightarrow M = 7$.

$M = 1$ *if* $b = 15$ provided that $(p/3) = (p/5) = 1$ but if $(p/3) = (p/5) = -1$, then $5x^2 + 3y^2 = p$.

Different kinds of results arise when $b = 14, 17$. Suppose first that $b = 14$. Then if $(2/p) = (p/7) = 1$, either $M = 1$ or $2x^2 + 5y^2 = p$ and we cannot remove the ambiguity. If $(2/p) = (p/7) = -1$, then either $M = 3$ or $2x^2 + 5y^2 = 3p$, and we cannot remove the ambiguity.

When $b = 17$, $M = 1$ or 2 if $(-1/p) = (p/17) = 1$ and we cannot remove the ambiguity. If $(-1/p) = (p/17) = -1$, $M = 3, 6, 7$, each implying the other two.

We now consider $b = 11$ in detail. Here $M < 2\sqrt{11} = 1, 2, 3, 4, 5, 6$. We can exclude $M = 2, 6$ since $x^2 + 11y^2 \equiv 0 \pmod 4$. If $M = 4$, the case when x, y are even reduces to $M = 1$.

We show that the case when x and y are both odd, and the cases $M = 3, 5$, each imply the other two.

Suppose $x^2 + 11y^2 = 4p$. From $1^2 + 11.1^2 = 12$, we deduce

$$A^2 + 11B^2 = 3p,$$

where

$$4A = x + 11y, \quad 4B = x - y; \qquad 3y = A - B, \quad 3x = A + 11B.$$

By choice of sign of y, A and B are integers. If A, B are given, we can take $A \equiv B \pmod 3$, and then x, y are integers.

Suppose next that $x^2 + 11y^2 = 5p$. From $2^2 + 11.1^2 = 15$, we deduce

$$C^2 + 11D^2 = 3p,$$

where

$$5C = 2x + 11y, \quad 5D = x - 2y; \qquad 3x = 2C + 11D, \quad 3y = C - 2D.$$

We can take $x \equiv 2y \pmod 5$ and later $C \equiv -D \pmod 3$, and then have integer correspondences.

We show that if these three cases occur, then $M = 1$ cannot occur and conversely. This is easy to see from $X^2 + XY + 3Y^2 = p$, but the result is a particular case of the

Theorem 2

The equations

$$ax^2 + by^2 = lp, \qquad ax_1^2 + by_1^2 = mp, \quad (x, y) = 1, (x_1, y_1) = 1.$$

cannot both be solvable if $a > 0$, $b > 0$, $(ab, p) = 1$, $l \neq m$, $lm < ab$.

We may take to mod p,

$$x \equiv ky, \qquad x_1 \equiv ky_1 \quad \text{where} \quad ak^2 + b \equiv 0.$$

Since

$$(axx_1 + byy_1)^2 + ab(xy_1 - x_1y)^2 = lmp^2,$$

on putting

$$axx_1 + byy_1 = pX, \qquad xy_1 - x_1y = pY,$$

where X, Y are integers, then

$$X^2 + abY^2 = lm.$$

Hence $Y = 0$, i.e. $x/y = x_1/y_1$, and then $x = \pm x_1$, $y = \pm y_1$, and this is not so.

3. We turn now to the case $ab < 0$. We write equation (1) in the form

$$x^2 - cy^2 = \varepsilon p, \quad \varepsilon = \pm 1.$$

Now $\qquad \left(\dfrac{c}{p}\right) = 1, \qquad x^2 - cy^2 = Mp, \qquad |M| < \sqrt{c}.$

Some results may be mentioned.

$M = 1$ if $c = 2, 5, 13, 17$. We also have here $M = -1$ since $x^2 - cy^2 = -1$ is solvable for these c on noting $y = 5$ for $c = 13$.

$M = \pm 1$ where $c = 3, 6, 7, 11, 14, 19$, and if

$$c \equiv 1 \ (\text{mod } 2), \qquad \left(\dfrac{-1}{p}\right) = \pm 1, \qquad \left(\dfrac{p}{c}\right) = \pm 1,$$

and if $\qquad c \equiv 0 \ (\text{mod } 2), \qquad \left(\dfrac{-2}{p}\right) = \pm 1, \qquad \left(\dfrac{p}{c/2}\right) = \pm 1.$

The $\pm$ sign corresponds to $M = \pm 1$.

$M = \pm 1$ if $c = 15$ and

$$\left(\dfrac{3}{p}\right) = \left(\dfrac{p}{5}\right) = 1, \quad p \equiv \pm 1 \ (\text{mod } 4).$$

$M = \pm 1 \ or \ \pm 2$ when $c = 10$ according as

$$\left(\dfrac{2}{p}\right) = \left(\dfrac{p}{5}\right) = 1 \text{ or } -1.$$

The details are comparatively simple except for $c = 19$ and so we give them. Here

$$\left(\dfrac{19}{p}\right) = \left(\dfrac{-1}{p}\right)\left(\dfrac{p}{19}\right) = 1, \qquad |M| = 1, 2, 3, 4,$$

$$x^2 - 19y^2 = Mp.$$

We can exclude $|M| = 4$ since this reduces to $|M| = 1$. We show that any of $M = 1, -2, -3$ implies each of the other two.

For from $\qquad x^2 - 19y^3 = p, \qquad 4^2 - 19.1^2 = -3,$

$$A^2 - 19B^2 = -3p,$$

where

$$A = 4x - 19y, \quad B = x - 4y; \qquad 3x = -4A + 19B, \quad 3y = -A + 4B.$$

Since we can take $A \equiv B \ (\text{mod } 3)$, $M = 1 \leftrightarrow M = -3$.

Next $M = -2 \leftrightarrow M = -3$. For from

$$x^2 - 19y^2 = -2p, \qquad 5^2 - 19.1^2 = 6,$$

$$C^2 - 19D^2 = -3p,$$

where

$$2C = 5x - 19y, \quad 2D = x - 5y; \qquad 3x = 5C - 19D, \quad 3y = C - 5D.$$

The result is now obvious since we can take $x \equiv y \pmod 2$, $C \equiv -D \pmod 3$. Similarly, we can show that each of $M = -1, 2, 3$ implies each of the others. Hence when $(-1/p) = 1$, we can take $M = 1$ since $M = -1$ is excluded by the congruence $x^2 - 19y^2 \equiv -p \equiv -1 \pmod 4$.

So when $(-1/p) = -1$, we have $M = -1$.

4. We now consider the representation[3] of numbers m, which we may suppose square free, by the special quaternary forms

$$f = f(x, y, z, w) = x^2 + bcy^2 + caz^2 + abw^2. \tag{6}$$

These forms admit a composition process. Thus if

$$f_1 = f(x_1, y_1, z_1, w_1) = x_1^2 + bcy_1^2 + caz_1^2 + abw_1^2,$$

then
$$f_2 = ff_1 = f(x_2, y_2, z_2, w_2), \tag{7}$$

where
$$x_2 = xx_1 - (bcyy_1 + cazz_1 + abww_1),$$

$$y_2 = yx_1 + xy_1 + a(zw_1 - wz_1),$$

$$z_2 = zx_1 + xz_1 + b(wy_1 - yw_1),$$

$$w_2 = wx_1 + xw_1 + c(yz_1 - zy_1).$$

Hence if f represents both m and m_1, then f represents mm_1.

Theorem 3

Integers $(x, y, z, w) \neq (0, 0, 0, 0)$ exist such that

$$f(x, y, z, w) = Mm, \qquad |M| \leqslant \sqrt{2|abc|}, \tag{8}$$

provided that the congruence

$$cA^2 + bB^2 + a \equiv 0 \pmod m \tag{9}$$

is solvable for A and B.

It is shown in Chapter 6 that the congruence is solvable if $(m, abc) = 1$, $m \not\equiv 0 \pmod 4$. Put $x = cAX + bBY + mZ, y = BX - AY + mW, z = X$, $w = Y$. From equations (6) and (9),

$$f(x, y, z, w) = F(X, Y, Z, W) = Mm, \tag{10}$$

where M is an integer, and the determinant D of F is $a^2b^2c^2m^4$.

There are several methods for estimating a minimum value μ or lower bound for a quaternary form $F(X, Y, Z, W)$ of determinant D. The most elementary is to use Hermite's[4] $|\mu| < (\frac{4}{3})^{3/2} \sqrt[4]{|D|}$, and so $M < 1{\cdot}54\sqrt{|abc|}$. Next perhaps is the application of Minkowski's theorem on linear forms in Chapter 5. Thus integers $(X, Y, Z, W) \neq (0, 0, 0, 0)$ exist such that, if $\delta = \sqrt[4]{|abc|}$, then

$$\delta|x| < \sqrt{|abcm|}, \qquad \delta|y| \leqslant \sqrt{|am|}, \qquad \delta|z| \leqslant \sqrt{|bm|}, \qquad \delta|w| \leqslant \sqrt{|cm|}.$$

This gives $|M| < 4\sqrt{|abc|}$. The estimate (8) follows from the well known more precise results of Korkine and Zolotareff[5] $|\mu| \leqslant \sqrt[4]{4|D|}$. These estimates are usually given for positive definite forms, but they also hold for indefinite forms although the results are not very sharp.

We commence with the case $c = 1$ and so

$$f = x^2 + by^2 + az^2 + abw^2 = Mm, \quad |M| \leqslant \sqrt{2|ab|}, \tag{11}$$

and

$$A^2 + bB^2 + a \equiv 0 \pmod{m}, \quad (m, ab) = 1 \tag{12}$$

The classical case is $a = b = 1$, Hermite's result gives $M < 1 \cdot 54$, i.e. $M = 1$. Minkowski's estimate gives $M < 4$ and so $M = 1, 2, 3$.

The case $M = 2$ can be written as

$$\left(\frac{x+y}{2}\right)^2 + \left(\frac{x-y}{2}\right)^2 + \left(\frac{z+w}{2}\right)^2 + \left(\frac{z-w}{2}\right)^2 = m,$$

since either x, y, z, w are all even or odd or only two odd, say x, y. The case $M = 3$ can be written as

$$\left(\frac{y+z+w}{3}\right)^2 + \left(\frac{x+y-z}{3}\right)^2 + \left(\frac{x+z-w}{3}\right)^2 + \left(\frac{x+w-y}{3}\right)^2 = m,$$

since we may suppose $x \equiv 0 \pmod{3}$, $y \equiv z \equiv w \equiv 1 \pmod{3}$.

The method shows that m is representable by f in equation (11) when $b = 1$, $a = \pm 3, \pm 5, -7, -11$ and also when $a = \pm 2$, $b = 3, -3$. It will suffice to take a few of these cases.

$b = 1, a = 3 \qquad M < \sqrt{6} = 1, 2, \qquad (m, 3) = 1.$

If $M = 2$, $\qquad\qquad x^2 + y^2 + 3(z^2 + w^2) = 2m.$ \hfill (13)

If $x \equiv y \pmod{2}$, then $z \equiv w \pmod{2}$, and

$$\left(\frac{x+y}{2}\right)^2 + \left(\frac{x-y}{2}\right)^2 + 3\left(\frac{z+w}{2}\right)^2 + 3\left(\frac{z-w}{2}\right)^2 = m,$$

and this is the case $M = 1$.

If $x \equiv y + 1 \pmod{2}$, then $z \equiv w + 1 \pmod{2}$, and so from equation (13)

$$1 + 3 \equiv 2m \pmod{4}, \quad m \equiv 0 \pmod{2}.$$

Hence $M = 1$ if $m \equiv 1 \pmod{2}$. If $m \equiv 0 \pmod{2}$, the argument applies to $\frac{1}{2}m$, and since 2 is representable by f so is m.

Finally if $m \equiv 0 \pmod{3}$, $\frac{1}{3}m$ is representable by f and so is 3 and hence also m.

$b = 1, a = -3 \qquad |M| = 0, 1, 2, \qquad (m, 3) = 1.$

Since -1 is representable, we need only consider $M \geqslant 0$.

Clearly $M = 0$ is impossible since this requires $x \equiv y \equiv 0 \pmod{3}$ and then $z \equiv w \equiv 0 \pmod{3}$. If $M = 2$, the argument above applies when $x \equiv y \pmod{2}$, $z \equiv w \pmod{2}$. For $x \equiv y + 1 \pmod{2}$, $z \equiv w + 1 \pmod{2}$, we need only consider

$$x \equiv 1 \pmod{2}, \qquad y \equiv 0 \pmod{2}, \qquad z \equiv 1 \pmod{2}, \qquad w \equiv 0 \pmod{2},$$

Since $$1^2 - 3.1^2 = -2,$$

we have

$$\left(\frac{x+3z}{2}\right)^2 - 3\left(\frac{x+z}{2}\right)^2 + \left(\frac{y+3w}{2}\right)^2 - 3\left(\frac{y+w}{2}\right)^2 = -m,$$

and this is the case $M = -1$. The case $m \equiv 0 \pmod 3$ is dealt with as above. $b = 1$, $a = 5$, then $(m, 5) = 1$ and this case is of some interest.

Here $$x^2 + y^2 + 5(z^2 + w^2) = Mm, \quad M = 1, 2, 3.$$

Clearly $M \neq 1$ for all m since 3 is not representable. It can be shown from the theory of the ternary quadratic that all integers > 3 are representable with $M = 1$. However, all integers are representable with $M = 2$. Thus if $M = 1$,

$$(x+y)^2 + (x-y)^2 + 5(z+w)^2 + 5(z-w)^2 = 2m.$$

If $M = 3$, compound with $1^2 + 5.1^2 = 6$. Then

$$\left(\frac{x+5z}{3}\right)^2 + 5\left(\frac{x-z}{3}\right)^2 + \left(\frac{y+5w}{3}\right)^2 + 5\left(\frac{y-w}{3}\right)^2 = 2m$$

is an integral representation. For

$$x^2 + y^2 \equiv z^2 + w^2 \pmod 3,$$

and we can take

$$x \equiv y \equiv 1, \qquad z \equiv w \equiv 1 \pmod 3,$$

and $$x \equiv 0, \qquad y \equiv 1, \qquad z \equiv 0, \qquad w \equiv 1 \pmod 3.$$

If $m \equiv 0 \pmod 5$, say $m = 5m_1$, from a representation

$$x_1^2 + y_1^2 + z^2 + w^2 = 2m_1,$$

$$(2x_1 + y_1)^2 + (x_1 - 2y_1)^2 + 5(z^2 + w^2) = 10m_1.$$

$b = 1$, $a = -7$ $\qquad |M| = 0, 1, 2, 3, \qquad (m, 7) = 1.$

Clearly $M = 0$ is impossible and we may suppose $M > 0$, since $3^2 + 2^2 - 7(1^2 + 1^2) = -1$.

For $M = 2$, $$x^2 + y^2 - 7(z^2 + w^2) = 2m.$$

The case $x \equiv y \pmod 2$, $z \equiv w \pmod 2$ is dealt with as for $a = \pm 3$. We need only consider $x \equiv 1$, $y \equiv 0$, $z \equiv 1$, $w \equiv 0$, all to mod 2. Since $3^2 - 7.1^2 = 2$, we need only note

$$\left(\frac{3x+7z}{2}\right)^2 - 7\left(\frac{x+3z}{2}\right)^2 + \left(\frac{3y+7w}{2}\right)^2 - 7\left(\frac{y+3w}{2}\right)^2 = m.$$

For $M = 3$, $$x^2 + y^2 - 7(z^2 + w^2) = 3m.$$

From $2^2 - 7.1^2 = -3$, we deduce

$$\left(\frac{2x + 7z}{3}\right)^2 - 7\left(\frac{x + 2z}{3}\right)^2 + \left(\frac{2y + 7w}{3}\right)^2 - 7\left(\frac{y + 2w}{3}\right)^2 = -m.$$

The brackets are integers since it suffices from $x^2 + y^2 \equiv z^2 + w^2 \pmod 3$, to consider only

$$x \equiv z \equiv 1, \qquad y \equiv w \equiv 0 \pmod 3,$$

and $$x \equiv y \equiv z \equiv w \equiv 1 \pmod 3.$$

When $m \equiv 0 \pmod 7$, it suffices to put $x = 7X, y = 7Y$.

We take finally $a = \pm 2, b = \pm 3, c = 1$. It is well known that the result for $a = 2, b = 3, c = 1$ follows from $a = b = c = 1$, since

$$x^2 + 2y^2 + 3z^2 + 6w^2$$
$$= x^2 + (y + z + w)^2 + (-y + z + w)^2 + (z - 2w)^2.$$

We have now the solvable equations with $(m, 6) = 1$,

I. $x^2 - 3y^2 - 2z^2 + 6w^2 = Mm$,

II. $x^2 + 3y^2 - 2z^2 - 6w^2 = Mm$,

III. $x^2 - 3y^2 + 2z^2 - 6w^2 = Mm$.

Here $|M| = 0, 1, 2, 3$. Since each of the forms represents -1, we need only consider $M = 0, 2, 3$.

Consider I. Clearly $M \neq 0$ since $x^2 - 2z^2 \equiv 0 \pmod 3$, gives $x = 3X$, $z = 3Z$, and then $y = 3Y, w = 3W$. If $M = 3, x = 3X, z = 3Z$

and so $$3X^2 - y^2 - 6Z^2 + 2w^2 = m,$$

and this is I with $M = -1$.

Suppose next $M = 2$. Then $x \equiv y \pmod 2$. If $x = 2X, y = 2Y$,

$$2X^2 - 6Y^2 - z^2 + 3w^2 = m,$$

and this is I with $M = -1$. If, however, $x \equiv y \equiv 1 \pmod 2$, apply composition with

$$1^2 - 3.1^2 - 2.1^2 + 6.1^2 = 2.$$

Then $x_2 = x + 3y + 2z - 6w,$ $y_2 = x + y - 2z + 2w,$

$z_2 = x + z + 3y - 3w,$ $w_2 = x + y - z + w,$

Hence if $w \equiv z \pmod 2$, $x_2 \equiv y_2 \equiv z_2 \equiv w_2 \equiv 0 \pmod 2$, and this gives I with $M = 1$.

We can reject $w \equiv z + 1 \pmod{2}$ since from I

$$-2 - 2(w - 1)^2 + 6w^2 \equiv 2m \pmod{4}, \quad \text{i.e. } m \equiv 0 \pmod{2}$$

which has been excluded.

When $m \equiv 0 \pmod{6}$ the representation holds for $m/6$ and for 6 and so for m.

When $m \equiv 0 \pmod{2}$, the representation holds for $\frac{1}{2}m$ and for 2 and so for m.

When $m \equiv 0 \pmod{3}$, the representation holds for $\frac{1}{3}m$ and for 3 and so for m.

We show now that each of I and II implies the other.

Multiply I with $M = 1$ by $1^2 - 2.1^2 = -1$. Then

$$(x + 2z)^2 - 2(x + z)^2 + 3y^2 - 6w^2 = -m.$$

Since $x + 2z = X$, $x + z = Z$ gives a 1–1 correspondence between integer sets (x, z) and (X, Z), and we have II with m replaced by $-m$.

Take finally III and multiply by $1^2 - 3.1^2 = -2$. Then

$$(x - 3y)^2 - 3(x - y)^2 - 4z^2 + 12w^2 = -2m.$$

Write this as $$PQ - 3RS = -2m,$$

where $$P = x - 3y + 2z, \quad Q = x - 3y - 2z,$$

$$R = x - y + 2w, \quad S = x - y - 2w,$$

Then x, y, z, w will be integers if

$$P \equiv Q \pmod{4}, \quad R \equiv S \pmod{4}, \quad P \equiv R \pmod{2}.$$

If $m \equiv 1 \pmod{2}$, we can solve III with $P \equiv Q \equiv R \equiv S \equiv 1 \pmod{4}$.
If $m \equiv 0 \pmod{2}$, III holds with $M = 1$ for $\frac{1}{2}m$, for 2 and so for m.

REFERENCES

1. B. A. Venkoff. "Elementary Theory of Numbers". (Russian.) (1937), 51.
2. L. J. Mordell. Solvability of the equation $ax^2 + by^2 = p$. *J. Lond. Math. Soc.*, **41** (1966), 517–522.
3. L. J. Mordell. The representation of numbers by some quaternary quadratic forms. *Acta Arith.*, **12** (1966), 47–54.
4. J. W. S. Cassels. "An Introduction to the Geometry of Numbers". Springer-Verlag, Berlin (1959), 31.
5. L. J. Mordell. Observation on the minimum of a positive quadratic form in 8 variables. *J. Lond. Math. Soc.*, **19** (1944), 3–6.

CHAPTER 20

Representation of Numbers by Homogeneous Forms in Several Variables

We give a few brief remarks about the general theory, for which various accounts[1-4] can be consulted.

1. Let $f(x) = f(x_1, x_2, \ldots, x_n)$ be a homogeneous form with integer coefficients of degree d in n variables. We discuss the integer solutions for $(x) = (x_1, x_2, \ldots, x_n)$ of the equation

$$f(x) = m \tag{1}$$

for given m. We may suppose that the representation of m is primitive, i.e. $(x_1, x_2, \ldots, x_n) = 1$. If $(p_1, p_2, \ldots, p_n)$ is such a solution, then by means of a unimodular substitution with integer coefficients and first column $\begin{pmatrix} p_1 \\ p_2 \\ \vdots \\ p_n \end{pmatrix}$, we can transform $f(x)$ into a form $g(x)$ in which m is the coefficient of x_1^d. Hence the problem of representation requires the following three steps.

1. To find all the forms $g(x)$ with the same invariants and covariants as $f(x)$ and with m as the coefficient of x_1^d.
2. To find those of the $g(x)$ which are equivalent to $f(x)$.
3. To find the substitutions S which transform $g(x)$ into $f(x)$.

If the first column of S is $\begin{pmatrix} p_1 \\ p_2 \\ \vdots \\ p_n \end{pmatrix}$, then $x = \not{p}$ gives all the representations.

We remark that all these substitutions are given by $S = S'A$ where S' is any one of them and A runs through all the automorphs of $f(x)$.

It can be shown[2] that reduced forms exist for $f(x)$ and that the class number is finite. This requires that the coefficients of the reduced form be bounded in terms of the invariants of $f(x)$. Then questions arise about the minimum value of $f(x)$ for integer x. There are very few results for general forms of degree $d \geqslant 3$. The theory of quadratic forms which arises when $d = 2$ has been thoroughly investigated. We outline the method[1].

Let
$$f(x) = \sum_{r,s=1}^{n} a_{rs}x_r x_s, \quad a_{rs} = a_{sr}, \tag{2}$$

with integer coefficients $a_{r,s}$ $(r, s = 1, 2, \ldots, n)$ and determinant

$$D = \|a_{rs}\| \neq 0.$$

We can then write $g(x)$ as

$$g(x) = \frac{1}{m}((mx_1 + h_1(x))^2 - h_2(x)), \tag{3}$$

where $h_1(x)$ is a linear form in $x_2, \ldots, x_n$, and $h_2(x)$ is a quadratic form in $x_2, \ldots, x_n$ of determinant $m^{n-2}D$. Then $g(x)$ has integer coefficients if and only if the congruence

$$h_1^2(x) \equiv h_2(x) \;(\mathrm{mod}\; m), \tag{4}$$

holds identically in the variables $x_2, \ldots, x_n$. Next we have to find all the quadratic forms $h_2(x)$, say $h_{2,s}(x)$, in $n - 1$ variables and of determinant $m^{n-2}D$ for which the congruence (4) is possible, and then all the solutions for $h_1(x)$ incongruent mod m. Let there be, say, ω_s solutions of $h_{1,s}^2(x) \equiv h_{2,s}(x)$ (mod m) for which $g(x) \sim f(x)$. This of course requires a knowledge of all the classes of quadratic forms in n variables of determinant D. Then if δ_s is the number of automorphs of $h_{2,s}$ and δ those of $f(x)$, the number of primitive representations, is $\sum_s \delta\omega_s/\delta_s$.

2. We illustrate the method by taking the simplest case

$$f(x, y, z) = x^2 + y^2 + z^2 = m,$$

for which no really elementary treatment is known.

Theorem 1

Every integer $m > 0$ not of the form $4^\lambda(8\mu + 7)$, $\lambda \geqslant 0$, $\mu \geqslant 0$, is the sum of three integer squares, i.e.

$$x^2 + y^2 + z^2 = m \tag{5}$$

is solvable.

Here $D = 1$, and we show that the class number is one. We require an estimate for the minimum value taken by a positive definite form for integers $(x, y, z) \not\equiv (0, 0, 0)$.

Lemma 1

Let $\quad g(x, y, z) = ax^2 + by^2 + cz^2 + 2fyz + 2gzx + 2hxy$

be a positive definite form with determinant

$$D = \begin{vmatrix} a & h & g \\ h & b & f \\ g & f & c \end{vmatrix}.$$

Then integers x, y, z not all zero exist such that

$$f(x, y, z) \leqslant \tfrac{4}{3}D^{1/3}.$$

We may suppose that the minimum is attained for integers x, y, z for which $(x, y, z) = 1$ and, by means of a unimodular substitution, we may suppose that a is the minimum. Then for all integers $(x, y, z) \neq (0, 0, 0)$,

$$g(x, y, z) \geqslant a.$$

Hence

$$(ax + hy + gz)^2 + (ab - h^2)y^2 + 2(af - gh)yz + (ac - g^2)z^2 \geqslant a^2.$$

We give y, z integer values $\neq (0, 0)$, which make the binary quadratic in y, z a minimum. Since we can satisfy

$$Py^2 + Qyz + Rz^2 \leqslant \sqrt{\frac{4PR - Q^2}{3}},$$

this minimum is

$$\leqslant (\tfrac{4}{3})^{1/2}((ab - h^2)(ac - g^2) - (af - gh)^2)^{1/2} = (\tfrac{4}{3}aD)^{1/2}.$$

We then give x an integer value such that

$$|ax + hy + gz| \leqslant \tfrac{1}{2}a.$$

Hence

$$\frac{a^2}{4} + \left(\frac{4aD}{3}\right)^{1/2} \geqslant a^2,$$

$$\frac{4aD}{3} \geqslant (\tfrac{3}{4}a^2)^2,$$

and so

$$a^3 \leqslant \frac{64D}{27}.$$

It may be noted that the best possible estimate is $a^3 \leqslant 2D$.

We prove now that the class number is one.

Lemma 2

If a, b, c, f, g, h are integers and $D = 1$, then

$$g(x, y, z) \sim x^2 + y^2 + z^2. \tag{6}$$

We may suppose that $a < 4/3$ and so $a = 1$. On writing $x - hy - gz$ for x, we may suppose that $g = h = 0$,

and so

$$g(x, y, z) \sim x^2 + by^2 + 2fyz + cz^2.$$

Here $by^2 + 2fyz + cz^2$ is a positive definite binary quadratic form of determinant -1 and so it is equivalent to $y^2 + z^2$.

This proves the lemma.

We now proceed with the representation of m. We must construct positive definite ternary forms $g(x, y, z)$ of determinant 1 and first coefficient m.

Then
$$mg(x, y, z) = (mx + qy + rz)^2 + Qy^2 + 2Syz + Rz^2,$$

say, where $QR - S^2 = m$, and to mod m,

$$q^2 + Q \equiv 0, \qquad r^2 + R \equiv 0, \qquad qr + S \equiv 0.$$

It is, however, simpler to take

$$g(x, y, z) = mx^2 + 2xz + by^2 + 2fyz + cz^2,$$

where $b > 0, c > 0, f$ are to be found, and $A = bc - f^2 > 0$.

Also
$$1 = \begin{vmatrix} m & 0 & 1 \\ 0 & b & f \\ 1 & f & c \end{vmatrix} = m(bc - f^2) - b.$$

Then
$$b = mA - 1, \qquad c = \frac{A + f^2}{b}.$$

Now we need only find $A > 0$ and f such that c is an integer. We shall take A to be a linear form defined mod 4 or mod 8, and $b = p$ or $2p$ where p is an odd prime which will be specified later. We have to satisfy $(-A/p) = 1$ and we note that $(b/A) = (-1/A)$, the symbols being the quadratic characters.

Various cases must be considered depending upon the form of m. Write $m = 4^\lambda m_1, m_1 > 0, m_1 \equiv 1, 2, 3 \pmod 4$. Then m is representable if and only if m_1 is representable. For from

$$x^2 + y^2 + z^2 = m \equiv 0 \pmod 4,$$

clearly
$$x \equiv y \equiv z \equiv 0 \pmod 2,$$

and so $x = 2x_1, y = 2y_1, z = 2z_1$. Hence we need only consider $\lambda = 0$.

The representation is impossible if $m \equiv 7 \pmod 8$, since $x^2 \equiv 0, 1, 4 \pmod 8$, and $x^2 + y^2 + z^2 \not\equiv 7 \pmod 8$.

Suppose next that $m \equiv 1, 2, 3, 5, 6 \pmod 8$. Take first $m \equiv 2, 6 \pmod 8$. We put $A = 4t + 1, b = 4tm + m - 1$. Since $(4m, m - 1) = 1$, we can take t by Dirichlet's theorem on the primes in an arithmetic progression so that b is a prime p, and $p \equiv 1 \pmod 4$.

Then
$$\left(\frac{-A}{p}\right) = \left(\frac{p}{A}\right) = \left(\frac{-1}{A}\right) = 1.$$

Suppose next that $m \equiv 1, 3, 5 \pmod 8$. Take

$$A = 8t + r, \qquad b = (8t + r)m - 1, \qquad r = 1 \text{ if } m \equiv 3; \quad r = 3 \text{ if } m \equiv 1, 5.$$

We can take t so that $b = 2p$, where p is an odd prime,

since
$$\left(4m, \frac{rm - 1}{2}\right) = 1.$$

Hence we have

$$m \equiv 1, \quad A \equiv 3, \text{(mod 8)}, \qquad p \equiv 1 \text{ (mod 4)},$$

$$m \equiv 3, \quad A \equiv 1, \text{(mod 8)}, \qquad p \equiv 1 \text{ (mod 4)},$$

$$m \equiv 5, \quad A \equiv 3, \text{(mod 8)}, \qquad p \equiv 3 \text{ (mod 4)}.$$

Hence in all cases $(-2/A) = 1$, and either $-A \equiv 1 \pmod 4$ or $p \equiv 1 \pmod 4$.

Then

$$\left(\frac{-A}{p}\right) = \left(\frac{p}{A}\right) = \left(\frac{-2p}{A}\right) = \left(\frac{-b}{A}\right) = \left(\frac{1}{A}\right) = 1.$$

This concludes the proof.

3. There are other simple results about the numbers which can be represented by the form

$$f(a, b) = x^2 + ay^2 + bz^2,$$

for particular values of a and b.

These can be proved by the general theory and sometimes by special methods. Thus an integer $m > 0$ cannot be represented by $f(a, b)$ for the a and b below if and only if,

$$a = 1, \quad b = 2, \quad m = 4^\lambda(16\mu + 14),$$

$$a = 1, \quad b = 3, \quad m = 9^\lambda(9\mu + 6),$$

$$a = 2, \quad b = 3, \quad m = 4^\lambda(16\mu + 10).$$

These results can be used to prove[5] that an integer m can be represented by some quaternary forms

$$f(a, b) = a(x^2 + y^2 + z^2) + bw^2.$$

We may suppose that $m \not\equiv 0 \pmod 4$, on putting $x = 2X$ etc.

Let us take $a = 1$. Then every positive integer is represented when $b = 1$, the classical case. For we need only take $w = 0$ if $m \equiv 1, 2 \pmod 4$ and $w = 1$ if $m \equiv 3 \pmod 4$.

When $b = -1$, every integer positive, negative or zero is represented. Thus if $m = 0$, we take $w = 1$. For other m, we take w such that $w^2 + m > 0$, and according as $m \equiv 1, 2 \pmod 4$, or $\equiv 3 \pmod 8$ or $\equiv 7 \pmod 8$, we take $w \equiv 0 \pmod 2$, $w \equiv 0 \pmod 4$, $w \equiv 2 \pmod 4$.

If $m > 0$, a representation is also possible for $1 \le b \le 7$. We may suppose that $m = 4^\lambda(8\mu + 7)$ as otherwise we can take $w = 0$. Suppose first that $b = 1, 2, 4, 5, 6$. Take $w = 2^\lambda$, then $m - bw^2 = 4^\lambda(8\mu + 7 - b)$ and is not of the form $4^\lambda(8\mu + 7)$. Suppose next that $b = 3$. If $\mu = 0$ we take $w = 2^\lambda$ and then $m - bw^2 = 4^{\lambda+1}$, and if $\mu \ge 1$ take $w = 2^{\lambda+1}$ and then $m - bw^2 = 4^\lambda(8\mu - 5)$.

Finally, let $b = 7$. If $\mu = 0, 1$ or 2, take $w = 2$ and then $m - bw^2 = 0, 2$ $4^{\lambda+1}$ or $4^{\lambda+2}$. If $\mu \ge 3$, take $w = 2^{\lambda+1}$. Then $m - bw^2 = 4^\lambda(8\mu - 21)$.

Some results on the representation of complex integers by special binary and ternary quadratic forms are very simple. Niven has proved the

Theorem 2

A representation of $m = a + 2ib$, where a and b are rational integers, as

$$x^2 + y^2 = m,$$

where x, y are complex integers, is always possible except when $a \equiv 2 \pmod 4$, $b \equiv 1 \pmod 2$.

We give a simpler proof[6]. Write

$$(x + iy)(x - iy) = a + 2ib.$$

If a is odd, a solution is given by

$$x + iy = a + 2ib, \qquad x - iy = 1.$$

Suppose $a = 2a_1$ is even. If a_1 and b are both even, take

$$x + iy = a_1 + ib, \qquad x - iy = 2.$$

If a_1 and b are of different parity, take

$$x + iy = (1 + i)(a_1 + ib), \qquad x - iy = 1 - i.$$

If a_1 and b are both odd, the representation is impossible. For if

$$x = X + iY, \qquad y = Z + iW,$$

$$X^2 - Y^2 + Z^2 - W^2 \equiv 2 \pmod 4, \qquad XY + ZW \equiv 1 \pmod 2.$$

Then say $ZW \equiv 1 \pmod 2$, $Z^2 - W^2 \equiv 0 \pmod 4$, and $X^2 - Y^2 \equiv 2 \pmod 4$ is impossible.

We use this theorem to prove

Theorem 3

A representation of $m = a + 2ib$, where a and b are rational integers, as

$$x^2 + y^2 + z^2 = m,$$

where x, y, z are complex integers, is always possible.

For take $z = X + iY$. Then we have a representation from Theorem 2, if the integers X, Y satisfy

$$a - X^2 + Y^2 \not\equiv 2 \pmod 4.$$

We take $X \equiv Y \equiv 1 \pmod 2$ if a is odd, and $X \equiv 1$, $Y \equiv 0 \pmod 2$ if a is even.

Mr. Makowski notes that a solution when $m = 2a + 2ib$ is $(1, a + ib, b + i - ai)$, and when $m = 2a + 1 + 2ib$, is $(2, a - 1 + ib, b + 2i - ia)$.

REFERENCES

1. P. Bachmann. "Die Arithmetik der quadratischen Formen", Part 1. Teubner (1898).
2. L. E. Dickson. "Studies in the Theory of Numbers", University of Chicago Press (1930). Also his "History", Vol. 3, Chapter XIV.
3. B. W. Jones. "The Arithmetic Theory of Quadratic Forms". Math. Assoc. of America and John Wiley and Sons (1950).
4. G. L. Watson. "Integral Quadratic Forms". Cambridge University Press (1960).
5. S. Ramanujan. "On the expression of a number in the form $ax^2 + by^2 + cz^2 + dw^2$". *Proc. Camb. Phil. Soc.*, **19** (1917), 11–21. Also in Collected Papers (1927), 169–178.
6. L. J. Mordell. The representation of a Gaussian integer as a sum of two squares. *Maths. Magazine*, **40** (1967), 209.

CHAPTER 21

Representation of Numbers by Polynomials

1. Let $f(x)$ be a polynomial in x which assumes only integer values when x is an integer. Such are

$$\frac{x(x-1)}{2!}, \quad \frac{x(x-1)(x-2)}{3!}, \quad \ldots.$$

Interesting problems arise about the existence of an integer s independent of n such that every integer n can be expressed with integers x in the forms

I. $n = f(x_1) + f(x_2) + \cdots + f(x_s),$

II. $n = f(x_1) + f(x_2) + \cdots + f(x_s), \quad x_1 \geqslant 0, \ldots, x_s \geqslant 0,$

III. $n = f(x_1) \pm f(x_2) \pm \cdots \pm f(x_s)$

with any combination of signs.

In II, when $f(x) = x^r$, we have Waring's problem. We will not discuss this and some other aspects of these questions since they involve considerations rather remote from those dealt with here. Some discussion of III when $f(x) = x^r$ is more relevant to our methods.

Theorem 1

Every integer can be expressed as an algebraic sum of three squares, i.e.

$$n = \pm x_1^2 \pm x_2^2 \pm x_3^2,$$

is solvable for some combination of signs.

The proof is obvious from

$$2n + 1 = (n + 1)^2 - n^2, \qquad 2n = n^2 - (n - 1)^2 + 1,$$

and so $s \leqslant 3$. Since $6 = x^2 \pm y^2$ is impossible, $s \geqslant 3$, and so the best possible value of s is 3.

Theorem 2

Every integer can be expressed as a sum of five integer cubes.

The result is obvious with four cubes for integers $\equiv 0 \pmod 6$, since

$$(x + 1)^3 + (x - 1)^3 - 2x^3 = 6x.$$

The theorem holds for all integers n as follows on putting for x, the integer $(n - n^3)/6$.

7+

2. The question arises whether fewer cubes are sufficient.
We have the still unproved

Conjecture
Every integer n can be expressed as a sum of the cubes of four integers.
This has been proved for all integers $n \not\equiv \pm 4 \pmod 9$.
Some results due to Richmond[1], and Mordell[2] are given by

Theorem 3
All integers $\equiv 3 \pmod 6$, ± 1, ± 7, $\pm 8 \pmod{18}$, *can be expressed as a sum of four integer cubes.*
We can easily verify that

$$k^3 + (-k + 4)^3 + (2k - 5)^3 + (-2k + 4)^3 = 6k + 3,$$

$$(3k + 30)^3 + (-3k - 26)^3 + (-2k - 23)^3 + (2k + 14)^3 = 18k + 1,$$

$$(k + 2)^3 + (6k - 1)^3 + (8k - 2)^3 + (-9k + 2)^3 = 18k + 7,$$

$$(k - 5)^3 + (-k + 14)^3 + (3k - 30)^3 + (-3k + 29)^3 = 18k + 8.$$

These results are found by putting

$$x = ak + p, \qquad y = bk + q, \qquad z = ck + r, \qquad w = dk + s$$

in
$$x^3 + y^3 + z^3 + w^3 = n.$$

Take
$$\sum a^3 = 0, \qquad \sum a^2 p = 0.$$

Then
$$n = 3 \sum ap^2 k + \sum p^3.$$

A special instance is given by $(a, b, c, d) = (1, 6, 8, -9)$, and then

$$p + 36q + 64r + 81s = 0.$$

An obvious solution is $(p, q, r, s) = (2, -1, -2, 2)$, giving $\sum ap^2 = 6$, $\sum p^3 = 7$ and so the formula for $18n + 7$.

It can be shown from Theorem 3, Chapter 8, that an infinity of integer solutions exist.

It has been shown very recently by Demjanenko[3] that integers of the form $18k \pm 2$ can be expressed in an infinity of ways as the sum of four cubes of either linear or quadratic polynomials in k. The proof is rather complicated since the coefficients are large numbers and depend upon the solution of the Pellian equation $x^2 - 3420y^2 = 1$.

There remains now only the question whether integers n of the form $9k \pm 4$ can be expressed as the sum of four cubes. He has verified that this is so for $n < 1000$.

Representations by linear polynomials do not exist when $n \equiv \pm 4 \pmod 9$, i.e. $n = 18k \pm 4, 18k \pm 5$. For if they did, $\sum ap^2 = 6$ and so

$$\sum p^3 \equiv \pm 4 \pmod 9, \quad \text{i.e. } p \equiv q \equiv r \equiv s \equiv \pm 1 \pmod 3,$$

say, $p = 3p_1 \pm 1$, etc. Then

$$\sum a^2(3p_1 \pm 1) = 0, \qquad \sum a(3p_1 \pm 1)^2 \equiv 0 \pmod 3,$$

and so $\qquad \sum a^2 \equiv 0 \pmod 3, \qquad \sum a \equiv 0 \pmod 3.$

Hence only one or all four of a, b, c, d are $\equiv 0 \pmod 3$.
For the first, we can take

$$a \equiv b \equiv c \equiv \pm 1, \quad d \equiv 0 \pmod 3.$$

But then $\qquad 0 = a^3 + b^3 + c^3 + d^3 \equiv \pm 3 \pmod 9.$

For the second, we take $a = 3a_1$, etc. and then

$$\sum a_1^3 = 0, \qquad \sum a_1(3p_1 \pm 1)^2 = 2.$$

These give the contradiction

$$\sum a_1 \equiv 0, \qquad \sum a_1 \equiv 2 \pmod 3.$$

It has just been shown by Schinzel[4] that there does not exist a representation of $9k \pm 4$ as a sum of cubes of four quartic polynomials.*

3. Theorem 4

If r is a given integer > 1, there exists a value of s independent of the integer n such that

$$\pm x_1^r \pm x_2^r \pm \cdots \pm x_s^r = n$$

for integers x.

This result is an immediate consequence of the identity

$$(x + r - 1)^r - \binom{r-1}{1}(x + r - 2)^r + \binom{r-1}{2}(x + r - 3)^r + \cdots$$
$$+ (-1)^{r-1}x^r = r!x + c_r,$$

where c_r is an integer independent of x. In fact $\pm x^r$ above can be replaced by an integer valued polynomial

$$f(x) = a_0x^r + a_1x^{r-1} + \cdots + a_r,$$

with $a_0 = a/r!$, say.

Write $\qquad \Delta f(x) = f(x + 1) - f(x),$

$$\Delta^2 f(x) = \Delta(\Delta f(x)) = f(x + 2) - 2f(x + 1) + f(x), \quad \text{etc.}$$

* See Addendum.

Then
$$\Delta f(x) = a_0 r x^{r-1} + \cdots,$$

$$\Delta^2 f(x) = a_0 r(r-1)x^{r-2} + \cdots,$$

$$\cdots$$

$$\Delta^{r-1} f(x) = a_0 r! x + c_r, \quad \text{say.}$$

This proves the identity above since its left-hand side is $\Delta^{r-1} x^r$. The theorem follows at once since any integer n can be expressed in the form

$$n = r!x + c_r + 1^r + 1^r + \cdots + 1^r,$$

with integer x and at most $r! - 1$ of the 1^r.

We consider the particular case $r = 4$. Then we have the

Theorem 5

If s is the best possible value for all n, then

$$9 \leqslant s \leqslant 10.$$

We show that $s \geqslant 8$ when $n \equiv 8 \pmod{16}$. Since $x^4 \equiv 0, 1 \pmod{16}$, clearly n cannot be expressed as an algebraic sum of less than eight fourth powers, and for eight powers only when these are all odd and have the same sign.

Then $s \geqslant 9$ since $\sum_{r=1}^{8} x_r^4 = 24$ is impossible.

The estimate $s \leqslant 12$ follows from

$$(x + 3)^4 - 3(x + 2)^4 + 3(x + 1)^4 - x^4 = 24x + 36.$$

This shows that eight fourth powers suffice when $n \equiv 12 \pmod{24}$. Four more will suffice for all n since the congruence

$$\pm a^4 \pm b^4 \pm c^4 \pm d^4 \equiv n \pmod{24},$$

is solvable for a, b, c, d. Since $a^4 \equiv 0, 1 \pmod 3$, the congruence is solvable mod 3. Since $a^4 \equiv 0, 1 \pmod 8$, it is also solvable for $n \equiv 0, \pm 1, \pm 2, \pm 3, 4 \pmod 8$.

To prove $s \leqslant 10$, Hunter[5] uses identities such as

$$48x + 4 = 2(2x + 3)^4 + (2x + 6)^4 + 2(2x^2 + 8x + 11)^4$$

$$- (2x^2 + 8x + 10)^4 - (2x^2 + 8x + 12)^4.$$

The problem of finding the best value of s in Theorem 4 is a very difficult one which has been solved only for $r = 2$. Some results are given in Hardy and Wright[6] but these are out of place here.

REFERENCES

1. H. W. Richmond. An elementary note upon Waring's problem for cubes, positive and negative. *Messenger Math.*, **51** (1922), 177–186.

2. L. J. Mordell. On the four integer cubes problem. *J. London. Math. Soc.*, **11** (1936), 208–218. Addendum. Also in **12** (1937), 80; Corrigendum. Also in **32** (1957), 383.

3. V. A. Demjanenko. On sums of four cubes. (Russian). *Izv. Vysŝ. Učebn. Zaved. Matematika*, **5** (54) (1966), 63–69.

4. A. Schinzel. On the sums of cubes of polynomials. *J. Lond. Math. Soc.*, **43** (1968), 143–145.

5. W. Hunter. The representation of numbers by sums of fourth powers. *J. Lond. Math. Soc.*, **16** (1941), 177–179.

6. G. H. Hardy and E. M. Wright. "An Introduction to the Theory of Numbers". Clarendon Press, Oxford (1945), §27–28.

Addendum

Mordell has found a simpler proof of Theorem 4. It may appear as "On the sum of cubes of polynomials" in the *Acta Arith.* for 1970.

CHAPTER 22

Thue's Theorem on the Integer Solutions of $f(x, y) = m$

1. A fundamental result is given by Thue's[1]

Theorem 1

The equation

$$f(x, y) = a_0 x^n + a_1 x^{n-1} y + \cdots + a_n y^n = m \neq 0, \tag{1}$$

where $n \geq 3$, and $f(x, y)$ is irreducible in the rational field, has only a finite number of integer solutions.

The cases when $f(x, y)$ is reducible are easily disposed of. If

$$f(x, y) = a(bx + cy)^n, \quad \text{or} \quad a(bx^2 + cxy + dy^2)^{n/2}, \tag{2}$$

there may be an infinity of solutions. If

$$f(x, y) = g(x, y)h(x, y), \tag{3}$$

where the polynomials $g(x, y)$, $h(x, y)$ are relatively prime to each other as functions of x and y, there can be only a finite number of integer solutions. For we have

$$g(x, y) = \delta, \qquad h(x, y) = m/\delta,$$

where δ is any divisor of m. Hence the result since these equations are independent of each other.

The case $f(x, y) = g(x, y)^l$ is included in the cases (1), (2), (3).

A trivial case of (1) is given by the

Theorem 2

If all the roots of $f(z, 1) = 0$ are complex numbers, there are only a finite number of solutions of $f(x, y) = m$.

If $y = 0$, there are at most two values for x.

Suppose then $y \neq 0$. For real z, $|f(z, 1)| > c > 0$, where c is independent of z. Hence

$$|m| = |f(x, y)| = |y|^n \left| f\left(\frac{x}{y}, 1\right) \right| > cy^n,$$

and so y is bounded.

Thue's proof depends on Diophantine approximation to an algebraic number θ of degree $n \geq 3$ by means of rational fractions. His result is included in Siegel's[2]

Theorem 3
There are only a finite number of integer solutions for x, y of the inequality

$$\left| \theta - \frac{x}{y} \right| < \frac{1}{|y|^\nu},\qquad(4)$$

where $\nu > n/(s + 1) + s$, and s is any one of $1, 2, \ldots, n - 1$.
On taking $\nu = \beta + \varepsilon$, $\beta = \min_{s=1,\ldots,n-1}(n/(s + 1) + s)$, and $\varepsilon, 0 < \varepsilon \leq 1$, such that ν is an integer,

$$\beta \leq \frac{n}{[\sqrt{n}] + 1} + [\sqrt{n}] < \frac{n}{\sqrt{n}} + \sqrt{n} = 2\sqrt{n}.$$

Thue proves the result for $\nu > n/2 + 1$.

It has been shown by Roth[3] that this theorem holds if $\nu > 2 + \varepsilon$ where $\varepsilon > 0$ is arbitrary. The 2 here is the best possible constant.

A particular instance of (4) is that the inequality

$$\left| \theta - \frac{x}{y} \right| < \frac{A}{|y|^n},\qquad(5)$$

where $A > 0$ is any given constant, has only a finite number of integer solutions.

Take $s = 1$, $\nu = n/2 + 1 + \frac{1}{4}$. Then for all large $|y|$,

$$\left| \theta - \frac{x}{y} \right| \geq \frac{1}{|y|^{n/2 + 5/4}} = \frac{|y|^{n/2 - 5/4}}{|y|^n} > \frac{A}{|y|^n} \quad \text{for } y > A^{1/(n/2 - 5/4)}.$$

Further if A is sufficiently small, the inequality (5) has no integer solutions in x, y. The result is trivial if $\theta = \zeta_1 + i\zeta_2$ is complex. For then $|\zeta_2| < A/|y|^n$, and so there are no solutions if $A < |\zeta_2|$.

Suppose next that θ is real. We may suppose $y > 0$, and that (5) holds. Let the roots of $f(z, 1) = 0$ in equation (1) be $\theta_1 = \theta, \theta_2, \ldots, \theta_n$. Then for $i = 2, \ldots, n$,

$$\left| \theta_i - \frac{x}{y} \right| \leq \left| \theta - \frac{x}{y} \right| + |\theta_i - \theta|,$$

$$\leq \frac{A}{y^n} + 2A_1, \quad A_1 = \max |\theta_i|, \ i = 1, 2, \ldots, n$$

$$\leq A + 2A_1 \quad \text{since } |y| \geq 1.$$

Hence

$$\left| f\left(\frac{x}{y}, 1\right) \right| < |a_0| \frac{A}{y^n}(A + 2A_1)^{n-1},$$

or

$$|f(x, y)| < |a_0|A(A + 2A_1)^{n-1}.$$

But for integers $(x, y) \neq (0, 0)$, $|f(x, y)| \geqslant 1$, and so

$$A(A + 2A_1)^n > 1/|a_0|.$$

This inequality, however, requires $A \geqslant A_2 = A_2(A_1, a_0)$, and so if $A < A_2$, there are no solutions of (5).

Assuming (5) for the present, we can prove Theorem 1. At most two solutions arise when $y = 0$, and so we can suppose $y > 0$. Then

$$\left| a_0 \prod_{i=1}^{n} (x - \theta_i y) \right| = |m|,$$

and so for at least one i, say $i = 1$, and $\theta_1 = \theta$, say,

$$|x - \theta y| \leqslant |m/a_0|^{1/n} = B_1, \quad \text{say.}$$

Then for $i \neq 1$, and large $|y|$,

$$|x - \theta_i y| = |x - \theta y + (\theta - \theta_i)y| \geqslant ||\theta - \theta_i|y - |x - \theta y||$$

$$\geqslant |B_2 y - B_1|, \quad B_2 = \min |\theta - \theta_i|, i = 2, \ldots, n.$$

$$> \tfrac{1}{2} B_2 |y|, \quad \text{for } y > 2B_1/B_2.$$

Hence $$|a_0(x - \theta y)(B_2 y/2)^{n-1}| < |m|,$$

that is, $$\left| \frac{x}{y} - \theta \right| < \frac{1}{|y|^n} \left| \frac{m}{a_0} \right| \left(\frac{2}{B_2} \right)^{n-1}.$$

Then from (5) only a finite number of values of x, y are possible.

We can deduce in a similar manner, the more general

Theorem 4

Let $P(x, y)$ be an irreducible binary form of degree $n > 2$, and let $Q(x, y)$ be a polynomial of degree $m < n - 2\sqrt{n}$. Then the equation

$$P(x, y) = Q(x, y), \tag{6}$$

has only a finite number of integer solutions.

Suppose that this is not so. By a linear transformation if need be, we may suppose that a_0, the coefficient of the highest power x^n in $P(x, y)$ is not zero, and so then

$$P(x,y) = a_0 \prod_{i=1}^{n} (x - \theta_i y),$$

say. Hence for one of the θ_i, say $\theta_1 = \theta$, $x - \theta y$ is very small for an infinity of integers x, y, corresponding to the solutions, and so

$$\prod_{i=2}^{n} |x - \theta_i y| > k_1 |y|^{n-1}, \quad |Q(x, y)| < k_2 |y|^m,$$

where k_1, k_2 are constants independent of x and y.

Then
$$|x - \theta y| < \frac{a_0 k_2/k_1}{|y|^{n-1-m}},$$

and
$$\left|\theta - \frac{x}{y}\right| < \frac{a_0 k_2/k_1}{|y|^{n-m}}.$$

This contradicts Siegel's theorem.

If the more precise result of Roth is used, the theorem will hold for $m < n - 2$. Schinzel has proved in the addendum to Chapter 28 that it suffices if $m < n$.

2. We now prove Siegel's Theorem 2. We require a number of preliminary lemmas.

Let $f_1(x), f_2(x), \ldots, f_m(x)$ be m polynomials with integer coefficients. They are called linearly independent or dependent according as a relation

$$\sum_{\lambda=1}^{m} c_\lambda f_\lambda(x) = 0 \tag{7}$$

with rational constants c implies $c_1 = c_2 = \cdots = c_m = 0$ or not. Denote by D the determinant (Wronskian)

$$D = D(f_1, f_2, \ldots, f_m) = \|f_\lambda^{(k)}(x)\|, \quad \lambda = 1, 2, \ldots, m; k = 0, 1, \ldots, m - 1,$$

where
$$f^{(k)}(x) = \frac{d^k f(x)}{dx^k}, \quad k > 0,$$

$$= f(x), \quad k = 0.$$

Lemma 1

$f_1(x), f_2(x), \ldots, f_m(x)$ *are linearly dependent if and only if* $D = 0$ *identically.*

For if a relation (7) holds, on differentiating $m - 1$ times, we have

$$\sum_{\lambda=1}^{m} c_\lambda f_\lambda^k(x) = 0, \quad k = 0, 1, \ldots, m - 1.$$

The elimination of the c's gives $D = 0$.

Suppose next that $D = 0$. We may assume $f_1 \not\equiv 0$ (i.e. not identically zero), as otherwise the lemma is true. We note, as is easily proved, that if $g(x)$ is a function of x differentiable $m - 1$ times, then

$$D(gf_1, gf_2, \ldots, gf_m) = g^m D(f_1, f_2, \ldots, f_m).$$

Thus the second row on the left is

$$g\frac{df_1}{dx} + f_1\frac{dg}{dx}, g\frac{df_2}{dx} + f_2\frac{dg}{dx}, \ldots.$$

This becomes on subtracting $(dg/dx)/g$ times the first row,

$$g\frac{df_1}{dx}, g\frac{df_2}{dx}, \ldots, \text{ etc.}$$

7*

We prove the lemma by induction, assuming it holds for $m - 1$, and then showing that it holds for m. Suppose that x lies in an interval I in which $f_1(x)$ does not vanish.

Take $g = 1/f_1$, then

$$D\left(1, \frac{f_2}{f_1}, \ldots, \frac{f_m}{f_1}\right) = 0.$$

Since the first column has 1 in the first row and zeros in the other rows, we have

$$D\left(\frac{d(f_2/f_1)}{dx}, \ldots, \frac{d(f_m/f_1)}{dx}\right) = 0.$$

Hence

$$\frac{d}{dx}\left(\frac{f_2}{f_1}\right), \ldots, \frac{d}{dx}\left(\frac{f_m}{f_1}\right)$$

are linearly dependent, and so for rational constants $c_2, \ldots, c_m$,

$$c_2 \frac{d}{dx}\left(\frac{f_2}{f_1}\right) + \cdots + c_m \frac{d}{dx}\left(\frac{f_m}{f_1}\right) = 0.$$

Then

$$c_2 f_2 + \cdots + c_m f_m = -c_1 f_1$$

where c_1 is a constant obviously rational. Since this relation holds for x in an interval I, and the f's are polynomials, it must hold for all values of x.

Lemma 2

Let $\quad y_i = a_{i1}x_1 + a_{i2}x_2 + \cdots + a_{in}x_n, \quad i = 1, 2, \ldots, m$

be m linear forms in $n > m$ variables with integer coefficients, with absolute values all $\leqslant A$, say. Then the equations

$$y_i = 0, \quad (i = 1, 2, \ldots, m),$$

have integer solutions for the x's, not all zero, and with absolute values satisfying

$$|x| < 1 + (nA)^{m/(n-m)}. \tag{8}$$

Let the x take the values $0, \pm 1, \pm 2, \ldots, \pm H$, where H will be defined presently, and so the y's take $(2H + 1)^n$ sets of integer values. Since $|y| \leqslant nAH$, there are at most $(2nAH + 1)^m$ different sets of values for the y. Hence if

$$(2nAH + 1)^m < (2H + 1)^n,$$

the same set of y values will arise from two different x sets. By subtraction, we obtain an x set not all zero and with $|x| \leqslant 2H$ for which all the y are zero. The H inequality will be satisfied if

$$(2H + 1)^n \geqslant (2nAH + nA)^m,$$

or

$$(2H + 1)^{n-m} \geqslant (nA)^m,$$

$$2H + 1 \geqslant (nA)^{m/(n-m)}.$$

Then we can take H to be an integer such that

$$(nA)^{m/(n-m)} - 1 \leqslant 2H < (nA)^{m/(n-m)} + 1,$$

since the interval for $2H$ is of width 2.

This lemma is a corollary to Theorem 3 in Chapter 5.

Lemma 3

Let θ be an algebraic integer of degree $n \geqslant 3$, and a, b, r non-negative integers such that

$$(a + 1)(b + 1) > rn.$$

Then there exist polynomials not identically zero,

$$R(x, y) = \sum_{\alpha=0}^{a} \sum_{\beta=0}^{b} c_{\alpha,\beta} x^{\alpha} y^{\beta}, \tag{9}$$

where the $c_{\alpha,\beta}$ are rational integers, such that

$$R(x, \theta) = (x - \theta)^{r} S(x), \tag{10}$$

and $S(x)$ is a polynomial in x. Further, if

$$R_{\lambda}(x, y) = \frac{1}{\lambda!} \frac{\partial^{\lambda} R(x, y)}{\partial x^{\lambda}}, \tag{11}$$

$R_{\lambda}(\theta, \theta) = 0$ for $\lambda = 0, 1, \ldots, r - 1$.

The vanishing for $x = \theta$ of a polynomial $R(x)$ with rational coefficients requires n conditions given by expressing the powers of θ in $R(\theta)$ in terms of $1, \theta, \ldots, \theta^{n-1}$, and then equating to zero the coefficients of these powers. These conditions are equivalent to the set

$$R(\theta_1) = 0, R(\theta_2) = 0, \ldots, R(\theta_n) = 0,$$

where $\theta_1 = \theta, \theta_2, \ldots, \theta_n$ are the conjugates of θ, and so since the θ are different, to the set,

$$\theta_1^t R(\theta_1) + \theta_2^t R(\theta_2) + \cdots + \theta_n^t R(\theta_n) = 0, \quad t = 0, 1, \ldots, n - 1.$$

These relations give linear conditions with rational coefficients for the coefficients of $R(\theta)$. Hence each condition $R_{\lambda}(\theta, \theta) = 0$ imposes n such conditions on the $c_{\alpha,\beta}$, and so there are rn conditions for the $(a + 1)(b + 1)$ variables $c_{\alpha,\beta}$. These can be satisfied by integer values of the $c_{\alpha,\beta}$ not all zero if $(a + 1)(b + 1) > rn$.

It is necessary to find an estimate for the $c_{\alpha,\beta}$.

This is given by

Lemma 4

Let b be a fixed integer with $0 \leqslant b < n$, δ a constant with $0 < \delta < 1$, and

$$a = \left[\left(\frac{n + \delta}{b + 1}\right) r\right], \tag{12}$$

where the square brackets denote the integer part. Then there exists in Lemma 3, an integer $c = c(\theta, \delta)$, and a polynomial $R(x, y)$ in equation (9) such that

$$|c_{\alpha, \beta}| \leqslant c^r, \quad 0 \leqslant \alpha \leqslant a, 0 \leqslant \beta \leqslant b. \tag{13}$$

We note that

$$(a + 1)(b + 1) > \left(\frac{n + \delta}{b + 1}\right) r(b + 1) > nr.$$

The conditions on the coefficients $c_{\alpha, \beta}$ are given by

$$\theta_1^t R_\lambda(\theta_1, \theta_1) + \theta_2^t R_\lambda(\theta_2, \theta_2) + \cdots + \theta_n^t R_\lambda(\theta_n, \theta_n) = 0,$$
$$t = 0, 1, \ldots, n - 1, \lambda = 0, 1, \ldots, r - 1.$$

Since
$$R_\lambda(\theta, \theta) = \sum_{\alpha = \lambda}^{a} \sum_{\beta = 0}^{b} \binom{\alpha}{\lambda} c_{\alpha, \beta} \theta^{\alpha - \lambda} \theta^\beta,$$

the coefficient of $c_{\alpha, \beta}$ in $R_\lambda(\theta, \theta)$ has an absolute value

$$\leqslant (1 + 1) \, {}^a max(1, \theta^{a + b})$$
$$< c_1^r, \quad c_1 = c_1(\theta, \delta).$$

Hence the coefficient of $c_{\alpha, \beta}$ in the conditions $R_\lambda(\theta, \theta) = 0$, has an upper bound given by

$$c_2^r(|\theta_1|^t + \cdots + |\theta_n|^t) < c_3^r, \quad c_3 = c_3(\theta, \delta),$$

where $c_2 = \max c_1$ for $\theta = \theta_1, \theta_2, \ldots$. Then Lemma 2 gives the estimate

$$|c_{\alpha, \beta}| < 1 + ((a + 1)(b + 1)c_3^r)^{rn/((a + 1)(b + 1) - rn)}.$$

Also
$$(a + 1)(b + 1) - rn > \delta r,$$

and
$$(a + 1)(b + 1)c_3^r < \left(\frac{n + 1}{b + 1} r + 1\right) (b + 1)c_3^r$$
$$< (n + 1)(r + 1)c_3^r < c_4^r, \quad c_4 = c_4(\theta, \delta).$$

Finally
$$|c_{\alpha, \beta}| < 1 + (c_4^r)^{n/\delta} < c_5^r, \quad c_5 = c_5(\theta, \delta).$$

Corollary

If
$$R_\lambda(x, y) = \sum_{\alpha = 0}^{a - \lambda} \sum_{\beta = 0}^{b} d_{\alpha, \beta} x^\alpha y^\beta,$$

then
$$|d_{\alpha, \beta}| < c_6^r, \quad c_6 = c_6(\theta, \delta).$$

For clearly
$$c_5^r \frac{\alpha . \alpha - 1 \ldots \alpha - \lambda + 1}{\lambda!} \leqslant 2^\alpha c_5^r < c_6^r, \quad c_6 = c_6(\theta, \delta).$$

We now have an estimate for $R_\lambda(x, y)$, when x, y are near θ, given by

Lemma 5

Write $x - \theta = u$, $y - \theta = v$, where $|u| \leqslant 1$, $|v| \leqslant 1$. Then

$$|R_\lambda(x, y)| \leqslant c_7^r(|u|^{r-\lambda} + |v|), \quad \lambda = 0, 1, \ldots, r - 1, \, c_7 = c_7(\theta, \delta).$$

For

$$R_\lambda(x, y) = \sum_{\alpha=0}^{a-\lambda} \sum_{\beta=0}^{b} d_{\alpha,\beta}(u + \theta)^\alpha(v + \theta)^\beta,$$

$$= \sum_{\alpha=0}^{a-\lambda} \sum_{\beta=0}^{b} e_{\alpha,\beta} u^\alpha v^\beta, \tag{14}$$

say, where,

$$|e_{\alpha,\beta}| \leqslant \sum_{\alpha=0}^{a-\lambda} \sum_{\beta=0}^{b} |d_{\alpha,\beta}|(1 + |\theta|)^\alpha(1 + |\theta|)^\beta$$

$$\leqslant (a + 1)(b + 1)c_6^r(1 + |\theta|)^{a+b}$$

$$< c_8^r, \quad c_8 = c_8(\delta, \theta).$$

Since $e_{\alpha,0} = 0$ for $0 \leqslant \alpha \leqslant r - 1 - \lambda$,

$$R_\lambda(x, y) = u^{r-\lambda} \sum_{\alpha=r-\lambda}^{a-\lambda} e_{\alpha,0} u^{\alpha-r+\lambda} + v \sum_{\alpha=0}^{a-\lambda} \sum_{\beta=1}^{b} e_{\alpha,\beta} u^\alpha v^{\beta-1}.$$

From this, since $|u| \leqslant 1$, $|v| \leqslant 1$,

$$|R_\lambda(x, y)| \leqslant |u|^{r-\lambda} \sum_{\alpha=r-\lambda}^{a-\lambda} c_8^r + |v| \sum_{\alpha=0}^{a-\lambda} \sum_{\beta=1}^{b} c_8^r$$

$$\leqslant |u|^{r-\lambda}(a - r + 1)c_8^r + |v|(a + 1)(b + 1)c_8^r$$

$$\leqslant c_7^r(|u|^{r-\lambda} + |v|), \quad c_7 = c_7(\delta, \theta).$$

Let now p_1/q_1, p_2/q_2 be two rational fractions with

$$(p_1, q_1) = 1, \quad (p_2, q_2) = 1, \quad q_1 > 0, q_2 > 0.$$

We shall show that p_1/q_1, p_2/q_2 cannot both be good approximations to θ. Put $x = p_1/q_1$, $y = p_2/q_2$ in the inequality for $R_\lambda(x, y)$.

Then

$$q_1^a q_2^b \left| R_\lambda \left(\frac{p_1}{q_1}, \frac{p_2}{q_2} \right) \right| \leqslant c_7^r \left(\left| \theta - \frac{p_1}{q_1} \right|^{r-\lambda} + \left| \theta - \frac{p_2}{q_2} \right| \right) q_1^a q_2^b.$$

The left-hand side is an integer. If it is not zero, and the proof of this which now follows is the most difficult part of the investigation, then the right-hand side $\geqslant 1$. Then one of the two terms $\geqslant \frac{1}{2}$ and so

$$c_9^r q_1^a q_2^b \max \left(\left| \theta - \frac{p_1}{q_1} \right|^{r-\lambda}, \left| \theta - \frac{p_2}{q_2} \right| \right) \geqslant 1, \quad c_9 = c_9(\delta, \theta).$$

This proves the statement.

Write now

$$R(x, y) = \sum_{m=0}^{b} f_m(x) y^m = \sum_{l=0}^{a} g_l(y) x^l, \tag{16}$$

where $f_m(x)$, $g_l(y)$ are polynomials in x, y respectively, and neither all the $f_m(x)$ nor all the $g_l(y)$ are identically zero.

The polynomials $f_m(x)$, $(m = 0, 1, 2, \ldots, b)$ are not necessarily independent. Suppose that $b' + 1$ $(0 < b' \leqslant b)$ of them, say

$$F_0(x), F_1(x), \ldots, F_{b'}(x),$$

are linearly independent. Then

$$\Delta = \| F_\beta^{(\alpha)}(x) \| \neq 0, \quad \alpha = 0, 1, \ldots, b'; \beta = 0, 1, \ldots, b'.$$

Write
$$R(x, y) = \sum_{\beta=0}^{b'} F_\beta(x) G_\beta(y),$$

where the coefficients in $F_\beta(x)$ are rational integers, and those in $G_\beta(y)$ are rational numbers. The $G_\beta(y)$ are also linearly independent since if they were not, then $R(x, y)$ could be expressed with less than b' of the $F(x)$.

Lemma 6

$$R\left(x, \frac{p_2}{q_2}\right) \neq 0 \quad \text{if } q_2 > c^r{}_{10}. \tag{17}$$

For otherwise

$$\sum_{l=0}^{a} g_l\left(\frac{p_2}{q_2}\right) x^l \equiv 0.$$

Then for some l for which $g_l(x)$ is not identically zero,

$$g_l\left(\frac{p_2}{q_2}\right) = 0, \quad \text{i.e.} \quad \sum_{\beta=0}^{b} c_{l,\beta} \left(\frac{p_2}{q_2}\right)^\beta = 0,$$

say.

On multiplying out by q_2^b, we see that $q_2 \mid c_{l,\beta'}$ where β' is the greatest number for which $c_{l,\beta} \neq 0$. This is impossible since $|c_{l,\beta}| \leqslant c^r$ by Lemma 4.

Lemma 7

Let k be any given rational number. If there exists an integer γ such that $\Delta^{(\gamma)}(h) \neq 0$, and $\gamma + b < r$, then there exists an $R_\lambda(h, p_2/q_2)$ with $0 \leqslant \lambda < r$ such that $R_\lambda(h, p_2/q_2) \neq 0$.

Since
$$R\left(x, \frac{p_2}{q_2}\right) = \sum_{\beta=0}^{b'} F_\beta(x) G_\beta\left(\frac{p_2}{q_2}\right) \neq 0,$$

there exists a β such that $G_\beta(p_2/q_2) \neq 0$, or by a slight change of notation, say $G_0(p_2/q_2) \neq 0$.

By repeated differentiation for x, we have, say,

$$\alpha! R_\alpha \left(x, \frac{p_2}{q_2}\right) = \sum_{\beta=0}^{b'} F_\beta^{(\alpha)}(x) G_\beta \left(\frac{p_2}{q_2}\right), \quad \alpha = 0, 1, \ldots, b'.$$

Here the $b' + 1$ linear equations in $G_\beta(p_2/q_2)$ can be solved on multiplying the equations by the usual cofactors, since the determinant $\Delta(x)$ formed from $F_\beta^{(\alpha)}(x)$ is not identically zero.

Hence

$$\Delta(x) G_0 \left(\frac{p_2}{q_2}\right) = \sum_{\alpha=0}^{b'} H_\alpha(x) R_\alpha \left(x, \frac{p_2}{q_2}\right),$$

where the $H_\alpha(x)$ are polynomials with integer coefficients. Differentiate γ times and put $x = h$. Then

$$\Delta^{(\gamma)}(h) G_0 \left(\frac{p_2}{q_2}\right) = \sum_{\lambda=0}^{b'+\gamma} h_\lambda R_\lambda \left(h, \frac{p_2}{q_2}\right),$$

where the h_λ are rational numbers. Since $b' + \gamma \leqslant b + \gamma < r$, the R_λ are defined, and clearly not all the $R_\lambda(h, p_2/q_2)$ are zero for $0 \leqslant \lambda \leqslant b' + \gamma$. We now find γ from

Lemma 8

Suppose $r > n$. Then there exists an integer $\gamma = \gamma(\theta, b, \delta, r, h)$ with

$$0 \leqslant \gamma \leqslant \delta r + n^2 - n, \qquad \Delta^{(\gamma)}(h) \neq 0. \tag{18}$$

From $\qquad \alpha! R_\alpha(x, y) = \sum_{\beta=0}^{b'} F_\beta^{(\alpha)}(x) G_\beta(y), \quad (\alpha = 0, 1, \ldots, b'),$

$$\alpha! R_\alpha(x, \theta) = \sum_{\beta=0}^{b'} F_\beta^{(\alpha)}(x) G_\beta(\theta).$$

The polynomial $R_\alpha(x, \theta)$ in x is divisible by $(x - \theta)^{r-\alpha}$, and so by $(x - \theta)^{r-b'}$ since $\alpha \leqslant b' < r$. On multiplying the last equations by the appropriate minors of $\Delta(x)$ and adding, $\Delta(x) G_0(\theta)$ is also divisible by $(x - \theta)^{r-b'}$. Now $G_0(y) \neq 0$, and $G_0(\theta) \neq 0$ since $G_0(\theta)$ is of degree $b < n$. Hence $\Delta(x)$ is divisible by $(x - \theta)^{r-b'}$, and so if

$$f(x) = x^n + a_1 x^{n-1} + \cdots + a_n = 0,$$

where the a are rational numbers, is the irreducible equation satisfied by θ,

$$\Delta(x) = f^{r-b'}(x) D(x),$$

where $D(x)$ is a polynomial with rational coefficients and of degree d, say. Hence since the elements of $\Delta(x)$ are polynomials of degree a at most,

$$d + n(r - b') \leqslant a(b' + 1),$$

$$d \leqslant \frac{n + \delta}{b + 1} r(b + 1) - nr + nb \leqslant \delta r + nb$$

$$\leqslant \delta r + n^2 - n.$$

Since h is rational, $f(h) \neq 0$, and so $\Delta(x)$ has a zero at $x = h$ of order γ at most equal to d.

Lemma 9

If $(p_1, q_1) = 1$, $(p_2, q_2) = 1$, $q_1 > 0$, $q_2 > c^r$, $r \geqslant 2n^2$, $\delta < \frac{1}{2}$, *there exists* $c_9 = c_9(\delta, \theta)$, *and an integer* $\lambda = \lambda(\theta, b, \delta, r, p_1, q_1, p_2, q_2)$ *with* $0 \leqslant \lambda < \delta r + n^2$, *i.e.* $\lambda < r$, *such that*

$$c_9^r q_1^a q_2^b \max \left(\left| \theta - \frac{p_1}{q_1} \right|^{r - \lambda}, \left| \theta - \frac{p_2}{q_2} \right| \right) > 1. \tag{19}$$

The lemma is trivial if either $|\theta - p_1/q_1| > 1$ or $|\theta - p_2/q_2| > 1$ with $c_9 = 1$, and so we may assume that

$$\left| \theta - \frac{p_1}{q_1} \right| \leqslant 1, \qquad \left| \theta - \frac{p_2}{q_2} \right| \leqslant 1.$$

From Lemma 7 with $h = p_1/q_1$, we can now find an $R_\lambda(x, y)$ such that $R_\lambda(p_1/q_2, p_2/q_2) \neq 0$. We take $h = p_1/q_1$ in Lemma 8, and so $\gamma = \gamma(\theta, b, \delta, r, p_1, q_1)$. Then

$$0 \leqslant \gamma \leqslant \delta r + n^2 - n,$$

$$\lambda \leqslant b + \gamma \leqslant \delta r + n^2 - n + b,$$

$$\lambda < \frac{r}{2} + \frac{r}{2} = r.$$

We have now disposed of the preliminary preparations and are in a position to prove Siegel's theorem.

Suppose first that θ is an integer. We need only consider solutions with $(x, y) = 1$. For if $(x, y) = d_1$, $x = d_1 X$, $y = d_1 Y$, $(X, Y) = 1$, and the inequality (4) becomes

$$\left| \theta - \frac{X}{Y} \right| < \frac{1}{d_1^\nu |Y|^\nu} \leqslant \frac{1}{Y^\nu}.$$

This has only a finite number of solutions from the case $d_1 = 1$. Also in equation (1), d_1 can have only a finite number of values.

Let us suppose there are an infinity of solutions of the inequality (4)

$$\left| \theta - \frac{x}{y} \right| < \frac{1}{y^\nu}, \quad (x, y) = 1,$$

where we may suppose that $y > 0$. We select two solutions (p_1, q_1), (p_2, q_2), $q_2 > q_1$, and define the integer r by

$$q_1^r \leqslant q_2 < q_1^{r+1}, \quad \text{i.e. } r = \left[\frac{\log q_2}{\log q_1}\right].$$ (20)

We can take $q_1 > c$, and $q_2 > c^r$ and also so great that $r \geqslant 2n^2$. We shall impose conditions on the choice of δ and q_1 which will contradict the assertion in Lemma 9, i.e. we shall make

$$A = c_9^r q_1^a q_2^b \left| \theta - \frac{p_1}{q_1} \right|^{r-\lambda} \leqslant 1,$$

$$B = c_9^r q_1^a q_2^b \left| \theta - \frac{p_2}{q_2} \right| \leqslant 1.$$

Write $\nu = n/(b+1) + b + \varepsilon$, where we can take $0 < \varepsilon < 1$, and so

$$\nu < \frac{n}{2} + n - 1 + 1 < 2n.$$

Now
$$A c_9^{-r} < q_1^{a + b(r+1) - \nu(r-\lambda)},$$

$$< q_1^{\frac{n+\delta}{b+1} r + br + b - \nu r + \nu\lambda},$$

$$< \left(q_1^{\frac{n+\delta}{b+1} + b + \frac{b}{r} - \nu + \frac{\nu\lambda}{r}} \right)^r,$$

$$< \left(q_1^{\frac{\delta}{b+1} - \varepsilon + \frac{b}{r} + \frac{\nu\lambda}{r}} \right)^r,$$

$$< \left(q_1^{\frac{\delta}{b+1} - \varepsilon + \frac{b}{r} + \delta\nu + \frac{n^2\nu}{r}} \right)^r.$$

We can take δ so small that $\delta/(b+1) + \delta\nu < \frac{1}{4}\varepsilon$, and r so great that $b/r + n^2\nu/r < \frac{1}{4}\varepsilon$. Then $A < (c_9 q_1^{-\varepsilon/4})^r$, and we can suppose q_1 so great that $A < 1$.

Next
$$B c_9^{-r} < q_1^{\frac{n+\delta}{b+1} r} q_2^{b-\nu},$$

$$< q_1^{\frac{n+\delta}{b+1} r + r(b-\nu)}, \quad \text{since } b < \nu,$$

$$< \left(q_1^{\frac{n+\delta}{b+1} + b - \nu} \right)^r = \left(q_1^{\frac{\delta}{b+1} - \varepsilon} \right)^r,$$

$$< (q_1^{-\varepsilon/2})^r.$$

Hence
$$B < (c_9 q_1^{-\varepsilon/2})^r < (c_9 q_1^{-\varepsilon/4})^r < 1$$

from the choice of q_1 for A.

This proves Siegel's theorem when θ is an algebraic integer.

Suppose next that θ is not an integer. Write $\theta = \phi/j$, where ϕ is an algebraic integer and j is a rational integer. The inequality (4) becomes

$$\left| \frac{\phi}{j} - \frac{x}{y} \right| < \frac{1}{y^\nu},$$

$$\left| \phi - \frac{jx}{y} \right| < \frac{j}{y^\nu}.$$

Then
$$\frac{j}{y^\nu} = \frac{j}{y^{\frac{n}{b+1} + b + \varepsilon}} < \frac{1}{y^{\frac{n}{b+1} + b + \frac{\varepsilon}{2}}}$$

for large y. Hence there can be only a finite number of values for jx and y.

3. The Thue–Siegel approximation result can be applied to equations other than (1). A corollary to Theorem 4 is given by

Theorem 5

Let $F(x, y)$ be a homogeneous irreducible polynomial of degree n and $G(x, y)$ a polynomial of degree m. Then the equation

$$F(x, y) = G(x, y)$$

has only a finite number of integer solutions for x, y if $m < n/2 - 1$.

The result is easily proved if all the linear factors of $F(x, y)$ are complex.

Suppose next that there are an infinity of solutions when there are real linear factors of $F(x, y)$. Then for large $|x|$, there exists a real linear factor $y - \alpha x$ such that $F(x, y)/(y - \alpha x)x^{n-1} \to c_1$ where c_1 is a constant. Hence say,

$$|y - \alpha x| \, |x^{n-1}| < c_2 |G(x, y)|,$$

and so
$$|y - \alpha x| < c_3 |x^m/x^{n-1}|,$$
$$< 1/|x^{n/2 + \varepsilon}|$$

for arbitrary $\varepsilon > 0$. Hence the result.

If Roth's result is used, we can take $m < n - 2$.

Other applications require an extension of the Thue–Siegel approximation theorem to approximation by algebraic integers. Siegel[2] has proved the

Theorem 6

Let K be an algebraic number field of degree n and α be the root of an equation of degree $d \geqslant 2$ irreducible in K. Let $\xi \neq 0$ be an algebraic number in K and let $H(\xi)$ be the maximum value of the absolute values of the coefficients of the irreducible equation satisfied by ξ. Then the inequality

$$|\xi - \alpha| \leqslant 1/(H(\xi))^{d/(s+1) + s + \varepsilon}, \quad 0 < s < d$$

has only a finite number of solutions in integers ξ of degree n.

The proof of the existence of only a finite number of integer solutions of

$$f(x, y) = m > 0, \qquad (21)$$

where $f(x, y)$ is a homogeneous polynomial of degree n irreducible over the rationals, can give estimates for the number of solutions. This, however, does not help in finding the solutions since the method is non-constructive. Recently, Baker[4] has shown that bounds can be given for the magnitude of the solutions. He has proved the

Theorem 7

Let $\alpha > n + 1$. *Then the solutions of* (21) *satisfy the inequality*

$$\max \left(|x|, |y| \right) < c e^{(\log m)^\alpha},$$

where c is an effectively computable constant depending only on n, α and the coefficients of $f(x, y)$.

Previously[5] he had proved some special results, for example, when $f(x, y) = x^3 - 2y^3$, then $|x| < M$, $|y| < M$ where $M = (3 \cdot 10^5 m)^{23}$.

Baker's results also imply that bounds can be found for the solution of some other equations whose solution can be made to depend upon equations such as (21), for example,

$$y^2 = ax^3 + bx^2 + cx + d,$$

as this can be reduced to the question of representing unity by a finite number of binary quartics as is shown in Chapter 27.

REFERENCES

1. A. Thue. Über Annäherungswerte algebraischer Zahlen. *J. reine angew. Math.*, **135** (1909), 284–305.
2. C. L. Siegel. Approximation algebraischer Zahlen. *Math. Z.*, **10** (1921), 173–213. Also Gesammelte Abhandlungen, **1** (1966), 6–46.
3. K. F. Roth. Rational approximations to algebraic numbers. *Mathematika*, **2** (1955), 1–20. Also Corrigendum. *Mathematika*, **2** (1955), 168.
4. A. Baker. On the representation of integers by binary forms. *Phil. Trans. R. Soc.*, **263** (1968), 173–191.
5. A. Baker. Rational approximations to $\sqrt[3]{2}$ and other algebraic numbers. *Q. J. Math.*, **15** (1964), 375–383.

CHAPTER 23

Local Methods or p-Adic Applications

1. One of the most important applications of p-adic numbers to Diophantine equations deals with the

Problem

Let $\omega_1, \omega_2, \ldots, \omega_n$ be a basis of the integers in an algebraic number field $K = Q(\theta)$. Denote by $N(\omega)$ the norm of ω in the field. Then it is required to discuss the solution in rational integers x of the equation

$$N(x_1\omega_1 + x_2\omega_2 + \cdots + x_n\omega_n) = a, \tag{1}$$

where the x satisfy the $n - m$ equation

$$g_l(x) = 0, \quad (l = 1, 2, \ldots, n - m) \tag{2}$$

for given $m \leqslant n$, and the $g(x)$ are polynomials in x with rational coefficients.
The simplest problem is when $x_{m+1} = x_{m+2} = \cdots = x_n = 0$.
From algebraic number theory, it is known that the general solution of equation (1) is given by

$$x_1\omega_1^{(s)} + x_2\omega_2^{(s)} + \cdots + x_n\omega_n^{(s)} = c^{(s)}\varepsilon^{(s)}, \quad (s = 1, 2, \ldots, n), \tag{3}$$

where $\omega^{(s)}$ denotes the conjugates of ω, the c belong to a finite set of numbers in K and ε is a unit in K. We recall that every unit ε can be written in the form

$$\varepsilon = \zeta\eta_1^{u_1}\eta_2^{u_2}\ldots\eta_r^{u_r}, \tag{4}$$

where ζ is a root of unity in K, the η are a set of fundamental units, and the u are arbitrary rational integers. Also $r = r_1 + r_2 - 1$ where r_1, r_2 denote respectively the number of real fields and pairs of complex fields among the conjugates of K. On substituting for the x from equations (3) and (4) in (2), we have $n - m$ equations in the r unknowns u which occur as exponents in the powers of the units η. If $r \leqslant n - m$, we should expect there to be only a finite number of solutions if the equations resulting from (2) are independent. As these equations are best dealt with by p-adic methods, we give a brief résumé of p-adic number theory where p is a rational prime. For simplicity we define the p-adic numbers over the rational field Q. Let x be any number in Q. We define a valuation $|x|_p$ as follows. If $x = 0$, $|x|_p = 0$. If $x \neq 0$, x

can be written in the form $x = p^\alpha x_1/x_2$, where x_1, x_2 are prime to p. Then $|x|_p = 1/p^\alpha$. The valuation has the properties

1. $|x|_p \geqslant 0$, and $|x|_p = 0$ if and only if $x = 0$,

2. $|x_1 x_2|_p = |x_1|_p |x_2|_p$,

3. $|x_1 \pm x_2|_p \leqslant |x_1|_p + |x_2|_p$.

This is the triangular inequality and may be sharpened to

$$|x_1 \pm x_2|_p \leqslant \max (|x_1|_p, |x_2|_p).$$

The p-adic field Q_p is defined as a field which contains the field Q and is such that if $X \in Q_p$, then

I. There is a valuation $|X|_p$ on Q_p which satisfies 1, 2 and 3 and coincides with $|x|_p$ when $X = x$ is an element of Q.

II. Limits are defined as for complex number theory, except that an absolute value $|x|$ there is replaced by $|x|_p$, and corresponding results exist for the p-adic field. Thus Cauchy's convergence principle holds, i.e. a sequence $X_1, X_2, \ldots$, tends to a limit if and only if $|X_m - X_n|_p < \varepsilon$ for $m, n > N(\varepsilon)$. This limit will be in Q_p and so the field Q_p is complete.

III. Every element of Q_p is a limit of a sequence of numbers of Q.

The discussion of convergence is now very simple since a series $\sum a_n$ converges if and only if $|a_n|_p \rightarrow 0$, and so there is no need for the concept of absolute convergence. The usual results on functions of a complex variable carry over to p-adic variables. There is, however, greater simplicity since if $|a_n|_p \rightarrow 0$, the series

$$f(x) = \sum_0^\infty a_n x^n$$

converges for $|x|_p \leqslant 1$.

We can define series which have the characteristic properties of the exponential and logarithmic functions.
Thus we have

$$e^x = 1 + x + \frac{x^2}{2!} + \cdots + \frac{x^n}{n!} + \cdots \qquad \text{if } |x|_p < \frac{1}{p-1}$$

$$\log (1 + x) = x - \frac{x^2}{2} + \cdots + \frac{(-1)^{n-1} x^n}{n} + \cdots \qquad \text{if } |x|_p < 1.$$

Similar results hold when x is a number in an algebraic number field K. If η is a unit in K, there exists a rational integer a such that if p is an odd prime, then $\eta^a \equiv 1 \pmod{p}$, but if $p = 2, \eta^a \equiv 1 \pmod 4$. Then $\eta^{av} = e^{v \log \eta^a}$ can be expanded as a power series in v with coefficients in K which converges for all p-adic integers v. Since $u = av + b, 0 \leqslant b < a$, we have a expansions for η^u. It follows at once that the product $\eta_1^{u_1}\eta_2^{u_2}\ldots$ can be expressed as a finite number of power series in $v_1, v_2, \ldots$ with coefficients in K which converge for all p-adic integers $v_1, v_2, \ldots$.

2. We now show by a method due to Skolem how p-adic theory can be applied to the equations arising from (2). It is obvious that equations will have only a finite number of rational solutions if they have only a finite number of p-adic solutions. The equations (2) can be replaced by a finite number of equations

$$g_l(u_1, u_2, \ldots, u_r) = 0, \quad (l = 1, 2, \ldots, n - m), \tag{5}$$

where the $g(u)$ are power series converging for all p-adic integers u. The coefficients may be taken as rational numbers whose denominators are prime to p since we are considering a set of conjugate equations.

The finiteness of the number of p-adic solutions can be proved from the following theorems.

Theorem 1

Let $f(x) = \sum_0^\infty a_n x^n$ where $|a_n|_p \to 0$ so that the series converges when $|x|_p \leqslant 1$. Then the equation $f(x) = 0$ has only a finite number of solutions for $|x|_p \leqslant 1$, i.e. for p-adic integers x.

More generally we have a result given by Strassmann[1]

Theorem 2

Let $f_0(x), f_1(x), \ldots$ be polynomials whose coefficients are p-adic integers, and suppose that $f_0(x)$ has at least one coefficient $\not\equiv 0 \pmod{p}$. Then the equation

$$\sum_{n=0}^\infty p^n f_n(x) = 0 \tag{6}$$

has only a finite number of solutions in p-adic integers.

There are extensions to several variables.

Theorem 3

Let $f_0(x, y), f_1(x, y), \ldots, g_0(x, y), g_1(x, y), \ldots$ be polynomials whose coefficients are p-adic integers and suppose that

$$\frac{\partial f_0}{\partial x}\frac{\partial g_0}{\partial y} - \frac{\partial f_0}{\partial y}\frac{\partial g_0}{\partial x} \not\equiv 0 \pmod{p}.$$

Then the simultaneous equations

$$\sum_0^\infty p^n f_n(x, y) = 0, \qquad \sum_0^\infty p^n g_n(x, y) = 0 \tag{7}$$

have only a finite number of p-adic solutions.

This also holds if f_0, g_0 are relatively prime mod p.

Skolem has proved many results by his methods. When the question is only to prove the existence of a finite number of integer solutions, the work may not be too complicated as can be seen from his[2,3] proof of

Theorem 4

Let $a_1, a_2, \ldots, a_n, b_1, b_2, \ldots, b_n$ be numbers in an algebraic number field K. Then the equation

$$\sum_{i=1}^{n} a_i b_i^x = 0 \tag{8}$$

has only a finite number of rational integer solutions for x, if none of the quotients b_i/b_j is a root of unity.

When the numerical values of the fundamental units of the relevant algebraic number field play no part in an investigation, and only an estimate for the number of solutions is required, the details may not be troublesome as in Skolem's proof of Theorem 5

Theorem 5

If d is an integer > 1, there is at most one rational integer solution of $x^3 + dy^3 = 1$ other than $x = 1, y = 0$.

Let us suppose there are two solutions (x_1, y_1) and (x_2, y_2). Write $\theta = \sqrt[3]{d}$. Then $\eta_1 = x_1 + y_1\theta$, $\eta_2 = x_2 + y_2\theta$ are positive units with norm 1 in the field $Q(\theta)$. Since there are no roots of unity in the field and there is only one fundamental unit, we have

$$\eta_1^{u_1} = \eta_2^{u_2} \tag{9}$$

with rational integers, u_1, u_2. We may suppose that u_1, u_2 are not both $\equiv 0 \pmod 3$, for if so, we would have $\eta_1^{u_1/3} = \eta_2^{u_2/3}$. Hence we may suppose that $u_2 \not\equiv 0 \pmod 3$. Then u_1/u_2 is a 3-adic integer and so we have, say, the 3-adic equation

$$\eta_1^u = \eta_2.$$

Suppose first that $y_1 \equiv 0 \pmod 3$ and so $x_1 \not\equiv 0 \pmod 3$. Then η_1^u is defined in the 3-adic field over $Q(\theta)$ and so

$$x_1^u \left(1 + \frac{y_1}{x_1}\theta\right)^u = \eta_2,$$

and the left-hand side can be expanded as a binomial series. Equating the coefficient of θ^2 to zero, we have

$$\binom{u}{2}\left(\frac{y_1}{x_1}\right)^2 + \binom{u}{5}\left(\frac{y_1}{x_1}\right)^5 d + \binom{u}{8}\left(\frac{y_1}{x_1}\right)^8 d^2 + \cdots = 0.$$

We show that the only solutions of this equation are $u = 0, 1$. For on dividing out by

$$2 \binom{u}{2} \left(\frac{y_1}{x_1}\right)^2,$$

we have

$$\frac{1}{2} + \binom{u-2}{3} \frac{d}{4.5} \left(\frac{y_1}{x_1}\right)^3 + \binom{u-2}{6} \frac{d^2}{7.8} \left(\frac{y_1}{x_1}\right)^6 + \cdots = 0.$$

This gives an impossible congruence mod 3, since $4, 5, 7, 8, \ldots$ are 3-adic units.

Suppose next that $y_1 \not\equiv 0 \pmod 3$. Since

$$\eta_1^3 = x_1^3 + 3x_1^2 y_1 \theta + 3x_1 y_1^2 \theta^2 + y_1^3 \theta^3$$

$$= 1 + 3x_1^2 y_1 \theta + 3x_1 y_1^2 \theta^2 = 1 + 3\delta,$$

say, η_1^u is defined for $u \equiv 0 \pmod 3$. Write $u = 3v + u_0$, $u_0 = 0, 1, 2$.

Then $\eta_1^{3v + u_0} \equiv \eta_2 \pmod 3, \qquad \eta_1^{u_0} \equiv \eta_2 \pmod 3.$

Comparing coefficients of θ^2, we see that $u_0 = 0, 1$.
Take first $u_0 = 0$. Then

$$(1 + 3\delta)^v = x_2 + y_2 \theta.$$

Denote by b_t the coefficient of θ^2 in δ^t. Then

$$\sum_{t=0}^{\infty} 3^t b_t \binom{v}{t} = 0,$$

or $$3x_1 y_1^2 v + 3^2 x_1^4 y_1^2 \binom{v}{2} + \cdots = 0.$$

Divide out by $3x_1 y_1^2$, and we have, say,

$$v + 3B_2 \binom{v}{2} + 3^2 B_3 \binom{v}{3} + \cdots = 0,$$

where the B are polynomials in x_1, y_1 with integer coefficients. This is impossible, for if 3^λ is the highest power of 3 dividing v, all the other terms are divisible by $3^{\lambda+1}$. For the general term is

$$3^{t-1} B_t \binom{v}{t} = 3^{t-1} \frac{v B_t}{t} \binom{v-1}{t-1}$$

and $3^{t-2}/t$ is a 3-adic integer. This is obvious on putting $t = t_0 3^\mu$ where 3^μ is the highest power of 3 dividing t.

Suppose next $u_0 = 1$. Then

$$(x_1 + y_1 \theta)\left(\sum_{t=0}^{\infty} 3^t \delta^t \binom{v}{t}\right) = x_2 + y_2 \theta.$$

Denote by c_t the coefficient of θ in δ^t. Then

$$x_1 \sum_{t=0}^{\infty} 3^t b_t \binom{v}{t} + y_1 \sum_{t=0}^{\infty} 3^t c_t \binom{v}{t} = 0.$$

Dividing out by $3x_1^2 y_1^2$, we have, say,

$$2v + 3c_1 \binom{v}{2} + 3^2 c_2 \binom{v}{3} + \cdots = 0,$$

and this is impossible as before.

3. When it is required to find all the integer solutions of an equation, the process may not be very complicated if fundamental units are not involved as in the following theorem. This deals with a conjecture enunciated by Ramanujan and first proved by Nagell. Many other proofs have been given and these have been analysed and discussed by Hasse. He has given a simpler version of Nagell's [4] proof as well as a generalization. We give Hasse's [5] proof of

Theorem 6

  The equation $x^2 + 7 = 2^n$ has only the positive integer solutions given by $x = 1, 3, 5, 11, 181$ corresponding to $n = 3, 4, 5, 7, 15$.

When n is even, $n = 4$ is the only solution since

$$(2^{n/2})^2 - x^2 = 7, \qquad 2^{n/2} \pm x = 7, \qquad 2^{n/2} \mp x = 1.$$

We may now suppose that n is odd, and we write the equation as

$$\frac{x^2 + 7}{4} = 2^y, \tag{10}$$

where y is odd and $y \geqslant 3$.

  We factorize the equation in the field $Q(\sqrt{-7})$, in which the integers have the form $(m + n\sqrt{-7})/2$ where $m \equiv n \pmod 2$, and in which unique factorization holds. Since

$$2 = \left(\frac{1 + \sqrt{-7}}{2}\right) \left(\frac{1 - \sqrt{-7}}{2}\right),$$

we have

$$\frac{x + \sqrt{-7}}{2} = \pm \left(\frac{1 \pm \sqrt{-7}}{2}\right)^y,$$

and so

$$\left(\frac{1 + \sqrt{-7}}{2}\right)^y - \left(\frac{1 - \sqrt{-7}}{2}\right)^y = \pm\sqrt{-7}. \tag{11}$$

  We show that the positive sign is impossible in equation (11). Write this as

$$a^y - b^y = a - b.$$

Then

$$a^2 \equiv (1 - b)^2 \equiv 1 \pmod{b^2},$$

since $ab = 2$, and so

$$a^y \equiv a(a^2)^{(y-1)/2} \equiv a \pmod{b^2},$$

$$a \equiv a - b \pmod{b^2},$$

which is false.
Hence we have

$$-2^{y-1} = \binom{y}{1} - \binom{y}{3} 7 + \binom{y}{5} 7^2 \cdots \pm \binom{y}{y} 7^{(y-1)/2}, \tag{12}$$

and so
$$-2^{y-1} \equiv y \pmod 7.$$

This has the odd solutions $y \equiv 3, 5, 13 \pmod{42}$. We prove that 3, 5, 13 are the only remaining solutions for y in equation (10).

It suffices to show that there cannot be two solutions y, y_1 with $y_1 - y \equiv 0 \pmod{42}$. Suppose that 7^l is the greatest power of 7 dividing $y_1 - y$. Then

$$a^{y_1} = a^y \cdot a^{y_1-y} = a^y(\tfrac{1}{2})^{y_1-y}(1 + \sqrt{-7})^{y_1-y}. \tag{13}$$

Now
$$(\tfrac{1}{2})^{y_1-y} = ((\tfrac{1}{2})^6)^{(y_1-y)/6} \equiv 1 \pmod{7^{l+1}}.$$

Also
$$(1 + \sqrt{-7})^{y_1-y} \equiv 1 + (y_1 - y)\sqrt{-7} \pmod{7^{l+1}}$$

as follows on raising $1 + \sqrt{-7}$ successively to powers $7, 7^2, \ldots, 7^l$ and then to the power $(y_1 - y)/7^l$.

Since
$$a^y \equiv \frac{1 + y\sqrt{-7}}{2^y} \pmod 7,$$

on substituting in equation (13), we have

$$a^{y_1} \equiv a^y + \frac{(y_1 - y)}{2^y} \sqrt{-7} \pmod{7^{l+1}}. \tag{14}$$

Similarly
$$b^{y_1} \equiv b^y + \frac{(y_1 - y)}{2^y} \sqrt{-7} \pmod{7^{l+1}}.$$

Since from equation (11),

$$a^y - b^y = a^{y_1} - b^{y_1},$$

then
$$(y_1 - y)\sqrt{-7} \equiv 0 \pmod{7^{l+1}},$$

and so since y_1, y are rational

$$y_1 - y \equiv 0 \pmod{7^{l+1}}.$$

This contradiction establishes the theorem.

4. When the numerical values of the fundamental units must be considered, in general, a great deal of detailed numerical work, and several cases may arise.

It is only exceptionally that little detail is required and then the result may perhaps be found more simply by classical methods. Thus we have the proof by Skolem[3] of

Theorem 7

The only integer solutions of the equation

$$x^4 - 2y^4 = 1 \tag{15}$$

are given by $y = 0$, $x = \pm 1$.

Clearly $y \equiv 0 \pmod 2$ and so we may replace the equation by the equation

$$x^4 - 32y^4 = 1. \tag{16}$$

It can be shown that the fundamental units in the field $Q(\theta)$, where $\theta = \sqrt[4]{2}$, are given by $1 + \theta$ and $1 + \theta^2$. Since $x + 2y\theta$ is a unit in the field, we have

$$(1 + \theta)^u (1 + \theta^2)^v = x + 2y\theta, \tag{17}$$

$$\left(1 + u\theta + \frac{u \cdot u - 1}{2!} + \cdots\right)(1 + v\theta^2 + \cdots) \equiv x \pmod 2,$$

and so $u \equiv 0 \pmod 2$.

Since the coefficients of θ^2, θ^3 vanish in the left-hand side of equation (17), we deduce the p-adic equations:

$$\binom{u}{2} + v + 2\left(\binom{u}{6} + \binom{u}{4}v + \binom{u}{2}\binom{v}{2} + \binom{v}{3}\right) + 2^2(\ldots) = 0,$$

$$\binom{u}{3} + uv + 2\left(\binom{u}{7} + \binom{u}{5}v + \binom{u}{3}\binom{v}{2} + u\binom{v}{3}\right) + 2^2(\ldots) = 0.$$

Multiply the first equation by u and subtract from the second. Then

$$-\tfrac{1}{3}(u + 1)u(u - 1) + 2\left\{\left(\binom{u}{7}\right) - u\binom{u}{6} + \left(\binom{u}{5}\right) - u\binom{u}{4}\right)v$$

$$+ \left(\binom{u}{3}\right) - u\binom{u}{2}\right)\binom{v}{2}\right\} + 2^2(\ldots) = 0. \tag{18}$$

If $u \neq 0$, suppose that $2^\lambda \parallel u$ and so $\lambda \geqslant 1$. Then

$$\binom{u}{2u + 1} = \frac{u}{2u + 1}\binom{u - 1}{2u} \equiv 0 \pmod{2^\lambda}.$$

Hence all the terms of equation (14) are $\equiv 0 \pmod{2^{\lambda+1}}$ except the first and so we must have $u = 0$.

Then
$$v + 2\binom{v}{3} + 2^2\binom{v}{5} + \cdots = 0,$$

and a similar argument shows that $v = 0$.

In the same way, it can be shown that the only integer solutions of

$$x^4 - 8y^4 = 1, \tag{19}$$

are given by $y = 0$, $x = \pm 1$. For now we have

$$(1 + \theta)^u (1 + \theta^2)^v = x + y\theta^3,$$

and the result is easily proved.

The most troublesome numerical details arise perhaps when Skolem's method cannot be applied directly because there are not as many equations as there are unknowns. It then becomes necessary to introduce relative units in an extension of the original algebraic number field. An illustration is given by the equation $x^3 - 3xy^2 - y^3 = 1$ noted by Nagell, and mentioned by Skolem as a possible application of his method. The equation was disposed of by Ljunggren[6] who proved

Theorem 8

The only integer solutions of the equation

$$x^3 - 3xy^2 - y^3 = 1 \tag{20}$$

are given by

$$(x, y) = (1, 0), (0, -1), (-1, 1), (1, -3), (-3, 2), (2, 1).$$

Here we have

$$N(x + \theta y) = 1,$$

taken in the cubic field $Q(\theta)$ where

$$\theta^3 - 3\theta + 1 = 0.$$

This equation is well known as an Abelian equation associated with the 9th roots of unity. Call the roots ξ, η, ζ. Then ξ, η may be taken as the fundamental units and so

$$x + \xi y = \xi^u \eta^v.$$

This gives

$$(\eta - \zeta)\xi^u \eta^v + (\zeta - \xi)\eta^u \zeta^v + (\xi - \eta)\zeta^u \xi^v = 0.$$

This is the only equation connecting the p-adic variables u, v. On writing

$$X = \xi^{u-v/2}\eta^{(u+v)/2}, \qquad Y = \xi^{(u-2v)/2}\eta^{u-v/2},$$

we find the equation

$$\zeta X^2 - \xi\zeta Y^2 = \xi.$$

We now consider the extension field arising from the adjunction of $\sqrt{\xi}$ to the field $Q(\xi)$. The new field is of degree 6 and there are now four fundamental units since only one of ξ, η, ζ is negative. Then $(X\sqrt{\zeta} + Y\sqrt{\zeta\xi})^2$ is a unit in $Q(\sqrt{\xi})$ with relative norm 1, and can be written in the form $\pm \varepsilon_1^h \varepsilon_2^k$, where $\varepsilon_1, \varepsilon_2$ are two of the fundamental units with the same property, and can be taken as

$$\varepsilon_1 = \sqrt{\zeta} + \sqrt{\xi\zeta}, \qquad \varepsilon_2 = \eta\sqrt{\zeta} + \eta\zeta\sqrt{\xi\zeta}.$$

Ljunggren finds X, Y in terms of $\varepsilon_1^h, \varepsilon_2^k$ and their relative norms. Since $N(X) = N(Y) = 1$, two equations are obtained for the h, k. The results follow on working in the 2-adic field.

The equation arises from the discussion of the equivalent equations

$$y^3 = x^2 + x + 1,$$

$$y^2 = x^3 - 48.$$

The theorem shows that the only solutions of the first one are $x = 0, -1, 18, -19$. A simpler method of proof is obviously desirable.

Skolem has given many other applications. He has proved Thue's theorem in Chapter 22, on the finiteness of the number of integer solutions of a polynomial equation $f(x, y) = m$, except in the case when all the roots of $f(x, 1) = 0$ are real. An account of this is given by Borevich and Shafarevich[7] in their book on number theory which also contains an excellent account of p-adic numbers and also of local methods.

5. Skolem has also shown that results can be obtained for diophantine equations in more than two variables. Thus he has proved

Theorem 9

Let a, b, c, be three linearly independent numbers in an algebraic number field K of degree five whose conjugates include only one real field. Then the equation

$$N(ax + by + cz) = n, \tag{21}$$

where N denotes the norm in K, has only a finite number of rational integer solutions for x, y, z.

In particular, he proved that the equation

$$N(x + y\sqrt[5]{2} + z\sqrt[5]{4}) = 1,$$

i.e. $$x^5 + 2y^5 + 4z^5 - 10xy^3z + 10x^2yz^2 = 1,$$

has at most six solutions in integers x, y, z, and of these three are known, namely $(x, y, z) = (1, 0, 0), (-1, 1, 0), (1, 1, -2)$.

Skolem's theorem 9 is included in the generalization due to Chabauty[8] and proved by applying results due to Skolem and Siegel, namely,

Theorem 10

Let K be a primitive algebraic number field of degree n, and let $r = r_1 + r_2 - 1$ where r_1 is the number of real fields conjugate to K and r_2 is the number of pairs of conjugate complex fields. Then if $r < n - 3$ and α, β, γ are three linearly independent integers in K, the equation

$$N(\alpha x + \beta y + \gamma z) = A, \tag{22}$$

where A is a given rational integer has only a finite number of rational integer solutions for x, y, z.

Recently other results have been found for equations typified by (22). Thus Nagell[9] has proved the

Theorem 11

Suppose that K is a biquadratic field having as its only quadratic subfield an imaginary one. Then if α, β, γ are as in Theorem 10, its result for (22) holds.

Though some of the new results are not proved by p-adic methods, an account of them may not be out of place here. By combining arithmetic methods with an application of Thue's theorem, Nagell[9] has proved

Theorem 12

Let p be a primes > 5, and m a rational integer such that $m(m - 1) \not\equiv 0$ (mod p). Then if ζ is a primative pth root of unity, the equation

$$N(x + \zeta y + \zeta^m z) = 1$$

has only a finite number of rational integer solutions for x, y, z.

Previously Siegel[10] had used his results on diophantine approximation, for example, the approximation of algebraic numbers by other algebraic numbers. Thus he proved

Theorem 13

Let θ be an algebraic integer of degree n and let h be a positive integer such that

$$n > h^2 \left(\frac{n}{s + 1} + s \right), \quad 2s = \sqrt{4n + 1} - 1.$$

Then the equation

$$N(x_0 + x_1 \theta + \ldots + x_h \theta^h) = A,$$

where A is a given rational integer, has only a finite number of rational integer solutions for $x_0, x_1, \ldots, x_h$.

Then if $n < 57$, $h = 1$; if $57 \leqslant n < 307$, $h = 1$ or 2; if $n \geqslant 307$, we can take $h = 3$. In general, we can take $n = 4h^4 - 2h^2 + 1$.

Very recently, new results on diophantine approximation have been given by Schmidt[11] who has found results for simultaneous approximation similar to those by Roth. He proves the

Theorem 14

Let α, β, be algebraic numbers such that α, β, 1 are linearly independent over the rational field Q. Then for every $\varepsilon > 0$, there are only a finite number of rational fractions x/z, y/z satisfying the inequalities

$$\left| \alpha - \frac{x}{z} \right| < |z|^{-3/2-\varepsilon}, \left| \beta - \frac{y}{z} \right| < |z|^{-3/2-\varepsilon}.$$

Let now K be an algebraic number field of degree $n > 3$, and let α, β, γ be three elements of K linearly independent over Q and such that $K = Q(\alpha/\gamma, \beta/\gamma)$. Schmidt[12] applies theorem 14 to show that if $f(x, y, z)$ is a polynomial, then subject to certain conditions, the equation

$$N(\alpha x + \beta y + \gamma z) = f(x, y, z),$$

has at most a finite number of rational integer solutions for x, y, z. In particular, he proves

Theorem 15

Suppose that $\alpha x + \beta y + \gamma z$ is not of the form $\lambda R + \mu S$ where R is a rational form and S is a real form whose coefficients are in a quadratic field. Then if $f(x, y, z)$ is a polynomial of degree $< n/4$, the equation

$$N(\alpha x + \beta y + \gamma z) = f(x, y, z),$$

has only a finite number of rational integer solutions for x, y, z.

REFERENCES

1. R. Strassmann. Über den Wertevorrat von Potenzreihen im Gebiet der p-adischen Zahlen. *J. reine angew. Math.*, **159** (1928), 13–28
2. T. Skolem. "Diophantische Gleichungen". Springer-Verlag, (1938), pp. 114–120. See also the references cited in this book.
3. T. Skolem. The use of p-adic method in the theory of diophantine equations. *Bull. Soc. Math. Belg.*, **7** (1955), 83–95.
4. T. Nagell. The diophantine equation $x^2 + 7 = 2^n$. *Arkiv matematik*, **4** (1960), 185–187.
5. H. Hasse. Über eine diophantische Gleichungen von Ramanujan-Nagell und ihre Verallgemeinerung. *Nag. Math. J.*, **27** (1966), 77–102.
6. W. Ljunggren. Einige Bemerkungen über die Darstellung ganzer Zahlen durch binäre kubische Formen mit positiver Diskriminante. *Acta Math.*, **75** (1942), 1–21.

7. Z. I. Borevich and I. R. Shafarevich. "Number Theory". Academic Press, New York and London (1966).
8. C. Chabauty. Sur certaines équations diophantiques ternaires. *Comptes rendus Acad. Sci. Paris* **202** (1936), 2117–2119.
9. T. Nagell. Remarques sur les formes à plusieurs variables décomposables en facteurs lineaires *Ark. mat.*, **7** (1967), 313–329.
10. C. L. Siegel. Approximation algebraischer Zahlen. *Math. Zeit.* **10** (1921) 173–213 or Gesammelte Abhandlungen **1** (1966), 6–46.
11. W. M. Schmidt. On simultaneous approximations of two algebraic numbers by rationals. *Acta Math.*, **119** (1967), 27–50.
12. W. M. Schmidt. Some diophantine equations in three variables with only finitely many solutions. *Mathematika*, **14** (1967), 113–120.

CHAPTER 24

Binary Cubic Forms

1. We now apply the general theory of Chapter 20 to the binary cubic

$$f(x, y) = ax^3 + bx^2y + cxy^2 + dy^3, \tag{1}$$

with integer coefficients and discriminant

$$D = -27a^2d^2 + 18abcd + b^2c^2 - 4ac^3 - 4bd^3, \tag{2}$$

where we suppose $D \neq 0$. Here D is the invariant

$$D = a^4 \Pi(\beta - \gamma)^2,$$

and α, β, γ are the roots of the equation

$$a\xi^3 + b\xi^2 + c\xi + d = 0.$$

There are quadratic and cubic covariants $H(x, y)$ and $G(x, y)$ given by

$$H = -\frac{1}{4} \begin{vmatrix} \dfrac{\partial^2 f}{\partial x^2} & \dfrac{\partial^2 f}{\partial x \partial y} \\ \dfrac{\partial^2 f}{\partial x \partial y} & \dfrac{\partial^2 f}{\partial y^2} \end{vmatrix} = (bx + cy)^2 - (3ax + by)(cx + 3dy),$$

$$= (b^2 - 3ac)x^2 + (bc - 9ad)xy + (c^2 - 3bd)y^2,$$
$$= Ax^2 + Bxy + Cy^2,$$

say, of discriminant $B^2 - 4AC = -3D$.

Also $\qquad G = \begin{vmatrix} \dfrac{\partial f}{\partial x} & \dfrac{\partial f}{\partial y} \\ \dfrac{\partial H}{\partial x} & \dfrac{\partial H}{\partial y} \end{vmatrix} = -(27a^2d - 9abc + 2b^3)x^3 + \cdots. \tag{4}$

The covariants G, H, and f are not algebraically independent.

Theorem 1

$$G^2 + 27Df^2 = 4H^3. \tag{5}$$

By a linear substitution of determinant unity with real or complex co-efficients, we can write, say,

$$f = ax^3 + dy^3, \qquad D = -27a^2d^2,$$
$$H = -9adxy, \qquad G = 27ad(ax^3 - dy^3).$$

The identity (5) follows at once.

8+

The following theorem is included in the general theorems, and has been known for many years, but an independent proof is worth while.

Theorem 2

The number of classes of binary cubics with given discriminant $D \neq 0$ is finite.

It suffices to prove that $f(x, y)$ is equivalent to a binary cubic all of whose coefficients are bounded in terms of D.

We consider two cases according as $D > 0$ or $D < 0$. Suppose first that $D > 0$ and so the roots α, β, γ are all real. Then $H(x, y)$ is a positive definite form since $H > 0$ unless $3ax + by = 0$, and $cx + 3dy = 0, bx + cy = 0$ have a solution other than $x = y = 0$. This requires $D = 0$. We now reduce $H(x, y)$ by means of a unimodular integral substitution, and so we may assume that

$$C \geqslant A \geqslant |B|, \quad A \leqslant \sqrt{D}, AC \leqslant D. \tag{6}$$

We apply the same substitution to $f(x, y)$, and we then call the new form reduced. We show that its coefficients are bounded in terms of D.

Write
$$H(x, y) = APQ,$$

$$P = x + \frac{B + \sqrt{-3D}}{2A} y, \quad Q = x + \frac{B - \sqrt{-3D}}{2A} y.$$

Then
$$f(x, y) = (p + q\sqrt{-3D})P^3 + (p - q\sqrt{-3D})Q^3,$$

where p, q are rational numbers whose denominators are seen from (6) to be bounded in terms of D.

Hence a, b, c, d are expressed as polynomials in p, q, A, B, D. Equating discriminants for the two forms of $f(x, y)$,

$$D = -27(p^2 + 3q^2D)^2(4A\sqrt{-3D})^6.$$

Since p, q have bounded denominators, their numerators are also bounded. Hence a, b, c, d are bounded in terms of D.

Suppose next that $D < 0$. Let α be the real root and β, γ the conjugate complex roots of $f(x, 1) = 0$.

Suppose first that $a = 0$. Write

$$f(x, y) = y(bx^2 + cxy + dy^2), \quad \Delta = c^2 - 4bd.$$

Then
$$D = b^2c^2 - 4db^3 = b^2\Delta,$$

and so b, Δ are bounded in terms of D. As we may suppose $|c| \leqslant b \neq 0$, then c, d are also bounded.

Suppose next that $a \neq 0$. Write

$$f(x, y) = \pm (x - \alpha y)(Px^2 + Qxy + Ry^2),$$

where the sign is taken so that $Px^2 + Qxy + Ry^2$ is positive definite. We reduce this form and so we may suppose that

$$-1 \leqslant \beta + \gamma \leqslant 1, \quad \beta\gamma \geqslant 1.$$

We apply the same substitution to $f(x, y)$ and call the new form reduced. We show that its coefficients are bounded in terms of D. We show that

$$|\beta - \gamma|^2 \geqslant 3, \quad (\alpha - \beta)(\alpha - \gamma) \geqslant \tfrac{3}{4}.$$

The first follows from

$$(\beta - \gamma)^2 = (\beta + \gamma)^2 - 4\beta\gamma \leqslant -3,$$

and the second from

$$(\alpha - \beta)(\alpha - \gamma) = \left(\alpha - \frac{\beta + \gamma}{2}\right)^2 - \left(\frac{\beta - \gamma}{2}\right)^2.$$

Then
$$|D| = a^4(\alpha - \beta)^2(\alpha - \gamma)^2|\beta - \gamma|^2 \geqslant \tfrac{27}{16}a^4.$$

Hence a and so P and Q are bounded in terms of D. Since

$$|D| \geqslant 3a^4\left(\alpha - \frac{\beta + \gamma}{2}\right)^4,$$

α is bounded in terms of D. Since

$$|D| > \tfrac{9}{16}a^4|\beta - \gamma|^2 \quad \text{and} \quad PR \leqslant \tfrac{1}{3}a^2|\beta - \gamma|^2,$$

then
$$|D| > \frac{27a^2}{16}PR,$$

and so R is bounded. This proves that the coefficients of $f(x, y)$ are bounded.

To prove that $f(x, y)$ in equation (1) is equivalent to a reduced binary cubic involves a special case of a general problem in the Geometry of Numbers. This is to find the minimum value m of a function $|g(x, y)|$ for integer values of x, y. For (1), it was shown by Mordell[1] that if $D < 0$, then $m \leqslant \sqrt[4]{-D/23}$, and that equality occurs when

$$f(x, y) \sim m(x^3 - xy^2 - y^3).$$

If $D > 0$, then $m \leqslant \sqrt[4]{D/49}$ and for equality

$$f(x, y) \sim m(x^3 + xy^2 - 2xy^2 - y^3).$$

2. We can use these results in 1 to find the solution in integers X, Y, Z of

$$X^2 + kY^2 = Z^3, \tag{7}$$

where k is a given integer.

This is suggested by the relation

$$G^2(x, y) + 27Df^2(x, y) = 4H^3(x, y),$$

which gives an integer solution in two parameters x, y of the equation

$$X^2 + 27DY^2 = 4Z^3.$$

It proves convenient in dealing with equation (7) to write $f(x, y)$ with binomial coefficients and to modify slightly the definition of the invariants and covariants.

Write now $\qquad f(x, y) = ax^3 + 3bx^2y + 3cxy^2 + dy^3,$

where a, b, c, d are integers. Use D_1, H_1, G_1 to denote invariants etc. for non-binomial coefficients, and D, H, G for the invariants for binomial coefficients.

Then $\qquad\qquad D_1 = 27D, \qquad H_1 = 9H, \qquad G_1 = 27G.$

Here $\qquad\qquad D = -a^2d^2 + 6abcd + 3b^2c^2 - 4ac^3 - 4db^3,$

$$H = (b^2 - ac)x^2 + (bc - ad)xy + (c^2 - bd)y^2$$

$$= Ax^2 + Bxy + Cy^2, = (A, B, C), \qquad (8)$$

say, of discriminant $B^2 - 4AC = -D,$

$$G = -(a^2d - 3abc + 2b^3)x^3 + \cdots.$$

Now $\qquad\qquad G^2(x, y) + Df^2(x, y) = 4H^3(x, y). \qquad (9)$

If $D = 4k$, $G(x, y) \equiv 0 \pmod 2$, and so integer values of X, Y, Z in equation (7) are given by taking

$$X = \tfrac{1}{2}G(x, y), \qquad Y = f(x, y), \qquad Z = H(x, y), \qquad (10)$$

where $f(x, y)$ is any binary cubic with binomial integer coefficients of discriminant $D = 4k$.

We prove now the [2]

Theorem 3

All the integer solutions of

$$X^2 + kY^2 = Z^3, \quad (X, Z) = 1 \qquad (7)$$

are given by the formulae (10) *above.*

For let $(X, Y, Z) = (g, f, h)$ be a solution such that

$$g^2 + kf^2 = h^3, \quad (g, h) = 1. \qquad (11)$$

We shall construct a binary cubic $f(x, y)$ with integer binomial coefficients and of discriminant $4k$ such that g, f, h are values assumed by $G(x, y), f(x, y), H(x, y)$ for integers x, y. Then all the solutions of equation (7), are given by taking for $f(x, y)$ a set of non-equivalent binary cubics of discriminant $D = 4k$, and letting x, y run through all integer values for which $(X, Z) = 1$.

Since from equation (11), $-k$ is a quadratic residue of h, there exist binary quadratics of discriminant $-4k$ with first coefficient h, for example, say,

$$(h, 2B, C) = hx^2 + 2Bxy + Cy^2, \quad \text{where } B^2 - hC = -k.$$

We take for B any solution of the congruence $fB \equiv -g \pmod{h^3}$.

We shall now construct a binary cubic (f, b, c, d) with discriminant $D = 4k$ and H in (8) given by $(h, 2B, C)$.

Since
$$h = b^2 - fc, \quad c = \frac{b^2 - h}{f},$$

we can take $b \equiv g/h \pmod{f}$ and, in particular,

$$bh = g + Bf, \quad \text{and so } b \equiv 0 \pmod{h^2}.$$

Then
$$h^2 c = \frac{(g + Bf)^2 - h^3}{f}$$

$$= -kf + 2gB + B^2 f.$$

We now find d. Since $bc - fd = 2B$,

$$fd = \left(\frac{g + Bf}{h}\right)\left(\frac{-kf + 2gB + B^2 f}{h^2}\right) - 2B.$$

On simplifying,

$$h^3 d = -kg - 3kfB + 3gB^2 + fB^3.$$

We show now that c and d are integers. We have

$$h^2 c \equiv -kf + 2g\left(-\frac{g}{f}\right) + \frac{g^2}{f} \pmod{h^2}$$

$$\equiv \frac{-hf^2 - g^2}{f} \equiv 0 \pmod{h^2}.$$

Hence c is an integer. Next

$$h^3 d \equiv -kg + 3kg + \frac{3g^3}{f^2} - \frac{g^3}{f^2} \pmod{h^3}$$

$$\equiv \frac{2g}{f^3}(kf^2 + g^2) \pmod{h^3}$$

$$\equiv 0 \pmod{h^3}.$$

Then d is an integer. This completes the proof.

There is an immediate application of Theorem 3 to the equation

$$y^2 = x^3 + k.$$

This shows at once that there are only a finite number of integer solutions if $(x, k) = 1$, as happens for example when k is square free. We must solve $f(x, y) = 1$ where $f(x, y)$ is a binary cubic with discriminant $-4k$. Since there are only a finite number of classes of forms with discriminant $-4k$, Thue's theorem in Chapter 22 shows at once that there are only a finite number of integer solutions for x, y.

The result holds for all k as is shown in Chapter 26.

3. We discuss in more detail the integer solutions of the general cubic equation

$$f(x, y) = ax^3 + bx^2y + cxy^2 + dy^3 = m. \tag{12}$$

It is known as a particular case of Thue's theorem of Chapter 22 that there are only a finite number of solutions if we suppose that $f(x, y)$ is irreducible. No necessary and sufficient condition for the existence of integer solutions of equation (12) nor a finite algorithm for finding them when they exist are known. However, Baker[3] has recently found an upper bound (a very large one indeed) for the magnitude of the solutions.

Some results are known about the number of solutions and some special equations of the form $ax^3 + dy^3 = m$ can be completely solved. We have seen that it suffices in (12), to consider the case when $m = 1$. Then if one solution is known, we may by means of a linear substitution suppose that $a = 1$.

Let $\theta, \theta', \theta''$ be the roots of the cubic equation

$$t^3 - bt^2 + ct - d = 0, \tag{13}$$

and let $K = Q(\theta)$ be the cubic field over the rational field generated by θ. Two cases arise according as the discriminant $D < 0$ or > 0.

Suppose first $D < 0$. Then combining results of Delaunay[4] and Nagell[5], we have the

Theorem 4

The equation (12) *for* $m = 1$ *has at most three integer solutions except when* $f(x, y) = (a, b, c, d) \sim (1, 0, 1, 1)$ *or* $(1, -1, 1, 1)$, *when there are exactly four solutions, or when* $f(x, y) \sim (1, 0, -1, 1)$, *when there are exactly five solutions.*

The proof requires a detailed investigation and so we shall give only a sketch of the method. We operate in the ring $Z[\theta]$. In this there is one fundamental unit η, and this may be taken to satisfy $0 < \eta < 1$. From equation (13),

$$(x + \theta y)(x + \theta'y)(x + \theta''y) = 1,$$

and so $x + \theta y$ is a unit in the ring. Hence

$$x + \theta y = \eta^m, \quad m = 0, \pm 1, \pm 2, \ldots \tag{14}$$

and we have to find the integer values of m for which this is possible. The first stage in the proof is to show that equation (14) can be replaced by

$$x + \eta y = \eta^m, \tag{15}$$

and that η is a root of an equation with $d = 1$. The next stage is to show that $m \geqslant 0$ except for the excluded case $\eta^3 + \eta^2 = 1$ when $\eta^{-2} = 1 + \eta$.

We show there is at most one unit for which $xy \neq 0$. Suppose that m_0 is the least positive integer for which a relation

$$x_0 + \eta y_0 = \eta^{m_0} \tag{16}$$

holds, and that x, y, m in equation (15) is a different set.

Put
$$m = qm_0 + r, \quad 0 \leqslant r < m_0.$$

It can be shown that $3 \leqslant r \leqslant m_0 - 2$. Put

$$\varepsilon = \eta^r = X + \eta Y + \eta^2 Z. \tag{17}$$

Then $Z \neq 0$ since $r < m_0$. From equations (15), (16)

$$x + \eta y = (x_0 + \eta y_0)^q (X + \eta Y + \eta^2 Z).$$

A congruence mod y_0 shows that $Z \equiv 0 \pmod{y_0}$ and so $|Z| \geqslant y_0$. From equation (17) and the conjugate equations,

$$\pm \sqrt{D} Z = (\eta' - \eta'')\varepsilon + (\eta'' - \eta)\varepsilon' + (\eta - \eta')\varepsilon''.$$

Also
$$\eta^3 \geqslant \eta^r = \varepsilon \geqslant \eta^{m_0 - 2},$$

$$|\varepsilon'| = |\varepsilon''| \leqslant |\eta'|^{m_0 - 2} = \left| \frac{x_0 + y_0 \eta'}{\eta'^2} \right| < \left| \frac{y_0}{\eta'} \right| + \frac{|y_0| - 1}{|\eta'^2|},$$

since $|x_0| < 1 + |\eta y_0| < 1 + |y_0|$ and $|x_0| = |y_0|$ implies $|y_0| = 1$.

Hence $$\sqrt{|D|}\,|y_0| < 2|\eta'|\varepsilon + 2(1 + |\eta''|) \left(\left| \frac{y_0}{\eta'} \right| + \frac{|y_0| - 1}{|\eta'^2|} \right).$$

Then $$|\eta_1^6 \varepsilon| \leqslant 1 \quad \text{since} \quad |\eta_1'^3 \eta''^3 \eta^3| = 1.$$

Hence, since $|\eta'| > 1$,

$$|\sqrt{D} y_0| < 2 + 4(|y_0| + |y_0| - 1) = -2 + 8|y_0|.$$

Then $-D < 64$, and then there can be at most three units.

The cases $D > -64$ arise only for $D = -23, -31, -44$ and these must be investigated in detail.

4. Theorem 4 does not enable us to find the existing integer solutions. All the solutions, however, can be found for some equations of the form

$$ax^3 + by^3 = c.$$

In particular, as was first shown by Delaunay, the equation

$$x^3 + dy^3 = 1,$$

does not present too much difficulty. The integer solutions are trivial when d is a perfect cube. Then if $|d| > 1$, the only solution is $x = 1, y = 0$, and when $|d| = 1$, there is another solution $x = 0, dy = 1$. We may suppose now that $d > 1$ and is free from cubed factors since these can be absorbed in y^3. We consider the cubic field $K = Q(\sqrt[3]{d})$. The integers in K of the form $x + y\sqrt[3]{d} + z\sqrt[3]{d^2}$, where x, y, z are rational integers, form a ring $Z[\sqrt[3]{d}]$, the units in which are those integers η whose norm $N(\eta) = \pm 1$. Let ε be the fundamental unit in the ring chosen so that $0 < \varepsilon < 1$. Then all the units in $Z[\sqrt[3]{d}]$ are given by

$$\eta = \pm \varepsilon^n,$$

where n takes all integer values. The $+$ sign must be taken for the positive units. Then if rational integers x, y satisfy

$$x^3 + dy^3 = 1, \quad \text{i.e.} \quad N(x + y\sqrt[3]{d}) = 1,$$

$\eta = x + y\sqrt[3]{d}$ is a positive unit in the ring. Such a unit will be called a binomial unit.

Theorem 5

 The equation $x^3 + dy^3 = 1$ $(d > 1)$ has at most one integer solution with $xy \neq 0$. This is given by the fundamental unit in the ring when it is a binomial unit, i.e. ε takes the form $\varepsilon = x + y\sqrt[3]{d}$.
 We require four lemmas.

Lemma 1

 There cannot exist units

$$\eta = P + Q\sqrt[3]{d} + R\sqrt[3]{d^2}, \quad |\eta| > 1, \quad QR = 0.$$

Suppose first that $R = 0$. Then $PQ < 0$, and

$$1/|\eta| = P^2 - PQ\sqrt[3]{d} + Q^2\sqrt[3]{d^2} \geqslant 1 + \sqrt[3]{d} + \sqrt[3]{d^2} > 3,$$

a contradiction.
So if $Q = 0, PR < 0$, and

$$1/|\eta| = P^2 - PR\sqrt[3]{d} + R^2\sqrt[3]{d^2} > 3.$$

Hence we have to find the positive integers n such that

$$\varepsilon^n = x + y\sqrt[3]{d}.$$

Lemma 2

 No unit of the types

$$(x + y\sqrt[3]{d})^n, \quad n = \pm 2, \pm 3, \ldots; \qquad (x + y\sqrt[3]{d^2})^n, \quad n = \pm 1, \pm 2, \ldots$$

can be a binomial unit.

We may suppose that the units are positive and so $n > 0$. Take the first type. Expand and equate to zero the terms in $\sqrt[3]{d^2}$, and put $t = dy^3$. This gives three different cases depending on the residue of n (mod 3). Then for $n \equiv 2$ (mod 3),

$$t^{(n-2)/3} + t^{(n-5)/3}x^3 \binom{n}{3} + t^{(n-8)/3}x^6 \binom{n}{6} + \cdots + (x^3)^{(n-2)/3}\binom{n}{2} = 0,$$

$n \equiv 1$ (mod 3),

$$t^{(n-4)/3}\binom{n}{2} + t^{(n-7)/3}x^3\binom{n}{5} + \cdots + (x^3)^{(n-4)/3}\binom{n}{2} = 0,$$

$n \equiv 0$ (mod 3),

$$t^{(n-3)/3}\binom{n}{1} + t^{(n-6)/3}x^3\binom{n}{4} + \cdots + (x^3)^{(n-3)/3}\binom{n}{2} = 0.$$

Since $t = dy^3$, $(x, t) = 1$. Suppose first that $d > 2$ and so $|x| > 1$. Let p be a prime divisor of x and let p^a be the greatest power of p dividing the binomial coefficient in the highest power of t in the equation above under discussion. We shall show that the remaining terms in the equation are divisible by p^{a+1} thus giving a contradiction.

It will suffice to take the case $n \equiv 1$ (mod 3). The general term with $r > 0$ is given by

$$t^{(n-3r-1)/3}x^{3r} \frac{n.n-1.\cdots.n-3r-1}{(3r+2)!}.$$

Write this as

$$2\left(\frac{n.n-1}{2!}\right)\left(\frac{n-2.n-3.\cdots.n-3r-1}{1.2.\cdots.3r}\right)\left(\frac{x^{3r}}{(3r+1)(3r+2)}\right)t^{(n-3r-1)/3}.$$

The first two terms in brackets are integers. Now if $p \geqslant 2$, $p^{3r} > 3r + 2$ since $2^{3r} > 3r + 2$, and so the term in the third bracket is divisible by p.

We now take the second type of units, and write $t = d^2y^3$. Three cases arise:
$n \equiv 2$ (mod 3),

$$\binom{n}{1}t^{(n-2)/3} + t^{(n-5)/3}x^3\binom{n}{4} + \cdots + (x^3)^{(n-2)/3}\binom{n}{1} = 0,$$

$n \equiv 1$ (mod 3),

$$t^{(n-1)/3} + t^{(n-4)/3}x^3\binom{n}{3} + \cdots + (x^3)^{(n-1)/3}\binom{n}{1} = 0,$$

$n \equiv 0$ (mod 3),

$$t^{(n-3)/3}\binom{n}{2} + t^{(n-6)/3}x^3\binom{n}{5} + \cdots + (x^3)^{(n-3)/3}\binom{n}{1} = 0.$$

An argument similar to that for the first type applies.
8*

Suppose finally that $d = 2$. Then it is known that the only rational solutions of $x^3 + 2y^3 = 1$ are $x = 1, y = 0; x = -1, y = 1$ (see Chapter 15), and that $-1 + \sqrt[3]{2}$ is the fundamental unit.

Lemma 3

The square of a unit $\eta \neq \pm 1$ cannot be a binomial unit.

Suppose that

$$\eta = P + Q\sqrt[3]{d} + R\sqrt[3]{d^2}.$$

Then

$$Q^2 + 2PR = 0. \tag{18}$$

Also

$$P^3 + Q^3 d + R^3 d^2 - 3dPQR = 1, \tag{19}$$

since η is a unit.

We shall show that the only integer solutions of these simultaneous equations are given by $P = 1, Q = R = 0$, and $P = Q = 0, R = 1, d = 1$, and these are obviously excluded.

From equation (19), $(P, R) = 1$, and so equation (18) gives four cases.

(A) $P = q^2,$ $\quad R = -2r^2,$ $\quad Q = \pm 2qr,$

(B) $P = -q^2,$ $\quad R = 2r^2,$ $\quad Q = \pm 2qr,$

(C) $P = 2q^2,$ $\quad R = -r^2,$ $\quad Q = \pm 2qr,$

(D) $P = -2q^2,$ $\quad R = r^2,$ $\quad Q = \pm 2qr.$

Here q, r are integers. Substituting these in equation (2), we have, on putting $p = dr^3$,

(A') $\quad -8p^2 \pm 20pq^3 + q^6 = 1,$

(B') $\quad -8p^2 \pm 20pq^3 + q^6 = -1,$

(C') $\quad p^2 \pm 20pq^3 - 8q^6 = 1.$

(D') $\quad p^2 \pm 20pq^3 - 8q^6 = -1.$

Clearly (B') and (D') are impossible on taking residues mod 4.
From (A'),

$$(4p \pm 5q^3)^2 = 27q^6 - 2.$$

This is Fermat's equation of which the only solutions are $q = \pm 1, p = 0$. Then $r = 0$, and $P = 1, Q = R = 0$.

Next equation (C') can be written as

$$(p \pm 10q^3)^2 - 108q^6 = 1,$$

or say

$$p_1^2 - 4q_1^3 = 1.$$

Hence $\qquad p_1 + 1 = 2q_2^3,$ $\qquad p_1 - 1 = 2q_3^3,$ $\qquad q_1 = q_2 q_3.$

Then

$$q_2^3 - q_3^3 = 1, \qquad q_2 = 1, \qquad q_3 = 0 \quad \text{or} \quad q_2 = 0, \qquad q_3 = -1.$$

Hence $\ q = 0,$ $\qquad p = \pm 1,$ $\qquad P = 0,$ $\qquad Q = 0,$ $\qquad R = d = 1.$

Lemma 4

 The cube of a unit $\eta \neq \pm 1$, cannot be a binomial unit.

Let $\qquad\qquad \eta = P + Q\sqrt[3]{d} + R\sqrt[3]{d^2}.$

Then equating to zero the coefficient of $\sqrt[3]{d^2}$ in q^3, we have

$$P^2R + PQ^2 + R^2Qd = 0. \tag{20}$$

Also $\qquad\qquad P^3 + Q^3d + R^3d^2 - 3PQRd = 1. \tag{21}$

We shall show that the only solutions of these equations are $P = 1$, $Q = R = 0$ or $P = R = 0$, $Q = 1 = d$, or $P = Q = 0$, $R = 1$, $d = 1$.
Write $(Q, R) = \delta$ and so $(P, d\delta) = 1$.
Then from equation (20)

$$R = \delta^2 r, \qquad Q = \delta q, \qquad (q, r) = 1,$$

and so $\qquad\qquad P^2r + Pq^2 + \delta^3 r^2 qd = 0,$

or $\qquad\qquad -r^2q\delta^3 d = P(Pr + q^2).$

But $\qquad\qquad (r, Pr + q^2) = 1, \quad \text{and so } P = pr^2,$

and $\qquad\qquad -q\delta^3 d = p(q^2 + pr^3).$

Also $(P, d\delta) = 1$ and so $(p, d\delta) = 1$, and $q = ps$.

Then $\qquad\qquad -\delta^3 sd = p(ps^2 + r^3).$

Hence $\qquad\qquad s = tp, \qquad -\delta^3 td = t^2p^3 + r^3.$

Now $t \mid s \mid q$, and since $t \mid r$ and $(q, r) = 1$, then $t = \pm 1$.

Hence $\qquad\qquad \pm \delta^3 d = p^3 + r^3. \tag{22}$

Substituting in equation (21) the values

$$R = r\delta^2, \qquad Q = \pm p^2\delta, \qquad P = pr^2, \qquad PQR = \pm r^3p^3\delta^3,$$

we get $\qquad\qquad p^3r^6 \pm p^6\delta^3 d + r^3\delta^6 d^2 \pm 3p^3 r^3\delta^3 d = 1.$

Replacing $\delta^3 d$ from equation (22), we have

$$p^3r^6 - p^6(p^3 + r^3) + r^3(p^3 + r^3)^2 + 3p^3 r^3(p^3 + r^3) = 1.$$

or $\qquad\qquad -p^9 + r^9 + 6p^3r^6 + 3p^6r^3 = 1. \tag{23}$

There are several ways of dealing with this equation.

Writing $pr^2 = l$, $r^3 - p^3 = m$, it becomes

$$9l^3 + m^3 = 1.$$

This is our equation with $d = 9$. The fundamental unit is $\varepsilon = -2 + \sqrt[3]{9}$. Also ε^n is a binomial unit only when $n = 1$. This proves the lemma.

Alternatively putting $p^3 = v$, $r^3 = u$, we can verify the identity

$$(u^3 + 6u^2v + 3uv^2 - v^3)U^3 = V^3 + W^3, \tag{24}$$

where

$$U = u^2 + uv + v^2, \qquad V = u^3 + 3u^2v - v^3, \qquad W = 3u^2v + 3uv^2.$$

Hence the only solutions of equations (23) and (24) are given by $UVW = 0$ and so $u = 0$, $v = -1$; $u = 1$, $v = 0$; $u = -1$, $v = 1$.

We can now prove that the nth power of a unit $\eta \neq \pm 1$, is not a binomial unit. We may assume that $0 < \eta < 1$ and $n > 0$. We need prove the statement for $n \equiv 1 \pmod 2$ and $n \not\equiv 0 \pmod 3$.

Write $\qquad\qquad X^n = (P + Q\sqrt[3]{d} + R\sqrt[3]{d^2})^n = x + y\sqrt[3]{d}.$

Then $\qquad\qquad\qquad X^n + \rho Y^n + \rho^2 Z^n = 0,$

where $\rho = e^{2\pi i/3}$, and Y, Z are the conjugates of X in K. This equation can be written in various forms depending upon the residue of $n \pmod 3$. Thus when $n \equiv 2 \pmod 3$,

$$X^n + (\rho^2 Y)^n + (\rho Z)^n = 0.$$

Hence $\rho^2 Y + \rho Z$ divides the unit X and so must be a unit, i.e. on substituting for Y, Z, then $-P + 2Q\sqrt[3]{d} - R\sqrt[3]{d^2}$ is a unit.

Hence $\qquad\qquad -P^3 + 8Q^3d - R^3d^2 - 6PQRd = \pm 1,$

also $\qquad\qquad\quad P^3 + Q^3d + R^3d^2 - 3PQRd = 1.$

By addition $\qquad\qquad\quad 9Qd(Q^2 - PR) = 0, 2,$

and so either $Q = 0$ or $Q^2 - PR = 0$.

If $Q = 0$, $\eta = P + R\sqrt[3]{d^2}$, and is excluded by Lemma 2.

If $Q^2 - PR = 0$,

$$\frac{1}{\eta} = \frac{1}{P + Q\sqrt[3]{d} + R\sqrt[3]{d^2}}$$

$$= P^2 + Q^2\sqrt[3]{d^2} + R^2\sqrt[3]{d^4} - dQR - PR\sqrt[3]{d^2} - PQ\sqrt[3]{d}$$

$$= P^2 - dQR + (R^2d - PQ)\sqrt[3]{d}$$

is a binomial unit > 1 and is excluded by Lemma 1.

Suppose next that $n \equiv 1 \pmod 3$. Then

$$X^n + (\rho Y)^n + (\rho^2 Z)^n = 0,$$

and so $\rho Y + \rho^2 Z$, i.e. $-P - Q\sqrt[3]{d} + 2R\sqrt[3]{d^2}$ is a unit. Hence

$$P^3 + Q^3 d - 8R^3 d^2 + 6PQRd = \pm 1.$$

Also

$$P^3 + Q^3 d + R^3 d^2 - 3PQRd = 1.$$

Hence

$$9Rd(r^2 d - PQ) = 0.$$

Then either $R = 0$ and $P + Q\sqrt[3]{d}$ is a binomial unit and so $n = 1$ is the only possibility from Lemma 2, or $R^2 d - PQ = 0$.

Then

$$1/\eta = P^2 - dQR + (Q^2 - PR)\sqrt[3]{d^2}$$

is a binomial unit > 1 and this is impossible.

This completes the proof.

Nagell[8] and Ljunggren[9] have generalized the method above and have found more comprehensive results given as

Theorem 6

Let a, b, c be positive integers, $a > b > 1$, $c = 1, 3$, $(ab, c) = 1$, $b = 1$ if $c = 3$. Then the equation

$$ax^3 + by^3 = c \qquad (25)$$

has at most one integer solution (x, y), and for this

$$c^{-1}(x\sqrt[3]{a} + y\sqrt[3]{b})^3$$

is either the fundamental unit or its square in the cubic field $Q(\sqrt[3]{d})$ defined by $Q(\sqrt[3]{ab^2})$, excluding, however, the equation $2x^3 + y^3 = 3$ which has the two solutions $(1, 1)$ and $(4, -5)$.

Further there is at most one equation (25) with given d which has integer solutions with $xy \neq 0$ except when $d = 2, 20$.

5. Suppose next that $D > 0$ in equation (12). There are now two fundamental units η_1, η_2 and so

$$x + \theta y = \eta_1^l \eta_2^m. \qquad (26)$$

It is not often that equations such as (26) are so easily dealt with as in Chapter 27. In general, they prove rather difficult and troublesome as was seen for the equation

$$x^3 - 3xy^2 + y^3 = 1$$

considered in Chapter 23.

Baulin[7] following Ljunggren's treatment of this equation showed that the only integer solutions of the equation

$$x^3 + x^2y - 2xy^2 - y^3 = 1$$

are given by $(1, 0,), (0, 1), (-1, 1), (-1, -1), (2, -1), (-1, 2), (5, 4), (4, -9), (-9, 5)$.

These two equations arise from the 7th and 9th roots of unity, and the last one gives the cubic field of least positive discriminant, namely 49.

The important only other known result when $D > 0$ is given by Siegel's[10]

Theorem 7

If D is sufficiently great, there are at most eighteen integer solutions of the equation $f(x, y) = 1$.

The proof depends upon ideas similar to those used in the proof of the Thue–Siegel theorem, but now the approximations to algebraic numbers are given by hypergeometric series.

6. We give a few results on the rational solutions of the equation

$$ax^3 + bx^2y + cxy^2 + dy^3 = e,$$

or in the homogeneous form

$$ax^3 + bx^2y + cxy^2 + dy^3 = ez^3, \tag{27}$$

where now x, y, z are integers and $(x, y, z) = 1$.

As seen in Chapter 6, the non-existence of integer solutions of equations of this form may be shown by simple congruence considerations, for example, by taking equation (27) as a congruence mod 9.

Most of the known results about equation (27) deal with special cases of the equation and equations derived from these, and in particular the equation

$$Ax^3 + By^3 + Cz^3 = 0, \tag{28}$$

and the derived equation

$$x^3 - 3xy^2 + y^3 = pz^3.$$

The equation (28) is a particular case of the equation

$$Ax^3 + By^3 + Cz^3 + Dxyz = 0,$$

already considered in Chapter 10.

Some results have already been given for special cases of equation (28). Selmer[11] has written an extensive memoir on this equation. The results are usually found by algebraic number theory. By a slight change in the variables, the equation (28) may be written in the form

$$x^3 - my^3 = nz^3. \tag{29}$$

The left-hand side is then split into linear factors. If $m = \pm 1$, we can apply the quadratic field $Q(\rho)$. If $m \neq \pm 1$, the cubic field $Q(\sqrt[3]{m})$ is required and its arithmetical properties must be studied. Thus if $\theta = \sqrt[3]{m}$, equation (29) leads to an ideal equation

$$(x - \theta y) = \eta a^3, \tag{30}$$

where η is an ideal taken from a finite set. Then we have an equation

$$x - y\theta = \mu a^3 = (e + f\theta + g\theta^2)(u + v\theta + w\theta^2)^3,$$

where u, v, w are rational integers and e, f, g are taken from a finite set of rational numbers. Multiplying out and equating the coefficient of θ^2 on the right-hand side to zero, we arrive at a homogeneous cubic equation, say,

$$f(u, v, w) = 0. \tag{31}$$

Sometimes congruence considerations applied to equations (30) or (31) may show there are no solutions. This may require the reciprocity laws in quadratic and cubic fields.

The equation (28) of most interest is the special case

$$X^3 + Y^3 = AZ^3 \tag{32}$$

where A is cube free. The application of the field $Q(\sqrt{-3})$ gives a method of descent which leads to equations of the form

$$ax^3 + by^3 + cz^3 = 0, \quad abc = A, (a, b) = (b, c) = (c, a) = 1. \tag{33}$$

If any of these equations with $1 < a \leqslant b \leqslant c$ are solvable, so is the equation (32). In fact, from a result due essentially to Euler, we can take

$$X + Y = -9abcx^3y^3z^3, \qquad X - Y = (ax^3 - by^3)(by^3 - cz^3)(cz^3 - ax^3),$$

$$Z = 3(abx^3y^3 + bcy^3z^3 + caz^3x^3)xyz.$$

Some such relation might be expected since both the equations (32) and (33), when a solution is known for a set a, b, c, are birationally equivalent to the cubic

$$y^2 = 4x^3 - 27A^2.$$

Some of the equations (33) may be of special interest since they may be everywhere locally solvable but have no solutions. The simplest such equation is

$$3x^3 + 4y^3 + 5z^3 = 0.$$

We now give some equations[12] with no rational solutions.

Theorem 8

The equation

$$(px + qy)^3 + kz^3 = (rx + sy)(x^2 + xy + 7y^2), \tag{34}$$

where $k = 2$ or 4, and the coefficients p, q, r, s are integers, has no integer solutions except $(0, 0, 0)$ if

$$p - r \equiv 1 \ (\text{mod } 2), \qquad p + q \not\equiv 0 \ (\text{mod } 3), \tag{35}$$

and if either

$$q^2 - qp + 7p^2 \not\equiv 0 \ (\text{mod } P_2) \text{ or } s^2 - sr + 7r^2 \not\equiv 0 \ (\text{mod } P_2) \tag{36}$$

where P_2 is a prime $\equiv 1$ (mod 3) for which 2 is a cubic non-residue.
From this is deduced

Theorem 9

The equation

$$Ax^3 + Dy^3 + kz^3 = 0, \quad k = 2, 4, \tag{37}$$

has no integer solutions except $(0, 0, 0)$ if

$$A = \tfrac{1}{2}p(q + p)(q - 2p), \qquad D = \tfrac{1}{2}q(7p + q)(7p - 2q), \tag{38}$$

$$p + q \not\equiv 0 \ (\text{mod } 3),$$

and either

$$p \equiv 1 \ (\text{mod } 2), \qquad q(q - p) \equiv 0 \ (\text{mod } 4), \tag{39}$$

or $\qquad\qquad\qquad p \equiv 2 \ (\text{mod } 4), \qquad\qquad q \equiv 1 \ (\text{mod } 2),$

and if either †

$$q^2 - qp + 7p^2 \not\equiv 0 \ (\text{mod } P_2) \quad \text{or} \quad pq(63p^2 - 34pq + 9q^2) \not\equiv 0 \ (\text{mod } P_2).$$

It is shown in due course that an instance is given by the equation

$$z^3 + 11y^3 + 20x^3 = 0.$$

This is of special interest since it has no integer solutions except $(0, 0, 0)$, but it is solvable locally everywhere. This is obvious since the congruence is solvable to moduli 9, 5, 11 since $5 \equiv 11 \equiv 2$ (mod 3). This result is given by Selmer and is proved in an entirely different way.

In equation (34), we may suppose that $(x, y, z) = 1$ and so $(x, y) = 1$.

Write $\qquad\qquad\qquad f(x, y) = x^2 + xy + 7y^2.$

We consider the possible prime factors d of $f(x, y)$. Clearly $d \neq 2$ since this requires $x \equiv y \equiv 0$ (mod 2). Next $d \neq 3$, since this requires $x \equiv y \equiv \pm 1$ (mod 3), and so

$$f(x, y) \equiv (x - 4y)^2 \equiv 0 \ (\text{mod } 9).$$

Then $z \equiv 0$ (mod 3), $px + qy \equiv 0$ (mod 3) contrary to the end of (35). Hence the only prime divisors of $f(x, y)$ are the primes $P \equiv 1$ (mod 3), and the odd primes $P' \equiv 2$ (mod 3) and then $x \equiv y \equiv 0$ (mod P') since $(-3/P') = 1$.

† See addendum.

The only prime divisors of the left-hand side of (34) that need be considered the common divisors of $px + qy$ and z, the primes $P_1 \equiv 1 \pmod 3$ for which 2 is a cubic residue; and this is so if and only if

$$P_1 = X_1^2 + 27 Y_1^2$$

with integers X_1, Y_1; the primes $P_2 \equiv 1 \pmod 3$ for which 2 is not a cubic residue and then $z \equiv 0 \pmod{P_2}$, $px + qy \equiv 0 \pmod{P_2}$; and the primes P'.

Let us consider next the divisor $d = P_2$.

Then $px + qy \equiv 0 \pmod{P_2}$, $f(x, y) \equiv 0 \pmod{P_2}$ and so $f(q, -p) \equiv 0 \pmod{P_2}$. By (36), $f(s, -r) \not\equiv 0 \pmod{P_2}$ and so $rx + sy \not\equiv 0 \pmod{P_2}$. Hence $f(x, y) \equiv 0 \pmod{P_2^3}$. Since P_2 can be expressed as

$$P_2 = x_2^2 + x_2 y_2 + y_2^2,$$

we have a factorization

$$f(x, y) = \prod_{P'} P'^2 \prod_{P_2} (x_2^2 + x_2 y_2 + y_2^2)^3 \prod_{P_1} (X_1^2 + 27 Y_1^2).$$

Also $\quad f(x, y) = \left(x + \frac{y}{2}(1 + \sqrt{-27})\right) \left(x + \frac{y}{2}(1 - \sqrt{-27})\right).$

Let δ be a common divisor of these two factors in $Q(\sqrt{-3})$, and so

$$2x + y \equiv 0 \pmod \delta, \quad y\sqrt{-27} \equiv 0 \pmod \delta, \quad 2x\sqrt{-27} \equiv 0 \pmod \delta.$$

Now δ is prime to 3 since $f(x, y)$ is prime to 3. If $\delta = 2$, $y \equiv 0 \pmod 2$. Then $x \equiv 0 \pmod 2$, since equation (34) taken as a congruence mod 2 becomes

$$(px)^3 \equiv rx^3 \pmod 2.$$

Hence $\delta = 1$.

Since unique factorization exists in $Q(\sqrt{-3})$,

$$x + \frac{y}{2}(1 + \sqrt{-27})$$

$$= \rho^\alpha \prod_{P'} P' \prod_{P_2} \left(x_2 + \frac{y_2}{2}(1 + \sqrt{-3})\right)^3 \prod_{P_1} (X_1 + Y_1\sqrt{-27}), \quad (35)$$

where $\rho = \frac{1}{2}(-1 + \sqrt{-3})$, $\alpha = 0, \pm 1$.

Write $\qquad x_2 + \frac{y_2}{2}(1 + \sqrt{-3}) = A + B\sqrt{-3},$

where A, B are either both integers or both halves of odd integers.

Then $\qquad (A + B\sqrt{-3})^3 = A^3 - 9AB^2 + 3\sqrt{-3}(A^2 B - B^3).$

Here $A(A^2 - 9B^2)$ and $B(A^2 - B^2)$ are both integers and so

$$(A + B\sqrt{-3})^3 = C + D\sqrt{-3},$$

where C, D are integers. Hence equation (35) can be written as

$$x + \frac{y}{2}(1 + \sqrt{-27}) = \rho^\alpha \prod \rho P'(X + Y\sqrt{-27}).$$

Suppose first that $\alpha = 0$. Then $y \equiv 0 \pmod 2$ and this is impossible. Suppose next that $\alpha = \pm 1$. Then

$$3y = \pm X - 3Y.$$

Then $X \equiv 0 \pmod 3$, and $f(x, y) \equiv 0 \pmod 9$ and this is also impossible. This completes the proof.

To prove Theorem 9, write equation (28) in the form

$$Ax^3 + Bx^2y + Cxy^2 + Dy^3 = kz^3,$$

where

$$A = r - p^3, \quad B = r + s - 3p^2q, \quad C = 7r + s - 3pq^2, \quad D = 7s - q^3.$$

Suppose now that $B = C = 0$. Then

$$7r + s = 3pq^2, \qquad r + s = 3p^2q,$$

and so

$$r = \tfrac{1}{2}pq(q - p), \qquad s = \tfrac{1}{2}pq(7p - q).$$

Hence

$$A = \tfrac{1}{2}pq(q - p) - p^3 = \tfrac{1}{2}p(q + p)(q - 2p),$$

$$D = \tfrac{7}{2}pq(7p - q) - q^3 = \tfrac{1}{2}q(7p + q)(7p - 2q).$$

We still have the condition $p + q \not\equiv 0 \pmod 3$. The condition $p - r \equiv 1 \pmod 2$ becomes

$$p - \tfrac{1}{2}pq(q - p) \equiv 1 \pmod 2.$$

This gives either

$$p \equiv 1 \pmod 2, \qquad q(q - p) \equiv 0 \pmod 4,$$

or

$$p \equiv 2 \pmod 4, \qquad q \equiv 1 \pmod 2.$$

The condition $f(s, -r) \not\equiv 0 \pmod{P_2}$ becomes

$$pq(63p^2 - 34pq + 9q^2) \not\equiv 0 \pmod{P_2}.$$

Take $p = 1, q = 4, r = 6, s = 6, A = 5, D = -22$. Then $f(q, -p) = 19 = P_2$ and $f(s, -r) = 9$, $6^2 \not\equiv 0 \pmod{P_2}$. On writing $2x$ for x etc., we get the equation

$$z^3 + 11y^3 + 20x^3 = 0$$

previously noted.

Addendum to Theorem 9

Prof. Schinzel points out that the condition, either $q^2 - qp + p^2 \not\equiv 0$ (mod P_2) or $pq(63p^2 - 34qp + 9q^2) \not\equiv 0$ (mod P_2) can be replaced by the condition $q \not\equiv 0$ (mod 7). For if neither statement is true, the identity

$$63p^2 - 34pq + 9q^2 = 9(q^2 - qp + 7p^2) - 25pq$$

shows that $pq \equiv 0 \,(\mathrm{mod}\, P_2)$, and then if $p \equiv 0 \,(\mathrm{mod}\, P_2)$, also $q \equiv 0 \,(\mathrm{mod}\, P_2)$; and if $q \equiv 0$ (mod P_2), then $7p \equiv 0$ (mod P_2). These are impossible if $(q, 7p) \not\equiv 0$ (mod P_2). Since a common divisor of p, q can be absorbed in x and y, we may suppose that $(p, q) = 1$ and so we require that $q \not\equiv 0 \,(\mathrm{mod}\, 7)$.

He also notes that the equation is locally solvable everywhere it either $q \equiv 4p$ (mod 9) or the cube free-kernel of $pq \equiv \pm 3 \,(\mathrm{mod}\, 9)$. Thus if $p = 2$, $q = 3$, we have the equation $10x^3 + 51y^3 + z^3 = 0$.

REFERENCES

1. L. J. Mordell. The minimum of a binary cubic form I, II. *J. Lond. Math Soc.*, **18** (1943), 201–219 and 210–217.
2. L. J. Mordell. The diophantine equation $y^2 - k = x^3$. *Proc. Lond. Math. Soc.*, (2) **13** (1913), 60–80.
3. A. Baker. On the representation of integers by binary forms. *Phil. Trans. R. Soc. Lond.*, **263** (1968), 173–208.
4. B. Delaunay. Über die Darstellung der Zahlen durch die binäre kubische Formen mit negativer Discriminante. *Math. Z.*, **31** (1930), 1–26.
5. T. Nagell. Darstellungen ganzer Zahlen durch binäre kubische Formen mit negativer Diskriminante. *Math. Z.*, **28** (1928), 10–29.
6. W. Ljunggren. Einige Bemerkungen uber die Darstellung ganzer Zahlen durch binäre kubische Formen mit positiver Diskriminante. *Acta Math.*, **75** (1942), 1–21.
7. V. I. Baulin. On an indeterminate equation of the third degree with least positive discriminant (Russian). *Tul'sk Gos. Ped. Inst. U'čen. Zap Fiz Mat. Nauk Vyp.*, **7** (1960), 138–170.
8. T. Nagell. Solution complète de quelques équations cubiques à deux indéterminées. *J. de Math.*, (9) **4** (1925), 209–270.
9. W. Ljunggren. On an improvement of a theorem of T. Nagell concerning the diophantine equation $Ax^3 + By^3 = C$. *Math. Scan.*, **1** (1953), 297–309.
10. C. L. Siegel. Über einige Anwendungen diophantischer Approximationen. *Abh. preuss. Akad. Wiss. Phys. Math.*, *Kl* (1929), Nr 1.
11. E. S. Selmer. The diophantine equation $ax^3 + by^3 + cz^3 = 0$. *Acta Math.*, **85** (1951), 203–362.
12. L. J. Mordell. Equations $ax^3 + bx^2y + cxy^2 + dy^3 = e$ with no rational solutions. *J. Lond. Math. Soc.*, **43** (1968), 433–438.

CHAPTER 25

Binary Quartic Forms

1. Let

$$F = F(x, y) = ax^4 + 4bx^3y + 6cx^2y^2 + 4dxy^3 + ey^4 = (a, b, c, d, e)(x, y)^4,$$

where a, b, c, d, e are integers. We shall require some results on the invariants and covariants of $F(x, y)$.

There are two invariants,

$$g_2 = ae - 4bd + 3c^2, \qquad g_3 = \begin{vmatrix} a & b & c \\ b & c & d \\ c & d & e \end{vmatrix}. \tag{1}$$

There are quartic and sextic covariants, $H(x, y)$, $G(x, y)$, defined by

$$H = H(x, y) = -\frac{1}{144} \begin{vmatrix} \dfrac{\partial^2 F}{\partial x^2} & \dfrac{\partial^2 F}{\partial x \partial y} \\ \dfrac{\partial^2 F}{\partial x \partial y} & \dfrac{\partial^2 F}{\partial y^2} \end{vmatrix}$$

$$= \begin{vmatrix} ax^2 + 2bxy + cy^2 & bx^2 + 2cxy + dy^2 \\ bx^2 + 2cxy + dy^2 & cx^2 + 2dxy + ey^2 \end{vmatrix}$$

$$= (b^2 - ac)x^4 + (2bc - 2ad)x^3y + (-ae - 2bd + 3c^2)x^2y^2$$

$$+ (2cd - 2be)xy^3 + (d^2 - ec)y^4. \tag{2}$$

Also

$$G = G(x, y) = -\frac{1}{8} \begin{vmatrix} \dfrac{\partial F}{\partial x} & \dfrac{\partial F}{\partial y} \\ \dfrac{\partial H}{\partial x} & \dfrac{\partial H}{\partial y} \end{vmatrix} = (a^2 d - 3abc + 2b^3)x^6 + \cdots \tag{3}$$

By means of a linear substitution with real or complex coefficients, $F(x, y)$, if it has no squared factor, as we suppose hereafter, can be reduced to the canonical form

$$F(x, y) = x^4 + 6mx^2y^2 + y^4.$$

Here
$$g_2 = 1 + 3m^2, \qquad g_3 = m - m^3,$$
$$H(x, y) = -m(x^4 + y^4) + (3m^2 - 1)x^2y^2,$$
$$G(x, y) = (1 - 9m^2)xy(x^4 - y^4).$$

The relation between the covariants of the quartic is given by

Theorem 1

$$G^2 = 4H^3 - g_2HF^2 - g_3F^3$$
$$= 4(H - e_1F)(H - e_2F)(H - e_3F), \qquad (4)$$

where e_1, e_2, e_3 *are roots of the equation*

$$4t^3 - g_2t - g_3 = 0.$$

It suffices to prove the result for the canonical form of the quartic. The e are roots of the equation

$$4t^3 - (1 + 3m^2)t - m + m^3 = 0,$$

or
$$(t + m)(4t^2 - 4mt + m^2 - 1) = 0,$$

and so
$$e_1 = -m, \qquad e_2 = \frac{m + 1}{2}, \qquad e_3 = \frac{m - 1}{2}.$$

We verify at once that

$$H - e_1F = (9m^2 - 1)x^2y^2,$$
$$H - e_2F = -\tfrac{1}{2}(3m + 1)(x^2 + y^2)^2,$$
$$H - e_3F = -\tfrac{1}{2}(3m - 1)(x^2 - y^2)^2,$$

and the theorem follows.
We have already proved in Chapter 18 the

Theorem 2

The class number for binary quartics with given invariants is finite.
The conditions for a reduced form cannot be expressed in very simple terms. Birch and Swinnerton-Dyer in their exhaustive study[2] of rational points on elliptic curves, found it convenient to develop a theory of reduction which is independent of Julia's geometric presentation but is more suitable for computational purposes.
2. We can now find[1] the integer solutions of the equation

$$Z^2 = X^3 - G_2XY^2 - G_3Y^3, \qquad (5)$$

where G_2, G_3 are given integers and the right-hand side has no squared linear factor.

Let $F(x, y)$ be a representative of the binary quartics with invariants $g_2 = 4G_2$, $g_3 = 4G_3$. Then from equation (4), a solution is given by

$$X = H(p, q), \qquad Y = F(p, q), \qquad 2Z = G(p, q), \qquad (6)$$

and X, Y, Z are all integers if p, q are integers.

If $(p, q) = \delta$, then X/δ^4, Y/δ^4, Z/δ^6 are integers and so we may take $\delta = 1$. We shall prove that all the integer solutions for which $(X, Y) = 1$ are included in these formulae. For let (h, a, g) be such a set of values for (X, Y, Z), and so

$$g^2 = h^3 - G_2 h a^2 - G_3 a^3, \quad (a, h) = 1.$$

We shall construct a quartic $(a, b, c, d, e)(x, y)^4$ with invariants $4G_2$, $4G_3$ with leading coefficients h, g for the quartic and sextic covariants respectively. Then if the quartic is equivalent to $F(x, y)$, we have

$$a = F(p, q), \qquad h = H(p, q), \qquad 2g = G(p, q),$$

and since $(a, h) = 1$, then $(p, q) = 1$. We have

$$h = b^2 - ac, \quad \text{and so} \quad (a, b) = 1.$$

We take
$$b \equiv g/h \,(\mathrm{mod}\ a^2),$$

and then
$$ac \equiv (g^2 - h^3)/h^2 \,(\mathrm{mod}\ a^2),$$

and so c is an integer.

We define d by

$$2g = a^2 d - 3abc + 2b^3.$$

Since $h = b^2 - ac$, $hb = b^3 - abc$, then

$$a^2 d = b^3 - 3bh + 2g \equiv g^3/h^3 - g \,(\mathrm{mod}\ a^2)$$

$$\equiv 0 \,(\mathrm{mod}\ a^2),$$

and so d is an integer.

Finally we define e by

$$4G_2 = ae - 4bd + 3c^2.$$

On substituting the values of c, d in here, we find

$$a^3 e = 4a^2 G_2 - 3h^2 + b^4 - 6b^2 h + 8bg.$$

Substituting in here the values of g, h, G_2, we find

$$4G_3 = ace + 2bcd - ad^2 - b^2 e - c^3,$$

and so the quartic has invariants G_2, G_3.

Since ae and $(ac - b^2)e$ are integers and $(a, b) = 1$, then e is an integer.

This completes the proof.

Considerable numerical detail may be involved in applications as is seen for the equation

$$z^2 = x^3 + y^3,$$

whose solution when y is odd and prime to x, is given by

$$x = -4p^3q + 4q^4, \qquad\qquad y = p^4 + 8pq^3,$$

$$x = -p^4 + 6p^2q^2 + 3q^4, \qquad y = p^4 + 6p^2q^2 - 3q^4,$$

$$x = p^4 + 6p^2q^2 - 3q^4, \qquad y = -p^4 + 6p^2q^2 + 3q^4,$$

$$x = 2p^4 - 4p^3q - 4pq^3 + 2q^4, \qquad y = p^4 + 4p^3q - 6p^2q^2 + 4pq^3 + q^4,$$

$$x = 4p^3q + 24p^2q^2 + 48pq^3 + 36q^4, \quad y = p^4 + 8p^3q + 24p^2q^2 + 24pq^3.$$

Here p, q take such integer values that y is odd and prime to x.

Results for equation (5) may sometimes be found by factorizing the right-hand side in the cubic field given by $\theta^3 - G_2\theta - G_3 = 0$, and in particular when unique factorization holds in the field.

Thus all[4] the rational integral solutions of

$$z^2 = x^3 + 4y^3,$$

where x, y, z are relative prime in pairs is included in

$$x = p(p^3 + q^3), \qquad y = q(q^3 - 2p^3), \qquad \pm z = p^6 - 10p^3q^3 - 2q^6.$$

The equation[3]

$$2z^2 = x^3 + y^3$$

has also been solved completely.

Three or four sets of formulae are required according as $(x, y) = 1$ or 2.

3. We can apply the theory of the binary quartic to prove the

Theorem 3

The equation

$$ey^2 = ax^3 + bx^2 + cx + d, \quad a \neq 0, \tag{7}$$

where the constants are integers and the right-hand side has no squared linear factor in x, has only a finite number of integer solutions.

The proof will be given in Chapter 27 and depends on Thue's theorem that the equation

$$f(x, y) = ax^4 + bx^3y + cx^2y^2 + dxy^3 + ey^4 = m, \tag{8}$$

where $f(x, y)$ is not a square in x, y, has only a finite number of integer solutions. In general, it is not too easy to find them, but the p-adic methods of Chapter 23 are sometimes useful.

A particular case of a theorem by Siegel, given in Chapter 28, states that the equation

$$kz^2 = f(x, 1)$$

has only a finite number of integer solutions. This is easily proved for the special case

$$kz^2 = ax^4 + cx^2 + e. \qquad (9)$$

For, writing it as

$$kz^2 = ax^4 + cx^2y + ey^2,$$

where $y = 1$, the general solution as shown in Chapter 8 is given by a finite number of expressions of the form

$$x^2 = lp^2 + mpq + nq^2, \qquad 1 = l_1p^2 + m_1pq + n_1q^2,$$

where p, q are integer parameters. The solution of the first is given by a finite number of expressions of the form

$$p = rX^2 + sXY + tY^2, \qquad q = r_1X^2 + s_1XY + t_1Y^2,$$

where X, Y are integer parameters. Substituting in the second equation gives finally a finite number of equations of the form

$$F(X, Y) = AX^4 + BX^3Y + CX^2Y^2 + DXY^3 + EY^4 = 1. \qquad (10)$$

Alternatively, as shown in Chapter 8, the solution of equation (9) can be expressed by a finite number of expressions of the form

$$x^2 = k_1T_n + k_2U_n,$$

where, say, $D = 4ak$ and

$$T_n + U_n\sqrt{D} = (T + U\sqrt{D})^n, \quad n = 0, \pm 1, \pm 2, \ldots$$

and T, U is the fundamental solution of

$$Y^2 - DX^2 = \pm 1.$$

The problem now is to find n. In some instances, the solution may be found by discussing various congruences satisfied by T_n, U_n. In others, the p-adic methods of Chapter 23 must be applied.

Some results on the number of solutions of irreducible equations such as (10), say (A, B, C, D, E) where $A > 0$, $E > 0$, have been given by Nagell.[5] Suppose that the equation $f(x, 1) = 0$ generates only imaginary biquadratic fields with at least one quadratic subfield. Thus he has proved

Theorem 4

The number N of solutions of equation (10) is always even and $N \leqslant 8$. Also $N = 8$ if and only if

$F(X, Y) \sim (1, 0, -1, 0, 1)$ *or* $(1, -1, -1, 1, 1)$; *and* $N = 6$ *if and only if* $F(X, Y) \sim (1, 0, r^2, -2r, 1)$ *or* $(1, 2r, r^2 + s, rs, 1)$ *or* $(1, 1, 1, 1, 1)$ *where r is an integer and* $s = 1$, *the case* $r = 2$, $s = 1$ *being excluded.*

REFERENCES

1. L. J. Mordell. Indeterminate equations of the third and fourth degrees. *Q. J. Pure appl. Maths.*, **45** (1914), 170–186.
2. B. J. Birch and H. P. F. Swinnerton-Dyer. Notes on elliptic curves, I. *J. reine angew. Math.*, **212** (1963), 7–25.
3. F. E. G. Rodeja. On the diophantine equation $x^3 + y^3 = 2z^2$. *Rivista Mat. Hisp. Am.* (1953), 4–13, 229–240.
4. C. Georgikopoulous. Rational solutions of the equations $x^3 + 4y^3 = z^2$, $x^3 + 2y^3 = z^2$. *Bull. Soc. Math. Grèce.*, **24** (1948), 13–19.
5. T. Nagell. Sur les représentations de l'unité par les formes binaires biquadratiques du premier rang. *Arkiv för Mat.*, **5** (1965), 477–521.

CHAPTER 26

The Equation $y^2 = x^3 + k$

1. *The Diophantine equation*[1]

$$y^2 = x^3 + k. \tag{1}$$

This has played a fundamental role in the development of number theory.
The earliest recorded result was given in 1621 by Bachet who noted that when
$k = -2$, and so $x = 3$ is a solution, other solutions can be found by the usual
tangent method. Then Fermat posed a problem for the English mathematicians to show that the only integer solutions of $y^2 = x^3 - 2$ are given by
$x = 3$. He asserted that, at first sight, this seemed to be a difficult question,
although an infinity of fractional solutions can be deduced by the method of
Bachet. He stated that he had discovered an exceedingly beautiful and subtle
method which enabled him to solve such questions in integers and which was
not known to Bachet. His proof was never published. A faulty proof was
given many years later by Euler.†

It may be remarked that the first *proof* of the existence of an infinity of
rational solutions was given by Fueter in 1930, and will be considered further
on.

We consider first various methods for discussing integer solutions of the
equation (1).

Congruence considerations

It has been known[2] for nearly a century that many equations can be proved
to have no integer solutions when they can be written in the form

$$y^2 + lm^2 = x^3 + n^3. \tag{2}$$

This is considered as a congruence mod $2^\alpha l$. Simple congruence considerations may eliminate some of the residues of x mod 4 or mod 8, or mod l, and
the other residues may often be eliminated by considering the quadratic
characters of $x + n$, $x^2 - xn + n^2$ mod 8 or mod l.

Some illustrations are now given.

The equation

$$y^2 + 4a^2 = x^3 + (4b - 1)^3, \tag{3}$$

where a has no prime factors $\equiv 3$ (mod 4).

Clearly

$$x \not\equiv 0 \;(\text{mod } 2), \qquad x \not\equiv -1 \;(\text{mod } 4), \quad \text{and so } x \equiv 1 \;(\text{mod } 4).$$

† For the early history, see Dickson's "History of the Theory of Numbers" II.

Then

$$x^2 - x(4b - 1) + (4b - 1)^2 \equiv 3 \ (\mathrm{mod}\ 4),$$

and is >0 and so cannot divide $y^2 + 4a^2$. Hence there are no solutions.

The equation

$$y^2 + (2a + 1)^2 = x^3 + (4b + 2)^3, \tag{4}$$

where $2a + 1$ has no prime factors $\equiv 3$ (mod 4).

Here $x \not\equiv 0$ (mod 2), $x \not\equiv -1$ (mod 4) and so $x \equiv 1$ (mod 4).
Then

$$x^2 - x(4b + 2) + (4b + 2)^2 \equiv 3 \ (\mathrm{mod}\ 4),$$

and so cannot divide $y^2 + (2a + 1)^2$.

We give instances of equation (2) when $l = \pm 2$.

The equation

$$y^2 - 2b^2 = x^3 - a^3, \tag{5}$$

where $a \equiv 2, 4$ (mod 8), $b \equiv 1$ (mod 2), *and b has no prime factor* $\equiv \pm 3$ (mod 8).

Here $x \not\equiv 0$ (mod 2), $x \not\equiv 1$ (mod 4) and so $x \equiv -1$ (mod 4), i.e. $x \equiv -1, 3$ (mod 8). When $x \equiv -1$ (mod 8), $x - a \equiv \pm 3$ (mod 8) and since $x - a > 0$, it cannot divide $y^2 - 2b^2$. When $x \equiv 3$ (mod 8),

$$x^2 + ax + a^2 \equiv 1 + 3a + a^2 \equiv \pm 3 \ (\mathrm{mod}\ 8),$$

and so cannot divide $y^2 - 2b^2$.

The equation

$$y^2 + 2b^2 = x^3 - a^3, \tag{6}$$

where $a \equiv 4$ (mod 8), $b \equiv 1$ (mod 2) *and b contains no prime divisors* $\equiv 5, 7$ (mod 8).

Here also $x \equiv -1, 3$ (mod 8). When $x \equiv -1$ (mod 8), $y^2 \equiv 5$ (mod 8), When $x \equiv 3$ (mod 8), $x - a \equiv 7$ (mod 8) and cannot divide $y^2 + 2b^2$.

Results may also be found if k can be written in several forms.

The equation

$$y^2 = x^3 + 45. \tag{7}$$

Clearly $x \not\equiv 0$ (mod 2), $x \not\equiv 1$ (mod 4) and so $x \equiv 3, 7$ (mod 8).

Write $\qquad\qquad y^2 - 2 . 6^2 = x^3 - 27.$

Here $x \not\equiv 0$ (mod 3) since if $x = 3X$, $y = 3Y$, $Y^2 = 3X^3 + 5$.

Then if $x \equiv 3 \pmod 8$, $x^2 + 3x + 9 \equiv 3 \pmod 8$ and so cannot divide $y^2 - 2.6^2$.

Write next $$y^2 - 2.3^2 = x^3 + 27.$$

Then if $x \equiv -1 \pmod 8$, $x^2 - 3x + 9 \equiv 5 \pmod 8$ and so cannot divide $y^2 - 2.3^2$.

Hence there are no integer solutions.

The equation

$$y^2 - 3b^2 = x^3 - a^3, \tag{8}$$

where $a \equiv 1 \pmod 4$, $b \equiv \pm 2 \pmod 6$ *and* b *has no prime factors* $\equiv \pm 5 \pmod{12}$.

Here $x \not\equiv 0 \pmod 2$, $x \not\equiv -1 \pmod 4$ and so $x \equiv 1 \pmod 4$. Also $x \equiv a, a + 1 \pmod 3$. We reject $x \equiv a$ since then $x^3 \equiv a^3 \pmod 9$ and so $y^2 \equiv 3 \pmod 9$. Hence

$$x^2 + ax + a^2 \equiv 1 \pmod 3, \equiv 3 \pmod 4, \equiv 7 \pmod{12}.$$

Then $x^2 + ax + a^2$ contains a prime factor $p \equiv \pm 5 \pmod{12}$ and since $(3/p) = -1$, it cannot divide $y^2 - 3b^2$.

We have the more general[2]

Theorem 1

The equation

$$y^2 - kb^2 = x^3 - k^3 a^3$$

has no integer solutions when

$$a \equiv -1 \pmod 4, \qquad b \equiv 0 \pmod 2,$$

k *is square free,* $k \equiv 3 \pmod 4$, $(k, b) = 1$, *and* $b \not\equiv 0 \pmod 3$ *if* $k \equiv 2 \pmod 3$; *and lastly* a *and* b *have no common prime factor* p *if the quadratic character* $(k/p) = -1$.

Since $y^2 \equiv x^3 - 1 \pmod 4$, $x \not\equiv 0, 2, 3 \pmod 4$, and so $x \equiv 1 \pmod 4$.

Write $$y^2 - kb^2 = (x - ka)(x^2 + kax + k^2 a^2),$$

and $$F = x^2 + kax + k^2 a^2 > 0.$$

Now $(x, k) = 1$ for if $q \mid (x, k)$, where q is a prime, then $q \mid y^2$ but $q^2 \nmid kb^2$ since $(k, b) = 1$. Hence $(F, k) = 1$.
Then since $F \equiv 3 \pmod 4$,

$$\left(\frac{k}{F}\right) = -\left(\frac{F}{k}\right) = -1,$$

and so F contains as a factor a prime p to an odd power such that $(k/p) = -1$.

Hence $y \equiv b \equiv 0 \pmod p$, and so p occurs to an even power as a divisor of $y^2 - kb^2$ and to an odd power in $x - ka$. Then

$$x - ka \equiv 0 \pmod p, \qquad x^2 + kax + k^2a^2 \equiv 0 \pmod p,$$

and so

$$3kax \equiv 0 \pmod p.$$

If $p = 3$, then $k \equiv 2 \pmod 3$ since $(k/p) = -1$ and we would have $b \equiv 0 \pmod 3$, and this has been ruled out.

If $x \equiv 0 \pmod p$, $ka \equiv 0 \pmod p$ whereas k is prime to p, and a is also prime to p since $p \nmid (a, b)$.

2. Applications of the quadratic field $Q(\sqrt k)$

We recall some well known results. We suppose that k is a square free integer. Two cases arise.

$k \equiv 2, 3 \pmod 4$. Then the integers x in the field are given by $x = x_1 + x_2\sqrt k$ where x_1 and x_2 are rational integers. Also x is a unit if $x_1^2 - kx_2^2 = \pm 1$.

$k \equiv 1 \pmod 4$. The integers are given by $x = x_1 + x_2\left(\dfrac{1 + \sqrt k}{2}\right)$ and x is a unit if $x_1^2 + x_1x_2 + \frac14(1 - k)x_2^2 = \pm 1$.

It is known that all units ε are given by $\varepsilon = \pm\eta^n$, where η is a fundamental unit and n takes all integer values.

If $k < 0$, the only units are ± 1 except that when $k = -1$, there are four units given by i^n, $n = 0, 1, 2, 3$, i.e. ± 1, $\pm i$, and that when $k = -3$, there are six units $\pm\rho^n$, $n = 0, 1, 2$, where $\rho = \dfrac{-1 + \sqrt{-3}}{2}$,

namely

$$\pm 1, \ \pm\left(\frac{-1 + \sqrt{-3}}{2}\right), \ \pm\left(\frac{-1 - \sqrt{-3}}{2}\right).$$

We begin with the case when h, the number of classes of ideals in the field $Q(\sqrt k)$ is not divisible by 3, and this of course is so when unique factorization holds in the field, for example, when $k = -1, -2, -3, -7, \ldots$, $k = 2, 3, 6, \ldots$.

Suppose now that $k \equiv 2, 3 \pmod 4$ or $5 \pmod 8$. This means that $x \not\equiv 0 \pmod 2$ in

$$y^2 - k = x^3.$$

Write

$$(y + \sqrt k)(y - \sqrt k) = x^3.$$

The two factors are relatively prime since any common divisor would divide $2\sqrt k$ but $(x, 2k) = 1$. Hence by the general theory of Chapter 15

$$y + \sqrt k = \varepsilon(a + b\omega)^3, \qquad y - \sqrt k = \varepsilon'(a + b\omega')^3,$$
$$x = N(a + b\omega), \tag{9}$$

where a, b are rational integers, $\varepsilon, \varepsilon'$ are conjugate units, ω, ω' are conjugate numbers and $\omega = \sqrt k$ if $k \equiv 2, 3 \pmod 4$, $\omega = (1 + \sqrt k)/2$ if $k \equiv 5 \pmod 8$.

Also if $k < 0$, $\varepsilon = \pm 1$, and if $k > 0$, $\varepsilon = 1$, η, η^{-1} where η is a fundamental unit of the field $Q(\sqrt{k})$ since a factor -1 can be absorbed in the cube.

Suppose, for example, that $k < 0$, $k \equiv 2, 3 \pmod 4$.

Then
$$y + \sqrt{k} = (a + b\sqrt{k})^3, \qquad x = a^2 - kb^2,$$

and so
$$1 = b(3a^2 + kb^2). \tag{10}$$

Solutions arise only when $b = \pm 1$, $k = \pm 1 - 3a^2$.

In particular, when $k = -2$, we have only $a = \pm 1$ and $x = 3$, as stated by Fermat. When $k = -13$, $h = 2$, and $a = \pm 2$, $x = 17$, $y = \pm 70$ are the only solutions.

Suppose next that $k > 0$, $k \equiv 2, 3 \pmod 4$. We may always take η to be the unit defined by $\eta = T + U\sqrt{k}$ where (T, U) is the fundamental solution of $T^2 - kU^2 = 1$. For if $\eta_0 = t + u\sqrt{k}$ where $t^2 - ku^2 = -1$, $\eta = \eta_0^2$ and then $\eta_0 = \eta_0^3/\eta$ and so η_0^3 can be absorbed in the cube. No solutions arise from $\varepsilon = 1$ since equation (10) holds. The units η, η^{-1} give

$$1 = T(3a^2b + kb^3) \pm U(a^3 + 3kab^2). \tag{11}$$

As shown in Chapter 7, congruences mod 9 or mod 7 sometimes suffice to prove that no integer solutions exist. We prove this for the two cases,

$$k \equiv 4 \pmod 9, \quad \text{if} \quad U \equiv 0 \pmod 9,$$

and
$$k \equiv 7 \pmod 9, \quad \text{if} \quad U \equiv \pm 3 \pmod 9.$$

From $T^2 - kU^2 = 1$, we have $U \equiv 0 \pmod 3$, $T \equiv \pm 1 \pmod 9$, and so from equation (11) as a congruence mod 3, $Tb \equiv 1$ and so $b \equiv \pm 1$. Then from equation (11) as a congruence mod 9,

$$1 \equiv 3a^2 + k \pm Ua,$$

and so $a \not\equiv 0 \pmod 3$ since $k \not\equiv 1 \pmod 9$. Also $a \not\equiv \pm 1 \pmod 3$ since $1 \not\equiv 3 + k \pm U \pmod 9$.

Instances are given by $k = 7, 34, 58, 70$.

On taking (11) as a congruence mod 7, we can show that the equation is impossible if $U \equiv 0 \pmod 7$ when $k \equiv 4 \pmod 7$. Then $x \equiv 0 \pmod 7$ since $y^2 - 4 \equiv x^3 \pmod 7$, and from $x = a^2 - kb^2$, $a \equiv \pm 2b \pmod 7$. Then equation (11) becomes

$$1 \equiv \pm(3a^2b + 4b^3) \equiv \pm 2b^3 \pmod 7,$$

and this is impossible. An instance is given by $k = 159$, $T = 1324$, $U = 105$.

We now consider some cases when the class number is divisible by 3. We suppose now that k is square free, $k \equiv 2, 3 \pmod 4$ and $h(Q(\sqrt{k})) \equiv 0 \pmod 3$.

In
$$(y + \sqrt{k})(y - \sqrt{k}) = x^3,$$

the two factors are relatively prime since $(x, 2k) = 1$. Hence we have the ideal equations

$$(y + \sqrt{k}) = a_1^3, \qquad (y - \sqrt{k}) = a_2^3.$$

Let ℓ_1 be an ideal in the inverse class of a_1. Then

$$\ell_1^3(y + \sqrt{k}) = (a_1\ell_1)^3 = (X + Y\sqrt{k})^3,$$

where X, Y are rational integers. Also

$$\ell_1^3 = (p + q\sqrt{k}), \qquad p^2 - kq^2 = (N(\ell_1))^3 = n^3, \text{ say,}$$

where p and q are rational integers.
Hence we have an ideal equation

$$N(\ell_1)^3(y + \sqrt{k}) = (p - q\sqrt{k})(X + Y\sqrt{k})^3,$$

i.e. an equation,

$$n^3(y + \sqrt{k}) = \eta(p - q\sqrt{k})(X + Y\sqrt{k})^3, \tag{12}$$

where η is a unit in $Q(\sqrt{k})$. If $k < 0$, we can take $\eta = 1$, and if $k > 0$, then $\eta = 1, \varepsilon, \varepsilon^{-1}$ where $\varepsilon = T + U\sqrt{k}$ is the fundamental solution of $T^2 - kU^2 = 1$. There will be as many sets of equations of this kind as there are classes of ideals ℓ whose cubes give the principal class. When $\ell \sim 1$, we take $n = 1$. If it is convenient to take ℓ to be a prime ideal, then n will be a prime.
The resulting cubic equation in X, Y takes the form

$$AX^3 + 3BX^2Y + 3CXY^2 + DY^3 = m^3,$$

and can sometimes be shown to be impossible by simple congruence considerations.
Let us now consider the equation

$$y^2 - k = x^3$$

when k is square free, $k < 0$, $k \equiv 1 \pmod 8$, $k \neq -7$, $h = 3$.
An integral basis in $Q(\sqrt{k})$ is $(1, \omega)$ where $\omega = (1 + \sqrt{k})/2$. We have an ideal factorization of 2 given by

$$(2) = (2, 1 + \omega)(2, 1 + \omega') = \mathscr{C}\mathscr{C}',$$

where ω, ω' are conjugate as are the ideals $\mathscr{C}$, $\mathscr{C}'$. Then $\mathscr{C}$ is not a principal ideal since for integers a, b,

$$2 \neq (a + b\omega)(a + b\omega'),$$

follows from

$$8 \neq (2a + b)^2 - kb^2.$$

Now $(y + \sqrt{k}, y - \sqrt{k}) = 2$ or 1 since $\mathscr{C} \neq \mathscr{C}'$. We have two cases. In the first, x is even and hence the ideal equation

$$(y + \sqrt{k}) = (2)\mathscr{C}a^3, \tag{13}$$

which is impossible since a^3 is a principal ideal.

In the second case, x is odd and we have

$$(y \pm \sqrt{k}) = a^3, \tag{14}$$

and this may be difficult to deal with. Other methods may be used to dispose of odd values for x. Suppose for instance that

$$y^2 + 31 = x^3.$$

Then $x \not\equiv 1 \pmod 4$ since $y^2 \not\equiv 2 \pmod 4$. Also $x \not\equiv -1 \pmod 4$ from

$$y^2 + 4 = (x - 3)(x^2 + 3x + 9).$$

Here $x^2 + 3x + 9 \equiv 3 \pmod 4$ and is > 0 and so cannot divide $y^2 + 4$.

3. Application of cubic residues

Another method of approach is to use cubic residues to a prime $p > 3$. We recall that the congruence

$$x^3 \equiv l \pmod p, \quad (l, p) = 1,$$

is always solvable if $p \equiv 2 \pmod 3$. If $p \equiv 1 \pmod 3$, solvability requires a condition on l, namely that l should be a cubic residue of p, written as $(l/p)_3 = 1$ and so $l^{(p-1)/3} \equiv 1 \pmod p$. If $l = 2$, the condition becomes the existence of integers r, s such that

$$r^2 + 27s^2 = p.$$

If $l = 3$, the condition is

$$r^2 + 243s^2 = 4p.$$

We now prove[3] the

Theorem 2

The equation

$$y^2 = x^3 + k, \qquad k = 2a^3 - 3b^2, \tag{15}$$

has no integer solutions if a, b are integers, $ab \neq 0$, $a \not\equiv 1 \pmod 3$, $b \not\equiv 0 \pmod 3$, and if when $b \equiv 0 \pmod 2$, then $a \equiv 1 \pmod 2$; and if 2 is a cubic residue of every odd prime $p \equiv 1 \pmod 3$ dividing a.

Write

$$x^3 + 2a^3 = y^2 + 3b^2. \tag{16}$$

The possible primes dividing the left-hand side are the common prime factors of x and a, 2, 3, primes $q \equiv 2 \pmod 3$, and primes $p \equiv 1 \pmod 3$ for which $(2/p)_3 = 1$.

We show first that the left-hand side, say L, is prime to 6. For if $x = 2x_1$, then $y \equiv b \pmod 2$, and so either $y \equiv b \equiv 0 \pmod 2$ or $y \equiv b \equiv 1 \pmod 2$. The first case is impossible since $a \equiv 1 \pmod 2$. The second case gives $x^3 + 2a^3 \equiv 4 \pmod 8$ and this is also impossible.

Next if $x^3 + 2a^3 \equiv 0 \pmod 3$, $y \equiv 0 \pmod 3$, and so $x^3 + 2a^3 \equiv 3 \pmod 9$. This is impossible since $a^3 \equiv 0, -1 \pmod 9$. Suppose now that a prime $q \equiv 2 \pmod 3$ divides L. Then $y \equiv b \equiv 0 \pmod q$. Hence we can write $y = Qy_1$, $b = Qb_1$, where Q is the product of factors q dividing L. Then Q^2 must divide out in both sides of equation (16) and the only other prime factors of L are primes $p = A^2 + 27B^2$.

Since factorization in the quadratic field $Q(\sqrt{-3})$ is unique, we have

$$(y_1 + b_1\sqrt{-3})\rho^\alpha = \prod_p (A + B\sqrt{-27}) = C + D\sqrt{-27},$$

where $\rho = \frac{1}{2}(-1 + \sqrt{-3})$, $\alpha = 0, \pm 1$. If $\alpha = 0$, then $b_1 \equiv 0 \pmod 3$ contrary to hypothesis. If $\alpha = \pm 1$, $y_1 + b_1 \equiv 0 \pmod 2$, and then $L \equiv 0 \pmod 2$, and this has been excluded.

Instances are given by $k = 51$, with $a = 3$, $b = 1$, and $k = 13$, with $a = 2$, $b = 1$.

A similar result[3] is

Theorem 3

The equation

$$x^3 + 4a^3 = y^2 + 3b^2, \quad ab \neq 0, \tag{17}$$

has no integer solution if $b \equiv \pm 1 \pmod 6$, $a \equiv 0, 2 \pmod 6$, and a has no prime factors $p \equiv 1 \pmod 3$.

A variant using the cubic character of 3 is given by

Theorem 4

The equation

$$x^3 + 3a^3 = y^2 + 3b^2, \tag{18}$$

has no integer solutions if $k/3 = a^3 - b^2 \not\equiv 0 \pmod 3$ unless that one of $b, b \pm (1 - k)$ which is divisible by 3 is also divisible by 9.

The left-hand side is not divisible by 3, for this would require $y \equiv 0 \pmod 3$, $x \equiv 0 \pmod 3$, $a^3 - b^2 \equiv 0 \pmod 3$. Hence

$$y \equiv \pm 1 \pmod 3, \qquad x^3 \equiv 1 \pmod 3, \qquad x^3 \equiv 1 \pmod 9,$$

and then

$$y^2 \equiv 1 + k \pmod 9, \qquad y \equiv \pm(1 - k) \pmod 9.$$

Hence the only possible divisors of the left-hand side are the common divisors of x and a, the primes $p \equiv 1 \pmod 3$ of which 3 is a cubic residue

9+

and the primes $q \equiv 2 \pmod 3$. If q is a divisor, then since $(-3/q) = 1$, $y \equiv 0 \pmod q$, $b \equiv 0 \pmod q$.

Hence
$$x^3 + 3a^3 = Q^2(y_1^2 + 3b_1^2),$$

where Q is a product of primes q. The factor Q^2 divides out and so

$$(y_1 + b_1\sqrt{-3})\rho^\alpha = \prod_p \left(\frac{A + B\sqrt{-243}}{2}\right) = \frac{C + D\sqrt{-243}}{2},$$

where C, D are integers and $\alpha = 0, \pm 1$.
If $\alpha = 0$, $b_1 \equiv 0 \pmod 9$ and so $b \equiv 0 \pmod 9$.
If $\alpha = \pm 1$, $y_1 \pm b_1 \equiv 0 \pmod 9$ and so $y \pm b \equiv 0 \pmod 9$.
The theorem now follows since $y \equiv \pm(1 - k) \pmod 9$.
   An illustration is given by $y^2 = x^3 - 24$ where $24 = 3 \cdot 3^2 - 3^2 \cdot 1^3$.

4. *Application of binary cubic forms*

   We consider now in more detail than in Chapter 24, the application of the binary cubic form to the equation

$$y^2 = x^3 + k.$$

Let $(x, y) = (p, q)$ be a solution. With it, we associate the binary cubic form

$$f(x, y) = x^3 - 3pxy^2 + 2qy^3 \tag{19}$$

with binomial coefficients and so of discriminant

$$D = -4q^2 + 4p^3 = -4k.$$

Hence $f(x, y)$ is equivalent to one of the finite number of binary cubics of discriminant $-4k$ representing unity. Conversely, since every such cubic is equivalent to a cubic

$$g(x, y) = x^3 + 3bx^2y + 3cxy^2 + dy^3, \tag{20}$$

this gives at once a solution of $y^2 = x^3 + k$ on writing $x - by$ for x in equation (20), and reducing it to the form (19). Since by Thue's theorem there are only a finite number of representations of unity by $g(x, y)$, $y^2 = x^3 + k$ can have only a finite number of solutions.

   In general, it is not an easy matter to find all the solutions, and even for some small values of k, a surprising amount of numerical detail may be required. When $k > 0$, the cubic $g(x, y)$ has negative discriminant, and so the representation results by Delaunay and Nagell in Chapter 21 are applicable. Thus all the equations with $0 < k \leqslant 100$ have been solved, and solutions are given in Hemer's thesis[4]. In particular, Nagell[5] has shown that there are exactly eight solutions when $k = 17$, namely,

$$x = -1, -2, 2, 4, \ 8, \ 43, \ 52, \ \ 5234,$$
$$y = \ \ 4, \ \ 3, 5, 9, 23, 282, 375, 378661.$$

When $k < 0$, the problem becomes much more difficult since there are no useful general theorems about the representation of unity by binary cubic forms of positive determinant. There are twenty unsolved equations for $0 > k \geqslant -100$. These correspond to irreducible cubic fields having two fundamental units. Since there is only one relation connecting them, the p-adic methods of Chapter 23 cannot be applied directly. It becomes necessary to introduce new units in fields containing the cubic field as a subfield. An illustration is given by the equation $y^2 = x^3 - 48$ which has only the solutions $(x, y) = (4, \pm 4)$, $(28, \pm 148)$ and is of particular interest. On replacing x by $4x$ and y by $8y + 4$, it becomes

$$y^2 + y + 1 = x^3 = (y - \rho)(y - \rho^2),$$

which has only the solutions $(x, y) = (1, 0)$, $(1, -1)$, $(7, 18)$. This follows since from the equation

$$y - \rho = \pm \rho^\alpha (p + q\rho)^3,$$

we easily deduce an equation

$$X^3 - 3XY^2 + Y^3 = 1.$$

Ljunggren[6] solves this completely in the manner indicated above, and some details are given in Chapter 23.

It is sometimes desirable to use the binary quartic equations which have been seen to arise. Now there are two fundamental units and two relations connecting them and so the p-adic method can be applied directly. In this way, Ljunggren[7] has shown that when $k = -7$, the only solutions are $(x, y) = (2, 1)$, $(32, 181)$; and that when $k = -15$, the only solution is $(x, y) = (1, 2)$.

When solutions exist for $y^2 = x^3 + k$, and we have no criterion for this, a computer may be very useful unless the solutions are exceedingly large numbers. Thus tables[6a, 6b] have been compiled for $|k| < 9999$ and $0 < y < 10^{10}$. This makes the range for x, $-21 \leqslant x < 4, 641, 589$.

5. *Rational solutions*

When one rational solution of the equation $y^2 = x^3 + k$ is known, it has been shown that in general a new solution can be found, and so an infinity of rational solutions can be expected. The first result, however, is due to Fueter[8] who proved the

Theorem 5

Let k be free from sixth power prime factors. Then if the equation $y^2 = x^3 + k$ has a rational solution $(x, y) = (p, q)$ with $pq \neq 0$, there are an infinity of rational solutions unless $k = -432$ when there is only the solution $x = 12$, $y = \pm 36$, and $k = 1$ when there are only the solutions $x = 0, -1, 2$.

His proof, however, is rather complicated since it depends upon the association of the equation with the related equation $y^2 = x^3 - 27k$. Another proof[9] can be given based on Bachet's idea. It may be recalled that Fermat stated without proof that when $k = -2$, this idea leads to an infinity of rational solutions.

It has been shown by putting $x = p + X$, $y = q + 3p^2X/2q$, that when $pq \neq 0$, a solution is given by

$$x = \frac{9p^4}{4q^2} - 2p, \qquad y = \frac{8q^4 - 36q^2p^3 + 27p^6}{8q^3}.$$

We have to investigate when this solution is different from (p, q). The numerator of y shows that $y \neq 0$, and $x = 0$ can arise only from $9p^3 = 8q^2$, i.e. $q = 3t^3$, $p = 2t^2$, $k = t^6$, and so effectively from $k = 1$. On putting $p = P/D^2$, $q = Q/D^3$,

$$Q^2 = P^3 + kD^6,$$

where $(P, Q, D) = 1$, $(P, D) = 1$, $(Q, D) = 1$.

Also $$D^2x = \frac{9P^4}{4Q^2} - 2P.$$

Hence we certainly have a new solution if $3P^2/2Q$ is not an integer, and so we may suppose that $3P^2/2Q$ is an integer. Then the special cases must be considered when $P \equiv 0 \pmod 2$ or $Q \equiv 0 \pmod 3$ or $(P, Q) > 1$. It can be shown that a similar procedure with the special cases leads to a solution which is not a special case. In this way, we find a solution which either has a greater denominator than D, or, if the denominator is D, the numerator is greater than P.

Equations with no rational solutions

Two general methods are known for proving the non-existence of rational solutions. The first depends essentially upon the study of quadratic fields, and the second upon cubic fields.

Some proofs may require a deep result from the theory of relative fields given by the

Lemma

If $Q(\sqrt{k})$ and $Q(\sqrt{-3k})$ are two quadratic fields, and if the class number for the imaginary field is prime to 3, then the class number for the real field is also prime to 3.

We need not use this lemma if we postulate the non-divisibility by 3 for both class numbers.

The first general result is due to Fueter[8] who proved the

Theorem 6

The equation $y^2 = x^3 + k$ has no rational solutions if k is a negative integer free from sixth power factors, and contains all odd prime factors to an odd power, and if also

$$k \equiv 2 \pmod 9, \qquad k \not\equiv 1 \pmod 4, \qquad k \not\equiv 4 \pmod{16},$$

and the class number h of $Q(\sqrt{k})$ is not divisible by 3.

It suffices to consider the equation

$$y^2 = x^3 + kt^6,$$

and to show that there are no integer solutions in (x, y, t) with $t \neq 0$ and $(x, y, t) = 1$. With such a solution, we could associate a cubic equation

$$u^3 - 3xu - 2y = 0$$

of discriminant $d = -108kt^6$.

The solution of the cubic is given by

$$u = (y + t^3\sqrt{k})^{1/3} + (y - t^3\sqrt{k})^{1/3}.$$

Two cases arise since either the equation is irreducible in the field $Q(\sqrt{-3k})$, or is reducible and so splits into a linear factor and a quadratic factor which is then reducible in $Q(\sqrt{-3k})$.

In the first case, it is shown that

$$(y + t^3\sqrt{k}) = a^3,$$

where a is a non-principal ideal. Then $h \equiv 0 \pmod 3$, a contradiction.

In the second case, it is obvious that

$$y + t^3\sqrt{k} = (r + s\sqrt{k})^3/n^3,$$

where r, s, n are integers and $(r, s, n) = 1$.

This gives

$$n^3t^3 = s(3r^2 + ks^2), \qquad n^3y = r(r^2 + 3ks^2).$$

The discussion of the first of these leads to an equation

$$y_1^2 = x_1^3 - 27kt_1^6$$

with an associated cubic equation

$$v^3 - 3x_1v - 2y_1 = 0$$

with discriminant $d_1 = (54t_1^3)^2k$.

Here again two cases arise according as the cubic is reducible or irreducible in the field $Q(\sqrt{k})$. In the first case the method of infinite descent applies and so no solution is possible. In the second case, it is shown by results on the relative discriminants of algebraic number fields that $h \equiv 0 \pmod 3$, a contradiction.

The second general method [10, 11, 12] is illustrated by the following Theorems 7, 8, and 9.

Theorem 7

The equation $y^2 = x^3 + k$ has no rational solutions if all the following conditions are satisfied.

I. k is positive and square free and $k \equiv 2$ or $3 \pmod 4$ and $k \equiv -2$ or $-4 \pmod 9$.

II. The number h of classes of ideals in the quadratic field $Q(\sqrt{-3k})$ is not divisible by 3.

III. The fundamental solution $(X, Y) = (U, T)$ of the equation $Y^2 - kX^2 = 1$ satisfies the conditions

III'. if $k \equiv -2 \pmod 9$, then $U \equiv \pm 3 \pmod 9$, and so $T \equiv \pm 1 \pmod 9$,

III''. if $k \equiv -4 \pmod 9$, then either $U \equiv \pm 3 \pmod 9$ and so $T \equiv \pm 1 \pmod 9$, or $U \equiv \pm 4 \pmod 9$ and $T \equiv \pm 3 \pmod 9$.

Instances are $k = 7$ since $h = 4$, and $U = 3$, and $k = 14$ since $h = 4$, $U = 4$, $T = 15$.

Theorem 8

The equation $y^2 = x^3 + k$ has no rational solutions if the following conditions are satisfied.

I. k is negative and square free, $k \equiv 2$ or $3 \pmod 4$, and $k \equiv 2, 4 \pmod 9$.

II. The number of classes of ideals in the quadratic field $Q(\sqrt{k})$ is not divisible by 3.

III. The fundamental solution $(X, Y) = (U, T)$ of the equation $Y^2 + 3kX^2 = 1$ satisfies the condition $U \not\equiv 0 \pmod 3$.

Instances are given by $k = -5, -14, -34, -41$ with $U = 1, 2, 10, 11$, respectively.

Theorem 9

The equation

$$y^2 = x^3 + k$$

has no rational solutions if the following conditions are satisfied.

I. k is negative, k is square free, $k \equiv 2, 3 \pmod 4$, $k \equiv 3 \pmod 9$.

II. The number h of classes of ideals in the quadratic field $Q(\sqrt{k})$ is not divisible by 3.

III. The fundamental solution $(X, Y) = (U, T)$ of the equation $Y^2 + \frac{1}{3}kX^2 = 1$ satisfies the condition, either $U \equiv \pm 3 \pmod 9$ or $T \equiv \pm 3 \pmod 9$.

Instances are given by $k = -33, -42, -69, -78, -105, -144$ corresponding to $U = 3$, $T = 15$, $T = 24$, $T = 51$, $T = 6$, $U = 6$, respectively.

The method will be sufficiently illustrated if we prove Theorem 8.

It suffices to consider the integer solutions of

$$y^2 = x^3 + kz^6, \qquad z \neq 0, \quad (x, y, z) = 1,$$

and suppose that z has its least positive value.

Then with integers A, B and $(A, B) = 1$,

$$y + z^3\sqrt{k} = (A + B\sqrt{k})^3, \qquad z^3 = B(3A^2 + kB^2).$$

Suppose first that B is prime to 3. Then

$$B = B_1^3, \qquad 3A^2 + kB_1^6 = z_1^3.$$

As a congruence mod 9 this gives

$$3A^2 + k = z_1^3,$$

and is impossible if $k \equiv 2$ or $4 \pmod 9$, since $z_1^3 \not\equiv 2, 4, 5, 7 \pmod 9$.

Suppose next that B is divisible by 3. Then clearly

$$B = 9B_1^3, \qquad A^2 + 27kB_1^6 = z_1^3.$$

Write this as

$$(A + 3B_1^3\sqrt{-3k})(A - 3B_1^3\sqrt{-3k}) = z_1^3.$$

Then $(z_1, 6) = 1$ since $(A, B_1) = 1$ and so the two factors are relatively prime. From the lemma, the class number for $Q(\sqrt{-3k})$ is prime to 3, and so

$$A + 3B_1^3\sqrt{-3k} = (T + U\sqrt{-3k})^\alpha(C + D\sqrt{-3k})^3, \quad (C, D) = 1, \alpha = 0, \pm 1.$$

Suppose first that $\alpha = \pm 1$. Then from a congruence mod $3\sqrt{-3k}$ applied to the irrational terms,

$$0 \equiv C^3U\sqrt{-3k}.$$

Now $C \not\equiv 0 \pmod 3$ since $A \not\equiv 0 \pmod 3$, and so $U \equiv 0 \pmod 3$, and this has been excluded.

Suppose finally that $\alpha = 0$. Then

$$B_1^3 = C^2D - kD^3.$$

Hence $D = D_1^3$, $C^2 - kD_1^6 = B_2^3$, and this is the same as the original equation for z.

Also $D_1 = \sqrt[3]{D} \leqslant \sqrt[3]{B_1^3} \leqslant \sqrt[3]{B/9} \leqslant z/\sqrt[3]{9}$, and so this contradicts the definition.

6. *Further application of algebraic number fields*

The finite basis theorem for cubic curves given in Chapter 16 applies to the special equation

$$y^2 = x^3 + k, \tag{21}$$

and so depends on the consideration of the cubic field $Q(\sqrt[3]{k})$. A simpler treatment has been given by Podsypanin [13] by using the quadratic field $Q(\sqrt{k})$, and we give an outline of his method. It is of special interest since it associates with equation (21) the related equation

$$y^2 = x^3 - 27k, \tag{22}$$

as had been previously done by Fueter. Thus if $P(x, y)$ is a solution of equation (21), then $P_1(x_1, y_1)$, where

$$x_1 = \frac{x^3 + 4k}{x^2}, \qquad y_1 = \frac{y(x^3 - 8k)}{x^3}, \tag{23}$$

is a solution of (22). Applying this result again to equation (22), it is easily shown that a solution of (21) is given by $P_2(x_2, y_2)$ where

$$x_2 = \frac{x_1^3 - 108k}{x_1^2}, \qquad y_2 = \frac{y_1(x_1^3 + 216k)}{x_1^3}. \tag{24}$$

This gives a solution of equation (21) if (x_1, y_1) is any solution of (22) even though this is not derived from (21) by (23).

Denote by G the additive group of the rational solutions of equation (21) and by H that of (22). Then if P_2 is derived from P by (23) and (24), it follows that $P_2 = 3P_1$, and so we have an inclusion relation

$$G \supset H \supset 3G.$$

An equivalence relation for solutions of equation (21) now arises. It can be shown that (x, y) is a point $3P$ if and only if

$$y + \sqrt{k} = \alpha^3, \tag{25}$$

where α is a number in the field $Q(\sqrt{k})$. Further, let $P_1(x_1, y_1)$, $P_2(x_2, y_2)$ be any rational solutions of (21), and denote by P_{12} the point $P_1 + P_2$. Then

$$(y_1 + \sqrt{k})(y_2 + \sqrt{k}) = \beta^3(y_{12} + \sqrt{k}),$$

where $$\beta x_{12} = x_1 y_2 - x_2 y_1 + (x_1 + x_2)\sqrt{d}.$$

For let $x = Ay + B$ be the equation of the line joining P_1, P_2. Then identically,

$$y^2 - k - (Ay + B)^3 = -A^3(y - y_1)(y - y_2)(y + y_{12}).$$

The result follows on putting $y = -\sqrt{k}$.

It can then be shown that the solution P_{12} is a solution of equation (22) derived from (21) if and only if

$$(y_1 + \sqrt{k})(y_2 + \sqrt{k}) = \gamma^3, \tag{26}$$

where γ is a number in the field $Q(\sqrt{k})$.

The relations (25), (26) define an equivalence process. In this way, Podsypanin finds for $|k| < 90$, the number of fundamental solutions and their values.

Several other authors have treated the equation by using cubic fields and Weil's ideas. Billing[14] has dealt exhaustively with the problem of finding the generators and has given them for $|k| \leqslant 25$.

The equation (21) was considered afresh by Cassels[15] who applied the ideas of Weil's proof. Cassels replaces (21) by

$$y^2 = x^3 + kz^6,$$

where x, y, z are integers. From this is deduced in the usual way

$$x - k_1\sqrt[3]{k_2} = \mu\alpha^2, \tag{27}$$

where $\mu > 0$ is an integer in $Q(\sqrt[3]{k})$ taken from a finite set and 6α is an integer in $Q(\sqrt[3]{k})$. Several cases are considered depending upon the parities of x, y, z. Then equation (27) is taken as a congruence whose modulus is an ideal factor of 2 and many special results are found. In this way, he finds for $|k| \leqslant 50$, the number of generators and solutions of the equations.

His work was amplified and completed by Selmer[16, 17].

The most extensive tables have been given by Birch and Swinnerton-Dyer who have found the number of generators for all $|k| < 400$ except -309. Their method[18] depends upon recent ideas as expounded in Cassels'[19] report and requires a detailed discussion of the reduction of binary quartic forms, both locally and globally. Cassels found the number of generators for $k = -309$.

A surprising result has been found very recently by Baker[20] who shows that all the integers solutions of the equation (1) satisfy

$$\max(|x|, |y|) < \exp(10^{10}|k|^{10^4}).$$

This depends upon his new proof of Thue's theorem which relies essentially on the study of linear forms in the logarithms of algebraic numbers.

REFERENCES

1. L. J. Mordell. "A Chapter in the Theory of Numbers". (1947). Cambridge University Press.
2. L. J. Mordell. The diophantine equation $y^2 - k = x^3$. *Proc. Lond. Math. Soc.*, (2) 13 (1913), 60–80.
9*

3. Marshall Hall. Some equations $y^2 = x^3 - k$ without integer solutions. *J. Lond. Math. Soc.*, **28** (1953), 379–383.

4. O. Hemer. On the diophantine equation $y^2 - k = x^3$. *Diss. Uppsala* (1952). See also Notes on the diophantine equation $y^2 - k = x^3$. *Arkiv för Mat.*, **3** (1954), 67–77.

5. T. Nagell. Einige Gleichungen von der Form $ay^2 + by + c = dx^3$. *Vid. Akad. Skrifter Oslo*, Nr. 7 (1930).

6. W. Ljunggren. Einige Bemerkungen über die Darstellung ganzer Zahlen durch binäre kubische Formen mit positiver Diskriminante. *Acta Math.*, **75** (1942), 1–21.

6a. M. Lal, M. F. Jones, W. J. Blundon. Tables of solutions of the diophantine equation $y^3 - x^2 = k$. *Dept. of Maths.*, *Memorial University of Newfoundland, St. Johns, Newfoundland*, (1968)—and 6b, Numerical solutions of the diophantine equation $y^3 - x^2 = k$. *Math. Comp.*, **20** (1966), 322–325.

7. W. Ljunggren. On the diophantine equation $y^2 - k = x^3$. *Acta Arith.*, **8** (1963), 451–463.

8. R. Fueter. Über kubische diophantische Gleichungen. *Commentarii Math. Helv.*, **2** (1930), 69–89.

9. L. J. Mordell. The infinity of rational solutions of $y^2 = x^3 + k$. *J. Lond. Math. Soc.*, **41** (1966), 523–525.

10. L. J. Mordell. On some diophantine equations $y^2 = x^3 + k$ with no rational solutions. *Archiv math. natur.*, **49** (1947), 143–150.

11. K. L. Chang. On some diophantine equations $y^2 = x^3 + k$ with no rational solutions. *Q. J. Maths.*, **1** (1948), 181–188.

12. L. J. Mordell. On some diophantine equations $y^2 = x^3 + k$ with no rational solutions. *Abhandlungen aus Zahlentheorie und Analysis zur Erinnerung an Edmund Landau* (1968), 225–232. VEB Deutscher Verlag der wiss. Berlin.

13. V. D. Podsypanin. On the indeterminate equation $x^3 = y^2 + Az^6$. (Russian). *Mat. Sbornik N.S.*, **24** (1949), 391–463.

14. G. Billing. Beiträge zur arithmetischen Theorie der ebenen kubischen Kurven vom Geschlecht Eins. *Diss. Uppsala* (1938).

15. J. W. S. Cassels. The rational solutions of the diophantine equation $y^2 = x^3 - D$. *Acta Math.*, **82** (1950), 243–273.

16. E. S. Selmer. The diophantine equation $y^2 = x^3 - D$. A note on Cassels' method. *Math. Scan.*, **3** (1955), 68–74.

17. E. S. Selmer. On Cassels' conditions for rational solubility of the diophantine equation $y^2 = x^3 - D$. *Archiv math. natur.*, **53** (1956), Nr. 7.

18. B. J. Birch and H. P. F. Swinnerton-Dyer. Notes on elliptic curves. I. *J. reine angew. Math.*, **212** (1963), 7–25.

19. J. W. S. Cassels. Diophantine equations with special reference to elliptic curves. *J. Lond. Math. Soc.*, **41** (1966), 193–291.

20. A. Baker. The diophantine equation $y^2 = x^3 + k$. *Phil. Trans. Roy. Soc., London*, **263** (1968), 193–208.

CHAPTER 27

The Equation $y^2 = ax^3 + bx^2 + cx + d$

1. The study of this equation has led to important developments and great advances in diophantine analysis.

The most important result[1,2] about its integer solutions is given by

Theorem 1

The equation

$$ey^2 = ax^3 + bx^2 + cx + d, \quad a \neq 0, \tag{1}$$

where the constants are integers and the right-hand side has no squared linear factor in x, has only a finite number of integer solutions.

Multiply by $81e$, and put $y_1 = 9ey$ and $x_1 = 3x$. The equation takes the form

$$y_1^2 = a_1 x_1^3 + 3b_1 x_1^2 + 3c_1 x_1 + d_1,$$

Put $t = 2a_1 y_1$, $s = a_1 x_1 + b_1$. The equation becomes, say,

$$t^2 = 4s^3 - g_2 s - g_3 \tag{2}$$

or $$(4t)^2 = (4s)^3 - 4g_2(4s) - 16g_3.$$

There are only a finite number of integer solutions for s, t. For in Chapter 25, we have seen that all the integer solutions of

$$Z^2 = X^3 - G_2 X Y^2 - G_3 Y^3 \quad (X, Y) = 1,$$

where the right-hand side has no squared linear factors, are given by

$$X = H(p, q), \qquad Y = F(p, q),$$

where $F(p, q)$ is a representative of the finite number of binary quartics with invariants

$$g_2 = 4G_2, \qquad g_3 = 4G_3.$$

Then by Thue's theorem, there are only a finite number of integer solutions of $F(p, q) = 1$.

We can show more directly that the equation

$$t^2 = 4s^3 - g_2 s - g_3, \qquad g_2^3 + 27g_3^2 \neq 0,$$

has only a finite number of integer solutions.

With the solution (s, t), we associate the binary quartic written with binomial coefficients,

$$f(x, y) = (1, 0, -s, t, e)(x, y)^4, \tag{3}$$

where $e = g_2 - 3s^2$. Its invariants are actually g_2, g_3 since

$$g_2 = e + 3s^2,$$

$$g_3 = \begin{vmatrix} 1 & 0 & -s \\ 0 & -s & t \\ -s & t & e \end{vmatrix} = -se - t^2 + s^3 = 4s^3 - g_2 s - t^2.$$

The quartic (3) is equivalent to one of a finite number of binary quartics $(a, b, c, d, e)(x, y)^4$ with invariants g_2, g_3. Hence

$$(1, 0, -s, t, e)(x, y)^4 = (a, b, c, d, e)(px + ry, qx + sy)^4,$$

where p, q, r, s are integers and $ps - qr = 1$, and so

$$1 = (a, b, c, d, e)(p, q)^4,$$

and by Thue's theorem, there are only a finite number of integer values for p, q. Further r, s are uniquely determined in terms of p, q since

$$r \frac{\partial f(p, q)}{\partial p} + s \frac{\partial f(p, q)}{\partial q} = 0.$$

Hence there are only a finite number of values for r, s.

There is an alternative method of dealing with equation (1).

Write it as

$$ey^2 = f(x) = a(x - \theta_1)(x - \theta_2)(x - \theta_3).$$

Then the θ, which are roots of $f(x) = 0$, define three fields $Q(\theta_1)$, $Q(\theta_2)$, $Q(\theta_3)$ whose nature depends upon the reducibility of $f(x)$. From the general theory of Chapter 15, we have for each θ and the corresponding field $Q(\theta)$, a relation

$$x - \theta = m(p + q\theta + r\theta^2)^2, \tag{4}$$

where p, q, r are rational integers and m takes only a finite number of values in $Q(\theta)$, and can be written as $p_0 + q_0\theta + r_0\theta^2$. Hence from equation (4) on replacing θ^4, θ^3 in terms of θ^2, θ, 1, and equating coefficients of θ, θ^2 on both sides, we have two equations of the form

$$f_1(p, q, r) = 0, \qquad f_2(p, q, r) = 1,$$

where f_1, f_2 are homogeneous quadratic forms. The solutions of the first of these is given by a finite number of expressions

$$p = j_1(u, v), \qquad q = j_2(u, v), \qquad r = j_3(u, v),$$

where the j are binary quadratics in the integers u, v. Substituting in the second equation, we have a finite number of equations $h(u, v) = 1$ where h is a binary quartic. Since equation (1) is of genus one, $h(u, v)$ cannot be a perfect square. Then by Thue's theorem, there are only a finite number of integer solutions for u, v and so for x, y.

From the particular case

$$y^2 = x(ax^2 + bx + c), \qquad b^2 - 4ac \neq 0,$$

it is obvious that the equation

$$y^2 = ax^4 + bx^2 + c$$

has only a finite number of integer solutions.

2. The problem of finding all the integer solutions of an equation (1) is in general a very difficult one, and only a few results have been found. An interesting one[3] is given by

Theorem 2

The equation

$$y(y + 1) = x(x + 1)(x + 2) \tag{5}$$

has only the integer solutions $x = -1, -2, 0, 1, 5$.

Hence 0, 6 and 210 are the only integers which can be expressed as both a product of two and three consecutive integers.

On replacing $2x + 2$ by x and $2y + 1$ by y, the equation becomes

$$2y^2 = x^3 - 4x + 2, \tag{6}$$

and we have to prove that its integer solutions are given by

$$x = 0, -2, 2, 4, 12.$$

The equation requires the study of the cubic field $Q(\theta)$ where

$$\theta^3 - 4\theta + 2 = 0.$$

We require the following arithmetical properties of the field $Q(\theta)$.

I. The integers are of the form $x = a + b\theta + c\theta^2$, where a, b, c are integers.

II. There are two fundamental units $\varepsilon = \theta - 1$, $\eta = 2\theta - 1$.

III. Unique factorization exists in $Q(\theta)$ since the number of ideal classes is one.

We note that $2 = \zeta\theta^3$ where ζ is a unit and it easily follows that θ is a prime in $Q(\theta)$.

Write equation (6) in the form

$$(x - \theta)(x^2 + \theta x + \theta^2 - 4) = \zeta\theta^3 y^2.$$

Then θ is a common divisor of the two factors. Also the prime $4\theta - 3$ with norm 37 is a possible common divisor since

$$3\theta^2 - 4 = (3\theta^3 - 4\theta)/\theta = (8\theta - 6)/\theta = 2(4\theta - 3)/\theta.$$

Hence

$$x - \theta = \pm\,\theta(4\theta - 3)^n \varepsilon^l \eta^m (a + b\theta + c\theta^2)^2,$$

where n is an integer $\geqslant 0$ and l, m are any integers, positive, negative or zero. If n is odd, on taking the norm of both sides, we find the impossible congruence

$$x^3 - 4x + 2 \equiv \pm 2\cdot 37 y^2 \pmod 8.$$

If n is even, $(4\theta - 3)^n$ can be absorbed in the square term. Hence it suffices to consider the four sets of simultaneous quadratic equations arising when

$$(l, m) = (0, 0),\ (1, 0),\ (0, 1),\ (1, 1).$$

These are given explicitly on noting that

$$(a + b\theta + c\theta^2)^2 = a^2 - 4bc + \theta(2ab + 8bc - 2c^2) + \theta^2(b^2 + 2ac + 4c^2).$$

Fortunately these equations can be dealt with by elementary considerations and congruence conditions, and then the desired result is obtained.

In problems of the present type, the simultaneous quadratic equations may lead to a large number of biquadratic equations. These may require a detailed study of arithmetical properties of many quartic fields. In general the equations can only be dealt with by the p-adic considerations of Chapter 23 applied to the units of the corresponding quartic fields, and this may involve considerable numerical work. Thus Avanesov[4] has proved a conjecture put forward by Sierpinski, here given as

Theorem 3

The only positive integer solutions of the equation

$$\tfrac{1}{2}y(y + 1) = \tfrac{1}{6}x(x + 1)(x + 2) = n$$

are given by $n = 1, 10, 120, 1540, 7140.$

The first interesting equation to be completely solved is given in

Theorem 4

The only integer solutions of the equation

$$6y^2 = x(x + 1)(2x + 1)$$

are $x = 0, -1, 1, 24.$

This is Lucas' problem of the square pyramid. Watson[5] gave a very complicated solution depending upon elliptic functions.

A proof based upon arithmetical considerations has been given by Ljunggren[6]. It depends upon a Pell equation in a quadratic field. A quartic field arises all of whose conjugate fields are imaginary. There is one fundamental unit and its properties must be investigated in detail.

Problem
   Are the only integer solutions of the equation

$$6y^2 = x^3 + 5x + 6 = (x + 1)(x^2 - x + 6)$$

given by

$$x = -1, 0, 2, 7, 15, 74?$$

The equation arises from

$$y^2 = 1 + x + \frac{x.x - 1}{2!} + \frac{x.x - 1.x - 2}{3!}.$$

3. Congruence considerations[7] enable us to construct many classes of equations

$$y^2 = ax^3 + bx^2 + cx + d$$

for which bounds can be given for the magnitude of the solutions. Equations can also be given with only one or two integer values for x.

Theorem 5
   Let $a > 0$, b, c be arbitrary integers and let d be odd and have no prime factors $\equiv 3 \pmod 4$. Then the equation

$$y^2 = 2ax^3 + (6 - 2a - 2c + 8b)x^2 + 2cx - d^2 \tag{7}$$

can only have integer solutions for which $x < 0$, $x \equiv 3 \pmod 4$, and so these are bounded in terms of a, b, c, d.
In particular, the equation

$$y^2 = 2ax^3 + (4 + 4b)x^2 + 2(1 - a + 2b)x - 1 \tag{8}$$

has only the solutions $(x, y) = (1, \pm 1)$ if $a > 0$, $3a > 1 + b$; and the equation

$$y^2 = 2ax^3 + (12a + 8)x^2 + (10a + 6)x - 1, \tag{9}$$

has only the solutions $(x, y) = (-1, \pm 1)$, $(-5, \pm 13)$ if $a > 0$.
   Clearly in equation (7), x is not even since $y^2 \not\equiv -1 \pmod 4$. Also $x \not\equiv 1 \pmod 4$ since then

$$y^2 \equiv 2a + 6 - 2a - 2c + 8b + 2c - 1 \equiv 5 \pmod 8.$$

Hence $x \equiv 3 \pmod 4$ and since $x \mid y^2 + d^2$, x must be negative.
   If in equation (7) we take $x = -1$, $y = 1$, $d = 1$, then $c = 1 - a + 2b$, then $c = 1 - a + 2b$, and we have with $a > 0$,

$$y^2 = 2ax^3 + (4 + 4b)x^2 + 2(1 - a + 2b)x - 1.$$

Any further solutions must satisfy $x \leqslant -5$. We show then that $y^2 < 0$. The condition for this can be written as

$$(x + 1)(2ax^2 + (4 - 2a + 2b)x - 2) < -1.$$

This holds if

$$10a - (4 - 2a + 2b) > 0, \quad \text{i.e. } 3a > 1 + b.$$

Another solution $x = -5$ of equation (8) arises if $b = 3a + 1$, and then with $a > 0$,

$$y^2 = 2ax^3 + (12a + 8)x^2 + (10a + 6)x - 1.$$

Any further solution of this must satisfy $x \leqslant -9$.

Write $y^2 - 1 = (x + 1)(2ax^2 + (10a + 8)x - 2).$

Then $y^2 < 0$ if $ax^2 + (5a + 4)x - 1 > 0$. This is true if $9a > 5a + 4$ or if $a > 1$. If $a = 1$, the equation becomes

$$y^2 = 2x^3 + 20x^2 + 16x - 1.$$

Then $x \neq -9$, since $y^2 \not\equiv -1 \pmod 3$. Another solution would satisfy $x \leqslant -13$. This is impossible since then

$$y^2 = 2x(x^2 + 10x + 8) - 1$$

and $x^2 + 10x + 8 > 0$.

The method is capable of considerable generalization[8]. Suppose that the cubic equation (1) can be written in the form

$$y^2 = ax^3 + bx^2 + cx + d = g(x)h(x) - kf^2(x) \tag{10}$$

where $f(x)$, $g(x)$, $h(x)$ are polynomials with integer coefficients and k is a square-free integer. Simple results arise if the factors of k are taken from the product $2.3.5.7$. Then conditions are imposed upon the coefficients of $f(x)$, $g(x)$, $h(x)$ so that $h(x)$ cannot be a divisor of $y^2 + kf^2(x)$, unless $h(x) < 0$. If $h(x) = x^{2n} + h_1x^{2n-1} + \cdots$, an upper bound is easily found for the magnitude of x in a solution (x, y).

A simple illustration of equation (10) is given by

$$y^2 + 2(x^2 + f_1x + f_2)^2 = (2x^2 + g_1x + g_2)(x^2 + h_1x + h_2),$$

where $g_1 \equiv 0 \pmod 8$, $g_2 \equiv 5 \pmod 8$. Then $g(x) = 2x^2 + g_1x + g_2 \equiv 7$ or $5 \pmod 8$ according as x is odd or even, and so if $g(x) > 0$, then -2 is a quadratic non-residue of $g(x)$. Now suppose $g(x)$ and $h(x)$ have no common factors $\equiv 5, 7 \pmod 8$. The condition for this is easily found since any common divisor must divide

$$(f_1^2 - 4f_2)(g_1^2 - 8g_2) - (4h_2 + 2g_2 - h_1g_1)^2.$$

Hence solutions of the equation can occur only when $g(x) < 0$. This means that an upper bound for x can be found from the roots of $g(x) = 0$.

The question arises whether such a result exists for all equations (1).

It has been noted in Chapter 22 that Baker has found bounds (very large ones indeed) for the magnitude of the solutions of equation (1).

REFERENCES

1. L. J. Mordell. Note on the integer solutions of the equations $Ey^2 = Ax^3 + Bx^2 + Cx + D$. *Messenger Maths.*, **51** (1922), 169–171.
2. L. J. Mordell. On the integer solutions of the equation $ey^2 = ax^3 + bx^2 + cx + d$. *Proc. Lond. Math. Soc.* (2), **21** (1923), 415–419.
3. L. J. Mordell. On the integer solutions of $y(y + 1) = x(x + 1)(x + 2)$. *Pacific J. Maths.*, **13** (1963), 1347–1351.
4. E. T. Avanesov. Solution of a problem on polygonal numbers (Russian). *Acta Arith.*, **12** (1967), 409–419.
5. G. N. Watson. The problem of the square pyramid. *Messenger Maths.*, **48** (1919), 1–22.
6. W. Ljunggren. New solution of a problem proposed by E. Lucas. *Norsk Mat. Tidsskrift*, **34** (1952), 65–72.
7. L. J. Mordell. The diophantine equation $y^2 = ax^3 + bx^2 + cx + d$ or fifty years after. *J. Lond. Math. Soc.*, **38** (1963), 454–458.
8. L. J. Mordell. The diophantine equation $y^2 = ax^3 + bx^2 + cx + d$. *R. Circ. Mat. Palermo* (II), **13** (1964), 1–8.

CHAPTER 28

Some Equations of Degree > 3

1. We show now that some general classes of equations of degree >3 have only a finite number of integer solutions. We commence with a result* due to Runge[1].

Theorem 1

   Let $f(x, y)$ be a polynomial of degree n with integer coefficients which is irreducible in the rational field Q, and suppose that the homogeneous part $f_n(x, y)$ of degree n of $f(x, y)$ is reducible in Q but is not a constant multiple of a power of an irreducible polynomial. Then the equation

$$f(x, y) = 0 \tag{1}$$

has only a finite number of integer solutions.

   For simplicity, we shall deal only with the case when the linear factors of $f_n(x, y)$ are all different. We may suppose that at least one linear factor has real coefficients as otherwise the theorem is trivially proved. Let α be a root of the equation $f(1, t) = 0$, and so α is of degree $n_1 < n$ if $f(x, y)$ is of degree n in y.

On writing
$$f(x, y) = (y - \alpha x)f_{n-1}(x, y) + g(x, y),$$

where $g(x, y)$ is of degree $<n - 1$, we see that we have for large values of x a convergent expansion for y in descending powers of x given by

$$y = \alpha x + \alpha_0 + \frac{\alpha_1}{x} + \frac{\alpha_2}{x^2} + \cdots, \tag{2}$$

where $\alpha_0, \alpha_1, \ldots$ are elements of the field $Q(\alpha)$.

   Suppose now that the equation (1) has an infinity of integer solutions. For these, (2) will hold with an appropriate α. We shall show that from (2), we can deduce a polynomial equation for x, y, say $h(x, y) = 0$, which is of degree $<n$ in y and so $h(x, y) = 0$ is independent of $f(x, y) = 0$. Hence these two equations give only a finite number of values of x and y.

   Consider the polynomial

$$h(x, y) = \sum_{p=0}^{P} \sum_{q=0}^{n_1-1} c_{p,q} x^p y^q, \tag{3}$$

*See Addendum 1.

where we have at our disposal the integer P and the $n_1(P + 1)$ integer constants $c_{p,q}$. On substituting from equation (2) in (3), we have an expansion

$$h(x, y) = \sum_{r \leq P + n_1}^{-\infty} d_r x^r.$$

The coefficients d_r can be expressed linearly in terms of the $c_{p,q}$ and $\alpha^0, \alpha^1, \ldots, \alpha^{(n_1 - 1)}$. We now impose the $d_r = (n_1 - 1)(P + n_1 + 1)$ conditions on the $c_{p,q}$ that the coefficients of $\alpha, \alpha^2, \ldots, \alpha^{n_1 - 1}$ in d_r for $r = P + n_1, \ldots, 1, 0$ should be zero. This will be possible if

$$n_1(P + 1) > (n_1 - 1)(P + n_1 + 1),$$

or

$$P \geqslant n_1^2 - n_1.$$

Then we have an identity

$$h(x, y) - \sum_{r=0}^{P+n_1} e_r x^r = \sum_{r<0} d_r x^r.$$

As the left-hand side is an integer, it must be zero since x is large. This completes the proof.

The most general result on the existence of only a finite number of integer solutions for an irreducible polynomial equation $f(x, y) = 0$ is due to Siegel[2] in 1929. He proved the

Theorem 2

There are only a finite number of solutions if the equation $f(x, y) = 0$ is not identically satisfied by a parametric representation,

$$x = A/L^n, \qquad y = B/L^n, \quad \text{or} \quad x = C/Q^n, \qquad y = D/Q^n,$$

where A, B, C, D are polynomials in t with integer coefficients and L is a linear polynomial and Q is an indefinite quadratic polynomial.

The proof is of a very advanced character.

2. We now consider some equations of the form

$$y^2 = a_0 x^n + a_1 x^{n-1} + \cdots + a_n, \tag{4}$$

where the a's are integers.

By applying the methods of Chapter 24, it is a simple matter to construct[3] equations of the form

$$y^2 + k = a_0 x^{2n+1} + a_1 x^{2n} + \cdots + a_{2n} x = f(x),$$

say, where $a_0 > 0$, which have only a finite number of integer solutions and for which an estimate in terms of the coefficients can be found for the magnitude of the solutions. Suppose for simplicity that k is a prime $\equiv 7 \pmod 8$ and that $a_{2n} \not\equiv 0 \pmod k$, $a_{2n} \neq \pm 1$. Clearly $x \not\equiv 0 \pmod k$. Denote by r the quadratic residues $r_1, r_2, \ldots, r_{(k-1)/2}$ of k and by n the quadratic non-residues $n_1, n_2, \ldots, n_{(k-1)/2}$.

Suppose first that x is congruent to a quadratic residue, say $x \equiv r$. This will be impossible if $f(r)$ is a quadratic non-residue of k, i.e. if

$$a_0 r^{2n+1} + a_1 r^{2n} + \ldots + a_{2n} r \equiv n \pmod{k},$$

where n is an arbitrary quadratic non-residue. If $2n + 1 > (k - 1)/2$, these congruences have a solution for the a.

Suppose next that x is congruent to a quadratic non-residue n. Let us assume first that $x > 0$. Let $x = 2^\alpha x_1$ where x_1 is odd and is also a quadratic non-residue of k since 2 is a quadratic residue. Then from equation (5),

$$1 = \left(\frac{-k}{x_1}\right) = \left(\frac{x_1}{k}\right) = -1.$$

This contradiction shows that $x < 0$. Then obviously from (5), x must be bounded and so can be easily found.

Results can also be found for equation (4) when n is even. Suppose for example that

$$y^2 + k^2 = (ax^2 + b)(a_0 x^{2n} + \cdots + a_{2n-1} x + a_{2n}) = f_1 f_2,$$

say, where k has no prime factors $\equiv 3 \pmod 4$, and

$$a \equiv 1 \pmod 4, \qquad b \equiv -2 \pmod 8, \qquad 2a_{2n-1} + a_{2n} \equiv 3 \pmod 4.$$

Then if $x \equiv 1 \pmod 2$, $f_1 \equiv -1 \pmod 4$; if $x \equiv 0 \pmod 4$, $\frac{1}{2} f_1 \equiv -1 \pmod 4$; if $x \equiv 2 \pmod 4$, $f_2 \equiv 3 \pmod 4$. Hence the only possible solutions must satisfy $f_1 < 0$, $f_2 < 0$ and so are finite in number.

We now prove an earlier Siegel's[4] result given by

Theorem 3

The equation

$$y^2 = a_0 x^n + a_1 x^{n-1} + \cdots + a_n \tag{5}$$

has only a finite number of integer solutions* if the right-hand side has at least three different linear factors.

Write
$$y^2 = a_0 (x - \alpha_1)(x - \alpha_2) \cdots (x - \alpha_n),$$

where we suppose the α define a field K and that $\alpha_1, \alpha_2, \alpha_3$ are all different. The general theory of Chapter 15 gives

$$x - \alpha_1 = \mu_1 \xi_1^2, \qquad x - \alpha_2 = \mu_2 \xi_2^2, \qquad x - \alpha_3 = \mu_3 \xi_3^2,$$

where the ξ are integers in K and the μ are a finite set of numbers in K.

Hence
$$\mu_2 \xi_2^2 - \mu_3 \xi_3^2 = \alpha_3 - \alpha_2 \neq 0,$$

$$\mu_3 \xi_3^2 - \mu_1 \xi_1^2 = \alpha_1 - \alpha_3 \neq 0,$$

$$\mu_1 \xi_1^2 - \mu_2 \xi_2^2 = \alpha_2 - \alpha_1 \neq 0.$$

* See Addendum 2.

Then in the field $K(\sqrt{\alpha_1}, \sqrt{\alpha_2}, \sqrt{\alpha_3}) = K'$, say,

$$\xi_2\sqrt{\mu_2} - \xi_3\sqrt{\mu_3} = \beta_1\varepsilon_1^l,$$

$$\xi_3\sqrt{\mu_3} - \xi_1\sqrt{\mu_1} = \beta_2\varepsilon_2^l,$$

$$\xi_1\sqrt{\mu_1} - \xi_2\sqrt{\mu_2} = \beta_3\varepsilon_3^l,$$

where l is an arbitrary large integer, $\varepsilon_1, \varepsilon_2, \varepsilon_3$ are units in K' and $\beta_1, \beta_2, \beta_3$ are numbers in K' belonging to a finite set. Then

$$\beta_1\varepsilon_1^l + \beta_2\varepsilon_2^l + \beta_3\varepsilon_3^l = 0,$$

or

$$\left(\frac{\beta_1}{\beta_3}\right)\left(\frac{\varepsilon_1}{\varepsilon_3}\right)^l + \left(\frac{\beta_2}{\beta_3}\right)\left(\frac{\varepsilon_2}{\varepsilon_3}\right)^l + 1 = 0.$$

By Siegel's Theorem[5] 2, this has only a finite number of solutions for $\varepsilon_1/\varepsilon_3$ and $\varepsilon_2/\varepsilon_3$, and then for ξ_4/ξ_3 and ξ_2/ξ_3 and then for ξ_1, ξ_2, ξ_3.

A particular case for which a simpler proof is known is given by Landau and Ostrowski[6], and Thue[7] as

Theorem 4

If a, b, c, d are integers, and $ad \neq 0$, $b^2 - 4ac \neq 0$, $n \geqslant 3$, the equation

$$ay^2 + by + c = dx^n, \tag{6}$$

has only a finite number of integer solutions.

On writing y for $2ay + b$, the equation takes the form

$$y^2 - k = lx^n, \quad kl \neq 0.$$

Suppose first that k is a perfect square, say $k = m^2$.

Then

$$(y + m)(y - m) = lx^n.$$

Since $y + m$, $y - m$ have only a finite number of common factors, we have with integers Y, Z,

$$y + m = f_1 Y^n, \qquad y - m = f_2 Z^n, \qquad x = fYZ,$$

where f_1, f_2, f belong to a finite set of integers, and $f_1 f_2 = lf^n$. Then

$$f_1 Y^n - f_2 Z^n = 2m.$$

By Thue's theorem, there are only a finite number of integer values for Y, Z.

Suppose next that k is not a perfect square.

Then

$$(y + \sqrt{k})(y - \sqrt{k}) = lx^n.$$

Then the results in Chapter 15 give at once

$$f(y + \sqrt{k}) = (g + h\sqrt{k})(u + v\sqrt{k})^n,$$

where f, g, h are integers taken from a finite set, and u, v are integer variables.

From this

$$2f\sqrt{k} = (g + h\sqrt{k})(u + v\sqrt{k})^n - (g - h\sqrt{k})(u - v\sqrt{k})^n.$$

This reduces to a binary equation in u, v, say $f(u, v) = m$, where $f(u, v)$ is clearly not a power of another form. Again by Thue's theorem in Chapter 22, there are only a finite number of integer values for u, v.

We give another proof, essentially Thue's, which is really independent of algebraic number theory. We may suppose that k is not a perfect square and so $x \neq 0$.

We require the

Lemma
Integers $(q, r) \neq (0, 0)$ exist such that

$$\left| \frac{qy}{x} - r \right| < \frac{1}{\sqrt{|x|}}, \qquad |q| \leqslant \sqrt{|x|}.$$

Proof obvious from Minkowski's theorem on linear forms.

Write $s = qy - rx$. Then $|s| < \sqrt{|x|}$, $s \equiv qy \pmod{x}$.
Put $t = (s^2 - kq^2)/x^n$. Then $t \neq 0$ since k is not a perfect square and $q \neq 0$. Also t is an integer since $s^2 - kq^2 \equiv q^2y^2 - kq^2 \equiv 0 \pmod{x}$. Next t is bounded independently of the values of x, y, and so is restricted to a finite set. For

$$|t| < \left(\frac{|x| + |k| \, |x|}{|x|} \right)^n = (1 + |k|)^n.$$

Write now $A + B\sqrt{k} = (s + q\sqrt{k})^n (y - \sqrt{k})/x^n.$

We prove that A, B are bounded integers independent of x and y. For

$$s + q\sqrt{k} = q(y + \sqrt{k}) - rx,$$

$$(s + q\sqrt{k})^n = (-1)^n r^n x^n + (y + \sqrt{k})(C + D\sqrt{k}),$$

where C, D are rational integers. Since $(y + \sqrt{k})(y - \sqrt{k}) = lx^n$, A and B are integers. Next for both signs,

$$|A \pm B\sqrt{k}| \leqslant (\sqrt{|x|} + \sqrt{|x|}\sqrt{|k|})^n (1 + \sqrt{|k|})|y|/|x|^n.$$

But $|y| \leqslant |k|^{1/2} + |l|^{1/2}|x|^{n/2} \leqslant (|k|^{1/2} + |l|^{1/2})|x|^{n/2}$

and so $|A \pm B\sqrt{k}| \leqslant (1 + \sqrt{|k|})^{n+1}(|k|^{1/2} + |l|^{1/2}).$

Hence A and B are bounded.
Finally

$$(A + B\sqrt{k})(s - q\sqrt{k})^n = (s^2 - kq^2)^n(y - \sqrt{k})/x^n = t(y - \sqrt{k}).$$

Then

$$(A + B\sqrt{k})(s - q\sqrt{k})^n - (A - B\sqrt{k})(s + q\sqrt{k})^n = -2t\sqrt{k}.$$

There are only a finite number of such equations for s, q since A, B, t are bounded. Since the left-hand side is not the power of a polynomial, Thue's theorem applies.

In general it is not easy to find the integer solutions of equation (4), or to prove that there are none. However, Baker has recently given an estimate for the magnitude of the solutions. An interesting example due to Rigge[8] and Erdös[9] is given by

Theorem 5

The equation

$$y^2 = x(x + 1)(x + 2)\ldots(x + n) = f(x), \tag{7}$$

say, has only the integer solutions given by $y = 0$.

On excluding these values, we easily deduce that

$$x + r = a_r x_r^2 \quad (r = 0, 1, \ldots, n - 1),$$

where the a are square free and have as factors only primes $< n$. Arguments rather different from those usually employed for diophantine equations lead to a proof. The first stage is to show that the a are all different. We do not proceed beyond this stage since a great deal of detail is involved. Further the proof shows first that the theorem holds for $n > 100$, and then the remaining values of n require special treatment.

We first prove Obláth's[10] result that $x > n^2$. Suppose first that $x \leqslant n$. By a theorem of Tchebycheff, there is a prime p such that

$$x + n > p \geqslant \tfrac{1}{2}(x + n) \geqslant x,$$

and so p but not p^2 divides $f(x)$, and this is impossible.

Since $x > n$, then by a theorem of Sylvester and Schur, $f(x)$ has a prime factor $q > n$. Then $q^2 \mid x + r$ for some $r \leqslant n - 1$, and so

$$x + r \geqslant (n + 1)^2, \qquad x > r^2.$$

Suppose next that the a's are not all different, say, $a_r = a_s$ where $r > s$. Then

$$n > a_r x_r^2 - a_s x_s^2 = a_s(x_r^2 - x_s^2) > 2a_r x_s$$
$$\geqslant 2\sqrt{a_r x_s^2} = 2\sqrt{(x + s)} > \sqrt{x},$$

and this is not so.

A more general result is

Theorem 6

The equation

$$y^m = x(x + 1)\ldots(x + n - 1) \tag{8}$$

has only the integer solutions given by $y = 0$.

A proof for $m = 2$ was found by Erdös,[11] and for all m, by Erdös and Selfridge, but this has not been published. Previously many special results had been proved by several authors, for example, Obláth[10], Rigge[12], Erdös[13], Johnson[14]. These in general require too much numerical detail for any account to be given here.

3. A few words may be said about the integer solutions of the quartic equation

$$ky^2 = ax^4 + bx^3 + cx^2 + dx + e. \tag{9}$$

By Siegel's Theorem 3, there are only a finite number of integer solutions when the right-hand side has no squared linear factors. Apart from this result, very little is known about the equation, and it is surprising what a variety of methods, some very complicated, have been employed in dealing with it. It had seemed impossible to find all the solutions except in particular cases. Recently Baker has formed an estimate (very large) for the magnitude of the solutions.

A simple instance [14a] of equation (9) is the equation

$$y^2 + k^2 = (px^2 - p - 1 - 4q)(rx^2 - s),$$

where k has no factors $\equiv 3 \pmod 4$, $p > 0$, $q \geqslant 0$, $s > r > 0$. When the two factors in x are positive, the first excludes $x \equiv 1 \pmod 2$, and the second, $x \equiv 0 \pmod 2$ if $s \equiv 1 \pmod 4$, and so solutions can arise only when these factors are negative. It is easy to construct equations with two values for x^2, but not with three values. In particular, the equation

$$y^2 + 1 = (4x^2 - 17)(60x^2 - 1025)$$

has only the integer solutions $x = 0, \pm 1, \pm 2$.

An interesting example is given by

Theorem 7

The only positive integer solutions of the equation

$$\left(\frac{x(x-1)}{2}\right)^2 = \frac{y(y-1)}{2}$$

are $(x, y) = (1, 1), (2, 2), (4, 9)$. *The others are* $x = 0, 1$, $y = 0, 1$ *and* $(x, y) = (-1, -1)\,(-3, -8)$.

This means that the only triangular numbers which are squares of triangular numbers are 0, 1, 36.

A complicated proof was given by Ljunggren[15] depending upon the p-adic methods of Chapter 23 applied to a quartic field. On putting $2x - 1 = X$, $2y - 1 = Y$, we have

$$Y^2 = 2\left(\frac{X^2 - 1}{4}\right)^2 + 1.$$

He uses the unit $1 + \sqrt{2}$ to construct integers in $Q(\sqrt[4]{2})$ with relative norm 9 over $Q(\sqrt{2})$. He then deduces an exponential equation in only one variable and shows that the only positive solutions are $(X, Y) = (1, 1)$ and $(7, 17)$.

A simple proof was given by Cassels[16] depending upon the properties of the quartic field $Q(\sqrt[4]{-2})$.

Special cases of equation (9) when $b = d = 0$ have been considered in Chapter 8, and also when $b = c = d = 0$. Then the equation becomes

$$ky^2 = ax^4 + e \tag{10}$$

which is of special interest. Results of various degrees of generality have been found by many authors, for example, Ljunggren[17,18,19,20], Mordell[21], Cohn[22], Podsypanin[22a] (cf. Ljunggren[18]) especially for the equations.

$$y^2 = Dx^4 \pm 1.$$

Sometimes elementary methods suffice for the rational solutions as was shown in Chapter 4. We now prove similarly

Theorem 8

The equation

$$y^2 = Dx^4 + 1 \tag{11}$$

has no integer solutions except $x = 0$ if

I. $D \not\equiv 0, -1, 3, 8 \pmod{16}$.

II. *D has no factorization $D = pq$, $(p, q) = 1$ where p is an odd number > 1 such that either*

$$p \equiv \pm 1, \quad \text{or} \quad p \equiv q \pm 1, \quad \text{or} \quad p \equiv 4q \pm 1 \pmod{16}.$$

We may suppose $x > 0$. Clearly equation (11) cannot be satisfied by odd values of x since $D + 1 \not\equiv 0, 1, 4, 9 \pmod{16}$, and so x is even. We now consider that solution of (11) for which x has its least positive value. Then

$$y \pm 1 = 2pa^4, \qquad y \mp 1 = 8qb^4, \qquad x = 2ab, \tag{12}$$

and $(p, q) = 1$, $a \equiv p \equiv 1 \pmod{2}$ for some decomposition $D = pq$.

Suppose first that $p = 1$, and so from equation (12)

$$a^4 - 4Db^4 = \pm 1. \tag{13}$$

The negative sign can be rejected and so

$$a^4 - 1 = 4Db^4.$$

Then with $D = rs$, $b = cd$,

$$a^2 + 1 = 2rc^4, \qquad a^2 - 1 = 2sd^4,$$

and so

$$c \equiv r \equiv 1 \pmod{2}.$$

Also

$$rc^4 - sd^4 = 1. \tag{14}$$

Suppose first that $r = 1$ and so

$$c^4 - Dd^4 = 1. \tag{15}$$

Then a solution of equation (11) is given by $x = 2acd$. Since $x \neq 0$, $d \neq 0$, then $d \leqslant \frac{1}{2}x$, and so equation (15) gives a contradiction.

Suppose next that $r > 1$ in equation (14). Then d cannot be even since from II, $r \not\equiv \pm 1 \pmod{16}$. Also d cannot be odd, for then from (14), $r - s \equiv 1 \pmod{16}$, and this is excluded by II.

Suppose finally that $p > 1$. Then from equations (12),

$$pa^4 - 4qb^4 = \pm 1.$$

Then b cannot be even since $p \not\equiv \pm 1 \pmod{16}$, and cannot be odd since $p - 4q \not\equiv \pm 1 \pmod{16}$. This completes the proof.

If D is a prime, $q = 1$, and then the proof does not apply when $D \equiv \pm 1, 3, 5 \pmod{16}$.

By the use of less elementary results, it can be proved that when D is a prime $\equiv 1 \pmod 4$, there are no integer solutions of $y^2 = Dx^4 + 1$ except $x = 0$ unless $D = 5$ when also $x = 2$. Two results are required. The first is that when $D = 2$, the only integer solutions are given by $x = 0$. This is easily proved for we deduce at once,

$$y \pm 1 = 2p^4, \qquad y \mp 1 = 16q^4, \qquad x = 2pq,$$
$$p^4 - 8q^4 = 1, \qquad p^2 + 1 = 2r^4, \qquad p^2 - 1 = 4s^4.$$

Clearly $s = 0$, $p^2 = 1$, $q = 0$, $x = 0$.

The other is a much deeper result noted a little further on that the only integer solutions of $y^2 = 2x^4 - 1$ are $\pm x = 1, 13$.

Ljunggren[20] proves the result for $D \equiv 1 \pmod 4$ by expressing x, y in terms of the solution of the Pell equation $Y^2 - DX^2 = -1$.

A proof, however, follows by a slight modification of the general proof. When $r > 1$ in equation (14), then $r = D$, $s = 1$, and we have $a^2 - 1 = 2d^4$ giving $a = \pm 1$ etc. Also equation (16) becomes

$$Da^4 - 4b^4 = 1$$
$$Da^4 = (2b^2 + 2b + 1)(2b^2 - 2b + 1).$$

Then
$$2b^2 \pm 2b + 1 = e^4$$
$$(2b \pm 1)^2 = 2e^4 - 1, \quad \text{etc.}$$

Ljunggren[19] has proved some results about the number of solutions of some equations of the form (10).

Theorem 9

The equation

$$y^2 = Dx^4 + 1, \tag{16}$$

where $D > 0$ and is not a perfect square, has at most two solutions in positive integers.

Denote by ε the fundamental unit in the quadratic field $Q(\sqrt{D})$. If there are two solutions, these are given by

either $\qquad y + x^2\sqrt{D} = \varepsilon, \varepsilon^2 \quad$ or by $\quad y + x^2\sqrt{D} = \varepsilon, \varepsilon^4,$

the latter occurring for only a finite number of values of D.
    It is much more difficult to deal with the equation

$$y^2 = Dx^4 - 1.$$

In particular for the special case

$$y^2 = 2x^4 - 1$$

it has been known for two centuries that solutions are given by $(x, y) = (1, 1)$ and $(13, 239)$. It was proved by Ljunggren[23] that these are the only positive integer solutions. The proof is exceedingly complicated. It is a particular case of his more general

Theorem 10

If the fundamental unit of the quadratic field $Q(\sqrt{d})$ is not also the fundamental unit of the ring $Z[\sqrt{d}]$, then the equation

$$y^2 = dx^4 - 1$$

has at most two possible solutions, and these can be found by a finite algorithm.
    We assume of course that the Pell equation

$$Y^2 - dX^2 = -1$$

is solvable, and so we write

$$\varepsilon = u + v\sqrt{d}, \qquad \varepsilon' = u - v\sqrt{d}$$

for the fundamental unit in the ring $Z[\sqrt{d}]$.
    Then $\varepsilon\varepsilon' = -1$ and so v is odd. We now take $x > 0$, $y > 0$ and so

$$y + x^2\sqrt{d} = \varepsilon^r, \qquad y - x^2\sqrt{d} = \varepsilon'^r, \quad r = 1, 3, 5, \ldots.$$

Hence $\qquad\qquad\qquad x^2 = v\left(\dfrac{\varepsilon^r - \varepsilon'^r}{\varepsilon - \varepsilon'}\right).$

We show that from this we can deduce an equation of the form

$$x_0^2 = \frac{\varepsilon^s - \varepsilon'^s}{\varepsilon - \varepsilon'}.$$

This is obvious if v is a square. Suppose next that $v = lk^2$ where $l > 1$ and is odd and square-free.

Then

$$\frac{\varepsilon^r - \varepsilon'^r}{\varepsilon - \varepsilon'} = lx_1^2,$$

say. Since $\varepsilon - \varepsilon' \equiv 0 \pmod{l}$, it follows that $r \equiv 0 \pmod{l}$, say $r = ls$. Write

$$PQ = \frac{\varepsilon^s - \varepsilon'^s}{\varepsilon - \varepsilon'} \frac{\varepsilon^{ls} - \varepsilon'^{ls}}{\varepsilon^s - \varepsilon'^s} = lx_1^2.$$

If $(P, l) = 1$, then $P = x_0^2$ as asserted. If $(P, l) > 1$ suppose that a prime p divides (P, l). On putting $(\varepsilon^s - \varepsilon'^s)/(\varepsilon - \varepsilon') = p^\alpha q$ where $(p, q) = 1$, then since l is square-free, it is easily seen that Q is exactly divisible by p. Then Q is exactly divisible by l and so again

$$\frac{\varepsilon^s - \varepsilon'^s}{\varepsilon - \varepsilon'} = x_0^2.$$

To find the integer values of x_0 is a particular case of the problem in Chapter 8 of finding the square numbers in a sequence defined by a recurrence formula.

Ljunggren shows that the p-adic considerations of Chapter 23 can be applied if we use an extension field of $Q(\sqrt{d})$. Thus from

$$(\varepsilon - \varepsilon')x_0^2 = \varepsilon^s - \varepsilon'^s,$$

$$\varepsilon^{2s} + 1 = \varepsilon^{s-1}(\varepsilon^2 + 1)x_0^2,$$

$$(\varepsilon^s)^2 - (\varepsilon^2 + 1)(x_0\varepsilon^{(s-1)/2})^2 = -1.$$

Then $\varepsilon^s + x_0\varepsilon^{(s-1)/2}(\varepsilon^2 + 1)^{1/2}$ is a unit with relative norm -1 in the ring $Z[1, v\sqrt{d}, \sqrt{\varepsilon^2 + 1}, v\sqrt{d}\sqrt{\varepsilon^2 + 1}]$. There are three fundamental units in the ring but he shows that it suffices to use only two of them.

4. Binomial equations

The equation

$$ax^m - by^n = c. \tag{17}$$

We may suppose that a, b, c, m, n are positive integers, and that either m or n is not less than 3.

Very little is known about the integer solutions of equation (19) for general m and n. The known results are of considerable interest, and in general are concerned with the existence of only a few solutions, often none, one or two. They can often be stated very simply in terms of fundamental units of algebraic number fields. Proofs are usually very complicated and may involve considerable detail, both theoretical and numerical, and so cannot be given here.

A few results, however, may be mentioned. Most of them deal with the case when $m = n$.

Some are included in the results for the integer solutions of the inequality

$$|ax^n - by^n| \leqslant c.$$

The first ones are due to Thue[24] and are particular cases of his general theorem for the inequality

$$|a_0 x^n + a_1 x^{n-1} y + \cdots + a_n y^n| \leqslant c.$$

This states * that if an integer solution is known for which $|x|$, $|y|$ are greater than a determinable constant M, then a constant N can be found such that all the solutions are numerically less than N. The method was extended and generalized by Siegel[25] who proved the fundamental

Theorem 11

The inequality

$$|ax^n - by^n| \leqslant c, \tag{18}$$

where a, b, c are positive integers and $n \geqslant 3$, has at most one solution in positive co-prime integers (x, y) if

$$(ab)^{(n/2)-1} \geqslant 4c^{2n-2} \left(n \prod_p p^{1/(n-1)} \right)^n, \tag{19}$$

where p runs through all the different prime factors of n.

In particular when n is a prime, we can replace condition (19) by the weaker and more practical condition

$$|ab|^{1/2} \geqslant 188c^4. \tag{20}$$

The idea in the proofs by Thue and Siegel can be made to depend essentially upon the approximation of algebraic functions by means of rational functions. This can be presented in different ways. Let $A_r(z)$, $B_r(z)$ be polynomials with rational coefficients and of degree r. Thue proved a relation of the form

$$A_r(z^n) - z B_r(z^n) = (z - 1)^{2n+1} C_r(z),$$

where $C_r(z)$ is a polynomial of degree $n(r - 2)$. His work is purely algebraic. Siegel, however, used a relation of the form

$$A_r(z) - (1 - z)^{1/n} B_r(z) = z^{2r+1} C_r(z).$$

Now $C_r(z)$ and the polynomials $A_r(z)$, $B_r(z)$ appear as hypergeometric series. Their properties are easily investigated, and the relations between them are given at once by using the hypergeometric differential equation.

* Hyyrö[27a] points out that N depends upon the first hypothetical solution. Since there is no limit to the first solution, the method fails to give an N.

Domar[26] by sharpening some of the inequalities in Siegel's proof, has obtained the two results given in

Theorem 12

The equation

$$ax^n - by^n = \pm 1, \tag{21}$$

where a, b are positive integers and $n \geqslant 5$, has at most two solutions in positive integers.

Theorem 13

The equation

$$x^n - Dy^n = \pm 1, \tag{22}$$

where $D > 0$ and $n \geqslant 5$, has at most one solution in positive integers x, y except possibly when $D = 2$, and when $n = 5$ or 6 and $D = 2^n \pm 1$.

Theorems 11 and 13 have been used by af Ekenstam[27] to prove a result given without proof by Tartakowski, namely, are

Theorem 14

If the equation

$$x^{2n} - Dy^{2n} = 1, \tag{23}$$

where D is a positive non-square integer and $n \geqslant 3$, has a solution (x_1, y_1) in positive integers, then if ε is the fundamental unit of the ring $Z[\sqrt{D}]$ and $N(\varepsilon) = 1$,

$$x_1^n + y_1^n \sqrt{D} = \varepsilon \text{ or } \varepsilon^2,$$

the ε^2 occurring in only a finite number of cases. If $N(\varepsilon) = -1$ there are only solutions with $y = 0$.

Some results for equation (19) may be noted when m, n have small values, for example 2, 4, 6 and c also has special values, for example, 1, 2, 4, 8, ... Thus Ljunggren[17,15] has proved

Theorem 15

The equation

$$ax^{2n} - by^{2n} = c, \tag{24}$$

where a, b, c are positive integers, has at most one solution in positive integers x, y when

$$n = 2, \quad c = 1, 2, 4, 8;$$

$$n = 3, \quad c = 1, 2, 3, 4, 6.$$

Further, among all the equations (24) corresponding to a given field

$$Q(\sqrt[2n]{d}) = Q(\sqrt[2n]{ab^{-1}}),$$

there is at most one solvable in positive integers except when $n = 2$, $d = 5$.
af Ekenstam,[27] by utilizing the results in Siegel's [25] paper, supersedes
Theorem 12 by

Theorem 16

Among all the equations

$$\left| ax^n - by^n \right| = 1, \qquad n \geqslant 5$$

corresponding to fields $Q(\sqrt[n]{d}) = Q(\sqrt[n]{ab^{-1}})$ with given d, there are at most two solvable in positive integers x, y.

He obtained a similar but more complicated result for the equations $\left| ax^n - by^n \right| = c$ where $1 < c < c'$, a number depending upon $|ab|$. Another of his results has been improved by Hyyrö,[27a] and is given as

Theorem 17

Let $d \geqslant 2$, $n \geqslant 5$ be given integers. Then the equation

$$\left| x^n - d^s y^n \right| = 1,$$

where $x \geqslant 2$, $y \geqslant 1$, $0 \leqslant s < n$, and $x \geqslant 3$ for $n = 5, 6$ has at most one solution s, x, y.

He has also improved Theorem 16.

Theorem 18

The equation

$$x^4 - Dy^4 = 1, \tag{25}$$

where D is a positive non-square integer has at most one integer solution. If this is (x_1, y_1) and ε is the fundamental unit in $Q(\sqrt{D})$ and $N(\varepsilon) = 1$, then

$$x_1^2 + y_1^2 \sqrt{D} = \varepsilon \text{ or } \varepsilon^2,$$

the latter occurring in only a finite number of solutions. If $N(\varepsilon) = -1$, there is no solution except when $D = 5$.

Ljunggren has shown that the ε^2 arises only in the case $D = 7140$ when

$$239^2 + 26^2 \sqrt{7140} = (169 + 2\sqrt{7140})^2 = \varepsilon^2.$$

By different methods Delone and Faddeev[29] have proved

Theorem 19

The equations

$$x^4 - Dy^4 = \pm 1 \tag{26}$$

have at most one solution in positive integers. This will be given by $x = A$, $y = B$ if the fundamental unit of the ring $Z[\sqrt[4]{-4D}]$ takes the form

$$\varepsilon = A^2 + AB\sqrt[4]{-4D} + B^2\sqrt{-D}.$$

The impossibility of non-trivial solutions of the equations

$$y^2 = x^m \pm 1, \quad m > 3$$
$$y^3 = x^m \pm 1, \quad m > 2$$

will be noted in Chapter 30.

Finally we give a result by Skolem[30].

Theorem 20

The equation

$$x^5 + Dy^5 = 1$$

has no solution in non-zero integers when $D = 4, 8, 16$, and only the solution $(-1, 1)$ when $D = 2$.

The proof depends upon the p-adic methods of Chapter 23.

From Siegel's theorem, it follows that there is at most one non-trivial solution if $D > 1250\sqrt[6]{20}$. It has been shown by Häggmark[31] that there are at most two solutions, a result contained in Theorem 12.

Addendum 1

Theorem 1 has been improved very recently by Schinzel[32] who following a suggestion by Davenport and Lewis, proved as follows,

Theorem 21

Let $f(x, y)$ be a polynomial of degree n with integer coefficients which is irreducible in the rational field Q and let $f_n(x, y)$ be its homogeneous part of degree n. If $f(x, y) = 0$ has infinitely many integer solutions, then except for a constant factor, $f_n(x, y)$ is a power of a linear form or of an irreducible quadratic form.

Suppose that $f(x, y) = 0$ has infinitely many integer solutions. Then by theorem 1, $f_n(x, y)$ is, except for a constant factor, a power of an irreducible form, and so either

$$f_n(x, y) = ax^n \quad \text{or} \quad by^n,$$

in accordance with the theorem, or

$$f_n(x, y) = a_0 x^n + \cdots + a_n y^n, \qquad (a_0 a_n \neq 0). \tag{27}$$

By Siegel's theorem 2, we have identically in t,

$$f(R(t), S(t)) = 0, \tag{28}$$

where either

I, $R(t)$, $S(t)$ are polynomials, not both constant, or

II, $R(t) = \dfrac{A(t)}{L(t)^m}, \qquad S(t) = \dfrac{B(t)}{L(t)^m},$

where A, B, L are polynomials, L is linear, $(A, B, L) = 1$, $m > 0$,

III, $R(t) = \dfrac{C(t)}{Q(t)^m}, \qquad S(t) = \dfrac{D(t)}{Q(t)^m},$

where C, D, Q are polynomials, Q is a quadratic, $(C, D, Q) \neq Q$, $m > 0$.

For I, from equations (27), (28), R and S are of the same degree and so if r and s are the leading coefficients of R and S, then $f_n(r, s) = 0$. Hence $f_n(x, y)$ is divisible by $sx - ry$ and so from theorem 1,

$$f_n(x, y) = c(sx - ry)^n.$$

For II, let t_0 be the zero of $L(t)$. Multiplying (27) by $L(t)^{mn}$ and then putting $t = t_0$, we see that $f_n(A(t_0), B(t_0)) = 0$. Hence $f_n(x, y)$ is divisible by $B(t_0)x - A(t_0)y$ and so from theorem 1,

$$f_n(x, y) = c(B(t_0)x - A(t_0)y)^n$$

For III, let t_1, t_2 be the zeros of $Q(t)$. We cannot have $C(t_i) = 0$, $D(t_i) = 0$, $(i = 1, 2)$ say, $D(t_i) \neq 0$. Multiplying (28) by $Q(t)^{mn}$ and then putting $t = t_1$, we obtain $f_n(C(t_1), D(t_1)) = 0$, and so $f_n(x, y)$ is divisible by $D(t_1)x - C(t_1)y$. Then either $C(t_1)/D(t_1)$ is rational, and

$$f_n(x, y) = c(D(t_1)x - C(t_1)y)^n,$$

or

$C(t_1)/D(t_1)$ and $C(t_2)/D(t_2)$ are conjugates in a quadratic field, and so

$$f_n(x, y) = c \prod_{i=1,2} (D(t_i)x - C(t_i)y)^{n/2},$$

and the product is a power of an irreducible quadratic.

A consequence of this theorem due to Davenport and Lewis replaces theorem 4 of Chapter 22 by

10

Theorem 22

The equation $f(x, y) = g(x, y)$ where f and g are polynomials of degrees n, m with integer coefficients, has only a finite number of integer solutions if $n > 2$, $m < n$, and f is an irreducible form.

Addendum 2

Siegel's theorem 3 does not enable one to find all the integer solutions of the equation

$$y^2 = a_0 x^n + a_1 x^{n-1} + \cdots + a_n = f(x),$$

say.

These can now be found from the following result just proved by Baker.[33]

Theorem 23

If $f(x)$ has at least three simple zeros, then all the integer solutions satisfy the inequality

$$\max\left(|x|, |y|\right) < \exp \exp \exp \left(n^{10n^3} A^{n^2}\right),$$

where $A = \max |a_r|$, $(r = 0, 1, \cdots n)$.

REFERENCES

1. C. Runge. Über ganzzahlige Lösungen von Gleichungen zwischen zwei Veränderlichen. *J. reine angew. Math.*, **100** (1887), 425–435.
2. C. L. Siegel. Über einige Anwendungen diophantischer Approximationen. *Abh. preuss. Akad. Wiss. Phys-Math. Kl.* (1929), Nr. 1.
3. L. J. Mordell. The diophantine equation $y^2 = ax^3 + bx^2 + cx + d$ or fifty years after. *J. Lond. Math. Soc.*, **38** (1963), 454–458.
4. C. L. Siegel. The integer solutions of the equation $y^2 = ax^n + bx^{n-1} + \cdots + k$. *J. Lond. Math. Soc.*, **1** (1920), 66–68.
5. C. L. Siegel. Approximation algebraischer Zahlen. *Math. Z.*, **10** (1961), 173–213 (205).
6. E. Landau and A. Ostrowski. On the diophantine equation $ay^2 + by + c = dx^n$. *Proc. Lond. Math. Soc.* ,(2), **19** (1920), 276–280.
7. A. Thue. Über die Unlösbarkeit der Gleichung $ax^2 + bx + c = dy^n$ in grossen ganzen Zahlen x und y. *Arch. Math. Naturv. Kristiania* Nr. 16, **34** (1917).
8. O. Rigge. Über ein diophantisches Problem. *IX. Skan. Math. Kongr. Helsingfors* (1938).
9. P. Erdös. Note on products of consecutive integers. *J. Lond. Math. Soc.*, **14** (1939), 194–198.
10. R. Obláth. Über Produkte aufeinander folgender Zahlen. *Tôhoku Math. J.*, **38** (1933), 73–92. See also Berichtigung.
11. P. Erdös. Note on the product of consecutive integers. II. *J. Lond. Math. Soc.*, **14** (1939), 245–249.
12. O. Rigge. On a diophantine problem. *Ark. Math. Astr. Fys.*, 27A, 3 (1940).
13. P. Erdös. On the product of consecutive integers, III. *Koninkl. Nederl. Akad. van Wetenschappen* (1955), 85–90.

14. L. Louis Johnson. On the diophantine equation $y^k = x(x + 1)\ldots(x + n - 1)$. *Am. Math. Mon.*, **47** (1940), 280–289.

14a. L. J. Mordell. The diophantine equation $dy^2 = ax^4 + by^2 + c$. *Acta Arith.* **15** (1969).

15. W. Ljunggren. Solution complète de quelques équations du sixième degré à deux indéterminées. *Arch. Math. Naturv.*, **48** (1946), Nr. 7, 26–29.

16. J. W. S. Cassels. Integral points on certain elliptic curves. *Proc. Lond. Math. Soc.* (3), **14** A (1965), 55–57.

17. W. Ljunggren. Einige Eigenschaften der Einheiten reeller quadratischer und rein biquadratischer Zahlkörper. *Oslo Vid-Akad Skrifter*, **1** (1936), No. 12.

18. W. Ljunggren. Über die unbestimmte Gleichung $Ax^2 - By^4 = C$. *Arch. Math. Naturv.*, **41** (1938), Nr. 10.

19. W. Ljunggren. Über die Gleichung $x^4 - Dy^2 = 1$. *Arch. Math. Naturv.*, **45** (1942), Nr. 5.

20. W. Ljunggren. Some remarks on the diophantine equations $x^2 - Dy^4 = 1$ and $x^4 - dy^2 = 1$. *J. Lond. Math. Soc.*, **41** (1966), 542–544.

21. L. J. Mordell. The diophantine equation $y^2 = Dx^4 + 1$. *J. Lond. Math. Soc.*, **39** (1964), 161–164.

22. J. H. E. Cohn. Eight diophantine equations. *Proc. Lond. Math. Soc.* (3), **16** (1966), 153–166. Addendum *Ibid.* (3) **17** (1967), 381.

22a. V. D. Podsypanin, On an indeterminate equation (Russian). *Izv. Akad. Nauk SSSR Mat.*, **5** (1941) 305–324.

23. W. Ljunggren. Zur Theorie der Gleichung $x^2 + 1 = Dy^4$. *Avh. Norske Vid. Akad. Oslo*, No. 5 1 (1942).

24. A. Thue, Berechnung aller Lösungen gewisser Gleichungen von der Form $ax^r - by^r = f$. *Vid. selskap Skrifter Kristiania mat. natur. Kl.* (1918), No. 4.

25. C. L. Siegel. Die Gleichung $ax^n - by^n = c$. *Math. Ann.*, **144** (1937), 57–68. Also Gesammelte Abhandlungen, II (1966).

26. Y. Domar. On the diophantine equation $|Ax^n - By^n| = 1$, $n \geqslant 5$. *Math. Scand.*, **2** (1954), 29–32.

27. A. af Ekenstam. Contributions to the theory of the diophantine equation $Ax^n - By^n = C$. *Dissertation* (1959) Uppsala, Almqvist and Wiksells.

27a. S. Hyyrö. Über die Gleichung $ax^n - by^n = z$ und das Catalansche Problem. *Ann. Acad. Sci. Fennicae, Series A*.1.355 (1964) 32.

28. V. A. Tartakowski. Auflösung der Gleichung $x^4 - \rho y^4 = 1$. *Izv. Akad. Nauk SSSR*, **20** (1926), 301–324.

29. B. N. Delone and D. K. Faddeev. "The Theory of Irrationalities of the Third Degree. *Translation of Math. monographs, Am. Math. Soc.*, **10** (1964), 370–380.

30. T. Skolem. En metode til behandling av ubestemte ligninger. *Chr. Michelsens Inst. Beretn*, IV (1934), Nr. 6, Bergen.

31. P. Häggmark. On a class of quintic diophantine equations. *Dissertation* Uppsala (1952).

32. A. Schinzel. An improvement of Runge's theorem on diophantine equations. *Commentarii Acad. Pontificiàe Scientiarum*, **2** (1969). (A generalization will appear in the same journal.)

33. A. Baker. Bounds for the solutions of the hyperelliptic equation. *Proc. Camb. Phil. Soc.*, **65** (1949), 439–444.

CHAPTER 29

Fermat's Last Theorem

1. The most famous of all Diophantine problems is due to Fermat and is called Fermat's theorem, namely,

Theorem 1

If n is an integer > 2, the equation

$$x^n + y^n = z^n \tag{1}$$

has no integer solutions except those given by $xyz = 0$.

Fermat stated that he had a proof of this, but it seems unlikely that this is so. The proof given when $n = 4$ in Chapter 4 is in principle due to him. The proof given when $n = 3$ in Chapter 16 goes back to Euler, but his proof was incomplete. Kummer made the greatest contributions to the subject. He introduced the algebraic numbers arising from the pth roots of unity, and this was the beginning of algebraic number theory which was later generalized by Dedekind and Kronecker.

It is obviously sufficient to prove the theorem when n is an odd prime p.

The proof is comparatively easy when p is a prime $\leqslant 19$ since then unique factorization holds in the field $Q(\zeta)$ where $\zeta^p = 1$. Kummer was at first under the impression that this held for all p.

No proof is known for general p but, as shown later, the theorem has been proved for many special values for p. We may suppose that $p > 3$ and write

$$x^p + y^p + z^p = 0. \tag{2}$$

Let $\zeta = e^{2\pi i/p}$ be a complex pth root of unity. Then the equation (2) can be written as

$$(x + y)(x + \zeta y)\ldots(x + \zeta^{p-1}y) = -z^p. \tag{3}$$

To apply the methods of Chapter 15, we require some knowledge of the cyclotomic field $Q(\zeta)$. For this the usual books on algebraic number theory may be consulted. For the applications to Fermat's last theorem, references may be made to the accounts by Hilbert[1], Bachmann[2], Dickson[3], Mordell[4], Landau[5], LeVeque[6], Borevich and Shafarevich[7], and Vandiver[8]. A complete study of the solvability of the equation (1) requires a detailed, intricate and advanced arithmetical investigation into which we cannot enter here.

We prove the impossibility in some comparatively simple cases and for this we require the following results. Most of them will be stated without proof, but a few will be proved.

I. The degree of the field is $p - 1$ since the equation

$$z^{p-1} + z^{p-2} + \cdots + z + 1 = 0$$

is irreducible in the rational field Q.

II. The integers in the field are given by

$$\xi = a_0 + a_1\zeta + \cdots + a_{p-2}\zeta^{p-2},$$

where the a are rational integers.

Clearly $\xi^p \equiv a \pmod{p}$ where a is a rational integer.

III. The only roots of unity in the field are $\pm\zeta^r$, $r = 0, 1, \ldots, p - 1$.

IV. The numbers $\varepsilon_r = (\zeta^r - 1)/(\zeta - 1)$ are units. For ε_r is an integer and has norm $N(\varepsilon_r) = 1$.

V. $\lambda = 1 - \zeta$ is a complex prime and $p = \varepsilon\lambda^{p-1}$, where ε is a unit. For put $u = 1$ in

$$u^{p-1} + \cdots + u + 1 = \prod_{r=1}^{p-1} (u - \zeta^r),$$

then

$$p = \prod_{r=1}^{p-1} (1 - \zeta^r) = \prod_{r=1}^{p-1} \left(\frac{1 - \zeta^r}{1 - \zeta}\right)(1 - \zeta)^{p-1}.$$

VI. Every unit ε can be expressed in the form $\varepsilon = \zeta^s\eta$ where $0 \leqslant s < p$ and η is a real unit.

Write $\varepsilon = \varepsilon_1 = f(\zeta)$, where $f(\zeta)$ is a polynomial with integer coefficients, and $\varepsilon_r = f(\zeta^r)$. Then

$$\frac{\varepsilon_r}{\varepsilon_{-r}} = \frac{f(\zeta^r)}{f(\zeta^{-r})}$$

is also a unit, and so

$$\prod_{r=1}^{p-1} \left(w - \frac{\varepsilon_r}{\varepsilon_{-r}}\right) = \prod_{r=1}^{p-1} (\varepsilon_{-r}w - \varepsilon_r)$$

has coefficients in Z. Since $|\varepsilon_r/\varepsilon_{-r}| = 1$, $\varepsilon_r/\varepsilon_{-r}$ is a root of unity by a well known theorem of Kronecker, and so

$$\varepsilon_1 = \pm\zeta^s\varepsilon_{-1},$$

say. We show that the negative sign does not hold, i.e. $\varepsilon_1 + \zeta^s\varepsilon_{-1} = 0$ is impossible.

For if this holds, we have identically in w,

$$a_0 + a_1w + \cdots + a_{p-2}w^{p-2}$$
$$+ w^{s+p}(a_0 + a_1w^{-1} + \cdots + a_{p-1}w^{-(p-2)})$$
$$= w^t(1 + w + \cdots + w^{p-1})g(w).$$

for some integer t and a polynomial $g(w)$ with integer coefficients. Put $w = 1$, then

$$a_0 + a_1 + \cdots + a_{p-2} \equiv 0 \pmod{p}.$$

Hence $\quad \varepsilon = a_0 + a_1\zeta + \cdots + a_{p-2}\zeta^{p-2}$

$$\equiv a_1(\zeta - 1) + \cdots + a_{p-2}(\zeta^{p-2} - 1) \pmod{\lambda}$$

$$\equiv 0 \pmod{\lambda},$$

and this is impossible.

VII. If p is a regular prime and ε is a unit in $Q(\zeta)$ for which $\varepsilon \equiv a \pmod{\lambda^p}$, where a is a rational integer, then $\varepsilon = \varepsilon_0^p$ where ε_0 is a unit in $Q(\zeta)$.

The proof requires too much detail to be given here.

The primes p are called regular or irregular according as the ideal class number h is not divisible by p. Kummer has shown that $h \not\equiv 0 \pmod{p}$, if p does not divide the numerator of the first $\frac{1}{2}(p - 3)$ Bernoulli numbers. These are defined by

$$\frac{t}{e^t - 1} = 1 - \frac{t}{2} + \sum_{n=1}^{\infty} \frac{(-1)^{n-1}B_n t^{2n}}{(2n)!}.$$

All the primes < 100 except $p = 37, 59, 67$ are regular. It has been proved that there are an infinity of irregular primes but it is not known if there are an infinity of regular primes. We shall prove Fermat's theorem for the regular primes. Kummer has proved the theorem for some classes of irregular primes.

2. We come back to equation (3). The common factors of $x + \zeta^r y$, $x + \zeta^s y$, $s > r$, are divisors of $(\zeta^r - \zeta^s)y$, and since $(x, y) = 1$, of $\zeta^r(1 - \zeta^{s-r})$, and these can only be 1 or λ. In the first case, all the factors $x + \zeta^r y$ are relatively prime. In the second, all the factors are divisible by λ, and so z is divisible by λ and hence by p. The cases $z \not\equiv 0 \pmod{p}$, $z \equiv 0 \pmod{p}$ are called the first and second cases respectively.

Theorem 2

If p is regular, the first case is impossible.

Each of the factors in equation (3) is a pth power except for a unit. Hence

$$x + \zeta y = \varepsilon \alpha^p, \tag{4}$$

where ε is a unit in $Q(\zeta)$. We may take $\varepsilon = \zeta^s \eta$ where $0 \leqslant s < p$, and η is a real unit. Since $\alpha^p \equiv a \pmod{p}$, where a is a rational integer,

$$x + \zeta y \equiv \zeta^s \xi \pmod{p},$$

and ξ is a real integer in $Q(\zeta)$. Hence also

$$x + \zeta^{-1}y \equiv \zeta^{-s}\xi \pmod{p}.$$

Then $\quad \zeta^{-s}(x + \zeta y) - \zeta^s(x + \zeta^{-1}y) \equiv 0 \pmod{p}.$

Since $1, \zeta, \ldots, \zeta^{p-2}$ form an integer basis for $Q(\zeta)$, then if $a_0, a_1, \ldots, a_{p-1}$ are rational integers,

$$a_0 + a_1\zeta + \cdots + a_{p-2}\zeta^{p-2} \equiv 0 \,(\text{mod } p)$$

if and only if

$$a_0 \equiv a_1 \equiv \cdots \equiv a_{p-2} \equiv 0 \,(\text{mod } p).$$

Write $\quad\quad \zeta^{p-s}(x + \zeta y) - (\zeta^s x + \zeta^{s-1} y) \equiv 0 \,(\text{mod } p).$

If $2 < s \leqslant p - 2$ and $s \neq (p + 1)/2$, the powers of ζ are all different and less than $p - 1$, and so $x \equiv y \equiv 0 \,(\text{mod } p)$, i.e. $z \equiv 0 \,(\text{mod } p)$.
If $s = (p + 1)/2$, then $x + \zeta y \equiv \zeta x + y \,(\text{mod } p)$, i.e. $x \equiv y \,(\text{mod } p)$.
Similarly $x \equiv z \,(\text{mod } p)$ and so $x^p + y^p + z^p \equiv 3x^p \equiv 0 \,(\text{mod } p)$, and this does not hold since $p > 3$.

If $s = 0$, $\quad\quad x + \zeta y - (x + \zeta^{-1}y) \equiv 0 \,(\text{mod } p).$

Then $y \equiv 0 \,(\text{mod } p)$, and similarly $x \equiv 0 \,(\text{mod } p)$.

If $s = 1$, $\quad \zeta^{-1}x + y \equiv \zeta x + y \,(\text{mod } p)$, i.e. $\quad x \equiv 0 \,(\text{mod } p)$,

and similarly $y \equiv 0 \,(\text{mod } p)$.

If $s = 2$, $x + \zeta y \equiv \zeta^4 x + \zeta^3 y$ and so $x \equiv y \equiv 0$.

If $s = p - 1$, $\quad\quad \zeta(x + \zeta y) \equiv \zeta^{-1}x + \zeta^{-2}y \,(\text{mod } p),$

i.e. $\quad\quad \zeta^3(x + \zeta y) \equiv \zeta x + y \,(\text{mod } p).$

Since $p \geqslant 5$, this gives $x \equiv y \equiv 0 \,(\text{mod } p)$.

Theorem 3

If p is regular, the second case is impossible.

It proves convenient now to consider solutions not in Z, but integer solutions in $Q(\zeta)$. We also consider the more general equation

$$x^p + y^p = \varepsilon\lambda^{np}z^p,$$

where ε is a unit and $n > 1$. We shall show that n must be greater than 1 and that if the equation is solvable for n, it is also solvable for $n - 1$. This leads to a contradiction. We have

$$\prod_{r=0}^{p-1} (x + \zeta^r y) = \varepsilon\lambda^{np}z^p. \tag{5}$$

One of the factors on the left-hand side, and so all of them, must be divisible by λ since $x + \zeta^r y - (x + \zeta^s y) = (\zeta^r - \zeta^s)y$. This also shows that λ is the greatest common divisor of any two of the factors. Hence one of these must be divisible by λ^{np-p+1}. By a slight change in the variables, we may suppose this occurs when $r = 0$. We now replace $\zeta^a x$, $\zeta^b y$ in the equation by x, y and show that we can choose a, b so that $x \equiv x_0$, $y \equiv y_0 \pmod{\lambda^2}$ where x_0, y_0 are rational integers.

In II we replace ζ by $1 - \lambda$, and so with rational integers $x_0, \ldots, x_{p-2}$,

$$x = x_0 + x_1 \lambda + \cdots + x_{p-2} \lambda^{p-2}.$$

Then since $\zeta = 1 - \lambda$, $\zeta^a x \equiv x_0 + \lambda(x_1 - ax_0) \pmod{\lambda^2}$. Since $x_0 \not\equiv 0 \pmod{\lambda}$, we can choose a so that $x_1 - ax_0 \equiv 0 \pmod{p}$.
Similarly for $y_1 - by_0 \equiv 0 \pmod{p}$. Hence $x + y \equiv x_0 + y_0 \pmod{\lambda^2}$, and so $x_0 + y_0 \equiv 0 \pmod{p}$. Then $x + y \equiv 0 \pmod{\lambda^2}$ and since $x + y \equiv 0 \pmod{\lambda^{np-p+1}}$, $n > 1$.

Write $\delta = (x, y)$ for the ideal common factor of x, y. Then we have the ideal equations

$$(x + y) = \delta \lambda^{np-p+1} a_0^p, \qquad (x + \zeta^r y) = \delta \lambda a_r^p,$$

or, say,

$$(x + \zeta^r y) = \delta \lambda^{t_r} a_r^p,$$

where a_0, a_r are ideals and $t_r = np - p + 1$ when $r = 0$, $t_r = 1$ when $r \neq 0$. Hence $a_0^p \sim a_r^p$ and since $(p, h) = 1$, $a_r \sim a_0$, and so $\delta_r a_r = \gamma_r a_0$ for algebraic integers δ_r, γ_r. Also we can write

$$\frac{x + \zeta^r y}{x + \zeta^s y} = \varepsilon_{r,s} \lambda^{t_r - t_s} \left(\frac{\gamma_r \delta_s}{\gamma_s \delta_r}\right)^p,$$

where $\varepsilon_{r,s}$ is a unit, and so

$$(\delta_r \gamma_s)^p (x + \zeta^r y) = \varepsilon_{rs} \lambda^{t_r - t_s} (\delta_s \gamma_r)^p (x + \zeta^s y).$$

In particular with $(r, s) = (0, 1)$ and $(r, s) = (2, 1)$, we can write, say,

$$\alpha_1^p (x + y) = \varepsilon_1 (x + \zeta y) \beta_1^p \lambda^{(n-1)p},$$

$$\alpha_2^p (x + \zeta^2 y) = \varepsilon_2 (x + \zeta y) \beta_2^p,$$

where ε_1, ε_2 are units, and the α, β are algebraic integers. Multiply the equations by $\zeta \alpha_2^p$, α_1^p respectively and add. Since

$$\zeta(x + y) + (x + \zeta^2 y) = (\zeta + 1)(x + \zeta y),$$

we can cancel a factor $x + \zeta y$ and so

$$\alpha_1^p \alpha_2^p (\zeta + 1) = \zeta \varepsilon_1 (\alpha_2 \beta_1)^p \lambda^{(n-1)p} + \varepsilon_2 (\alpha_1 \beta_2)^p.$$

Since ε_1, ε_2 and $\zeta + 1 = (\zeta^2 - 1)/(\zeta - 1)$ are units, we have an equation of the form

$$X^p + \varepsilon_3 Y^p = \varepsilon_4 \lambda^{(n-1)p} Z^p,$$

where X, Y, Z, are integers in $Q(\zeta)$. Now $X^p \equiv x_0$, $Y^p \equiv y_0 \pmod{p}$ where x_0, y_0 are rational integers and $x_0 y_0 \not\equiv 0$. Hence since $n > 1$,

$$x_0 + \varepsilon_3 y_0 \equiv 0 \pmod{\lambda^p}.$$

Then $\varepsilon_3 \equiv -x_0/y_0 \pmod{\lambda^p}$ and so $\varepsilon_3 = \varepsilon_5^p$ where ε_5 is a unit, and

$$X^p + (\varepsilon_5 Y)^p = \varepsilon_4 \lambda^{p(n-1)} Z^p,$$

an equation with n replaced by $n - 1$. This proves the theorem.

3. Other methods are known for dealing with the first case when x and y are rational integers. These depend upon arithmetical considerations different from those previously considered and we can give only brief mention of the results. Kummer showed by multiplying together an appropriate set of the equations (4), that solvability implies some polynomial congruences. He proved

Theorem 4

Denote by t the quotient of any two of x, y, z, where $xyz \not\equiv 0 \pmod{p}$. Write

$$\phi_n(t) = t - 2^{n-1}t^2 + 3^{n-1}t^3 - \cdots + (-1)^{p-2}(p-1)^{n-1}t^{p-1}.$$

Then solvability of equation (1) *implies*

$$\phi_n(t)B_{(p-n)/2} \equiv 0 \pmod{p}, \quad n = 3, 5, \ldots, p - 2. \tag{6}$$

From this, polynomial congruences can be found for the t if some or all of the $B_{(p-n)/2}$ are not divisible by p.

The congruence (6) can be replaced by

$$\phi_{p-n}(t)\phi_n(t) \equiv 0 \pmod{p}, \quad n = 2, 3, \ldots, \frac{p-3}{2},$$

$$\phi_{p-1}(t) \equiv 0 \pmod{p}.$$

From these Wieferich deduced the criterion

$$2^{p-1} \equiv 1 \pmod{p^2}. \tag{7}$$

Mirimanoff showed that also

$$3^{p-1} \equiv 1 \pmod{p^2}. \tag{8}$$

For $p < 31{,}059{,}000$ congruence (7) is satisfied[10] only by $p = 1093$, $p = 3571$, and (8) only by $p = 11$, $p = 1{,}006{,}003$ for $p < 10{,}752{,}000$.

Furtwängler has also proved (7), (8) by applying the general law of reciprocity in the cyclotomic field $Q(\zeta)$. He showed that if a prime q is a divisor of xyz, then

$$q^{p-1} \equiv 1 \pmod{p^2}. \tag{9}$$

It has been proved by various writers that this result holds for all primes $q \leqslant 43$. The Lehmers have used such results to prove the impossibility of the first case for $p \leqslant 253, 747, 887$.

Results for the irregular primes were also found by Kummer. It has been proved by K. L. Jensen[9] that there are an infinity of irregular primes. Of the

11+

302 primes less than 2,000, only 118 are regular. The work of Vandiver and the Lehmers[11] has settled the insolvability for $p < 2000$. Selfridge, Nicol and Vandiver[13] do this for $p < 4002$. It now holds[12] for $p < 25,000$.

REFERENCES

1. D. Hilbert. Die Theorie der algebraischen Zahlkörper. *Jahresbericht der Deutschen Mathematiker Vereinigung*, **4** (1897), 175–546. Also "Gesammelte Abhandlungen", I (1932), Springer, Berlin. Also "Théorie des Corps de nombres algébriques" (1913), A. Hermann et fils. (Translation by A. Levy and Th. Got.)
2. P. Bachmann. "Das Fermatproblem in seiner bisherigen Entwicklung" (1919). Walter de Gruyter & Co., Berlin und Leipzig.
3. L. E. Dickson. "History of the Theory of Numbers, II". Carnegie Inst. Washington Pub. 256 Roman Cap, 1920. (Reprint: Stechert, New York, 1934).
4. L. J. Mordell. "Three Lectures on Fermat's Last Theorem" (1921) Cambridge University Press, Cambridge.
5. E. Landau. "Vorlesungen über Zahlentheorie", III (1927), S. Hirzel, Leipzig.
6. W. J. Le Veque. "Topics in Number Theory", II (1956), Addison-Wesley, Reading, Massachusetts.
7. Z. I. Borevich and I. R. Shafarevich. "Number Theory" (1966), Academic Press, New York & London. (Translation from the Russian.)
8. H. Vandiver. Fermat's last theorem; its history and the nature of the results concerning it. *Am. Math. Month.*, **53** (1946), 555–578. See also A supplementary note to a 1946 article on Fermat's Last Theorem. *Amer. Math. Monthly*, **60** (1953), 164–167.
9. K. L. Jensen. Om talteoretiske Egenskaber ved de Bernoulliske Tal. *Nyt. Tidskr. Math.*, **26B** (1915) 73–83.
10. K. E. Kloss. Some number theoretic calculations. *J. Res. Nat. Bur. Standards Sect. B*, **693** (1965), 335–336.
11. D. H. Lehmer, E. Lehmer, H. S. Vandiver. An application of high speed computing to Fermat's Last Theorem. *Proc. Nat. Acad. Sci. U.S.A.*, **40** (1954), 25–33.
12. J. L. Selfridge and B. W. Pollock. *Notices Amer. Math. Soc.*, **11** (1967), 97. (*Abstract 608–138*).
13. J. L. Selfridge, C. A. Nicol, H. S. Vandiver. Proof of Fermat's last theorem for all prime exponents less than 4002. *Proc. Nat. Acad. U.S.A.*, **41** (1955), 970–973.

CHAPTER 30

Miscellaneous Results

1. *The equation $z = f(x, y)$.*

Let $f(x, y)$ be the quotient of two polynomials in x, y with integer co-efficients. Two kinds of problems arise according as the integers x, y, z are all non-negative or not. Two of the first type will be discussed. The first deals with the exceedingly interesting

Conjecture (Erdös, Straus),
The equation

$$\frac{4}{n} = \frac{1}{x} + \frac{1}{y} + \frac{1}{z},\tag{1}$$

where n is an integer > 3 is solvable in positive integers x, y, z.

It has been verified for $n < 5000$ by Straus, $n < 8000$ by Bernstein[1], $n < 20{,}000$ by Shapiro, $n < 106{,}128$ by Obláth[2], and $n < 10^7$ by Yamamoto[3]. The proofs show that the equation is solvable if n satisfies one of an infinite set of congruences, or equivalently, if n is representable by one of an infinite set of arithmetic progressions.

Obviously if equation (1) is solvable for n, and in particular when n is a prime, it is also solvable for any multiple of n.

For some simple general results, let a, b, c, d be arbitrary positive integers. Then if

$$a + bn + cn = 4abcd,\tag{2}$$

there is a representation

$$(x, y, z) = (bcdn, acd, abd).$$

If

$$na + b + c = 4abcd,\tag{3}$$

there is a representation

$$(x, y, z) = (bcd, nabd, nacd).$$

Representations when $n \equiv 2, 3 \pmod 4$ follow from (3). For if

$$a = 2, \quad b = 1, \quad c = 1, \quad \text{then } n = 4d - 1,$$
$$a = 1, \quad b = 1, \quad c = 1, \quad \text{then } n = 4d - 2.$$

When $n \equiv 0 \pmod 4$, we have $x = y = z = 3n/4$.

Hence we need only consider the case $n \equiv 1 \pmod 4$.

If in equation (3), $a = 1, b = 1, c = 2, n \equiv -3 \pmod 8$, and so we need only consider $n \equiv 1 \pmod 8$.

Write equation (3) as

$$na + b = c(4abd - 1) = cq, \tag{4}$$

where

$$q + 1 \equiv 0 \pmod{4ab}.$$

Take $q = 3, a = b = 1$, then $n \equiv -1 \pmod 3$.

Since for $n = 3$, we have $(x, y, z) = (3, 2, 2)$, equation (1) is solvable for $n \equiv 0 \pmod 3$, and so we may suppose that $n \equiv 1 \pmod 3$.

Take $q = 7$, and then $ab|2$, and equation (4) gives

$$n \equiv -1, -2, -4 \pmod 7.$$

Since for $n = 7$, we have $(x, y, z) = (2, 28, 28)$, we may suppose that $n \equiv 1, 2, 4 \pmod 7$.

Take $q = 15$, then $ab|4$, and with $(a, b) = (1, 2), (2, 1)$, we have

$$n + 2 \equiv 0 \pmod{15}, \qquad n + 8 \equiv 0 \pmod{15}.$$

Since $n \equiv 1 \pmod 3$, we have

$$n \equiv -2, -3 \pmod 5.$$

Hence we may suppose that $n \equiv 1, 4 \pmod 5$.

Gathering these results together, the conjecture is proved except possibly when

$$n \equiv 1, 121, 169, 289, 361, 529 \pmod{840}.$$

Since the first prime in this set is 1009, the conjecture holds for $n < 1009$.

Write $l = \frac{1}{4}(n + 3)$. Then with arbitrary m,

$$\frac{4}{n} = \frac{1}{l + m} + \frac{4m + 3}{n(l + m)}.$$

Hence a representation exists if for positive integers m, d, d_1, d_2, d_3,

$$d(4m + 3) = d_1 + d_2,$$

$$l + m = d_1 d_2 d_3,$$

Many results can be found in this way.

The conditions (2) and (3) are sufficient for solvability. We now investigate necessary conditions. Let n be a prime $p > 3$. Then all three of x, y, z cannot be divisible by p. Hence either only one, say x, is divisible by p, or only two, say, y, z, are divisible by p. We replace equation (1) by the two equations

$$\frac{4}{p} = \frac{1}{px} + \frac{1}{y} + \frac{1}{z}, \quad xyz \not\equiv 0 \pmod p, \tag{5}$$

$$\frac{4}{p} = \frac{1}{x} + \frac{1}{py} + \frac{1}{pz}, \quad x \not\equiv 0 \pmod p, \tag{6}$$

We now prove a result due to Rosati[3a] who also verified the conjecture for $n < 171,649$.

Theorem 1

A representation (5) exists if and only if for positive integers a, b, c, d,

$$(x, y, z) = (bcd, acd, abd),$$

where $(a, b) = (b, c) = (c, a) = 1, p \nmid abcd$, and

$$a + bp + cp = 4abcd. \tag{7}$$

A representation (6) exists if and only if for positive integers a, b, c, d,

$$(x, y, z) = (bcd, abd, acd),$$

where $(a, b) = (b, c) = (c, a) = 1, p \nmid bcd$, and

$$pa + b + c = 4abcd. \tag{8}$$

To prove representation (5), write $(y, z) = \delta, y = \delta b, z = \delta c$ and so $(bc\delta, p) = 1$. Then

$$\delta bc + p(b + c)x = 4\delta bcx.$$

Since $(b + c, bc) = 1, x = bcd$, say, and so

$$\delta + pd(b + c) = 4\delta dbc.$$

Then $\delta = da$, say, and $(ad, p) = 1$. Hence

$$a + p(b + c) = 4abcd.$$

To prove representation (6), write $(y, z) = \delta, y = \delta b, z = \delta c$. Then

$$p\delta bc + cx + bx = 4x\delta bc.$$

Here

$$x = bcd, \qquad p \nmid bcd$$

$$p\delta + (b + c)d = 4x\delta bcd.$$

Then $\delta = ad$ and

$$pa + b + c = 4abcd.$$

We note that $a \equiv 0 \pmod p$, i.e. $y \equiv z \equiv 0 \pmod p$ is a possibility.

L. Bernstein[1] has shown that an infinity of congruences can be derived for p from equations (7) and (8). To illustrate his method, it will suffice to deal with (8).

We may suppose $p = 8s + 1$. We shall find values for b and c. From (8),

$$b + c = a(4bcd - p) = a(4t - 1), \quad \text{say.} \tag{9}$$

Then

$$2s + t = bcd, \qquad 2s + t \equiv 0 \pmod{bc}. \tag{10}$$

We require another equation for b, c. We can take for this

$$c - b = a(2gt + 1) - 2f,$$

since $a + b + c$ is even. Then

$$c = at(2 + g) - f, \qquad b = a(2t - tg - 1) + f.$$

Then equation (10) becomes

$$2s + t \equiv 0 \bmod (at(2 + g) - f)(a(2t - tg - 1) + f)). \tag{11}$$

Here we can take $g = 0, \pm 1, \pm 2, \ldots$, a an arbitrary integer, and $(f, a) = 1$, $f = \pm 1, \pm 2, \ldots$.

Yamamoto[3] deals rather differently with equations (7), (8). Write (8) as

$$pa + b = c(4abd - 1) = cq.$$

Then if $(a, p) = 1$, and this is a restriction,

$$p \equiv -\frac{b}{a} \pmod{q}, \qquad q \equiv -1 \pmod{4ab}. \tag{12}$$

Then the Legendre–Jacobi quadratic character

$$(p/q) = -1. \tag{13}$$

Suppose first that a and b are odd. Then

$$\left(\frac{p}{q}\right) = \left(\frac{-ab}{q}\right) = (-1)^{(ab+1)/2}\left(\frac{q}{ab}\right) = (-1)^{(ab+1)/2}(-1)^{(ab-1)/2} = -1.$$

Suppose next that ab is even, say $ab = 2^{\alpha}k$, k odd, $q \equiv -1 \pmod 8$. Then

$$\left(\frac{-ab}{q}\right) = \left(\frac{-2^{\alpha}k}{q}\right) = \left(\frac{-k}{q}\right) = (-1)^{(k+1)/2}\left(\frac{q}{k}\right) = (-1)^{k} = -1.$$

In (7), put $q = 4abd - p$. Then $p \equiv -a/b \pmod{q}$, and $p \equiv -q \pmod{4ab}$. This can be written as

$$p \equiv -s \pmod{4abq}, \qquad s \equiv q \pmod{4ab}, \qquad s \equiv a/b \pmod{q}. \tag{14}$$

If we use the Kronecker quadratic character, we can show similarly that $(s/4abq) = 1$.

In (8), put $b + c = as$. Then

$$p + s = 4bcd, \qquad p \equiv -s \pmod{4bc}. \tag{15}$$

In (7) put $b + c = as$. Then

$$1 + ps = 4bcd, \qquad p \equiv -1/s \pmod{4bc}. \tag{16}$$

In both of these cases, the Kronecker character

$$\left(\frac{-s}{4bc}\right) = -1.$$

2. *The equation yz + zx + xy = d*

The problem here is to find explicit expressions for non-negative integer solutions of the equation

$$yz + zx + xy = d, \tag{17}$$

and what is more important, their number. The problem is connected with the class number for binary quadratic forms. Let

$$[x, y, z] = xX^2 + 2yXY + zY^2 \tag{18}$$

be a binary quadratic form with negative determinant $-d$ and so

$$xz - y^2 = d > 0. \tag{19}$$

The results will be simpler if weights are attached to special forms, thus $[x, 0, x]$ and $[x, x, x]$ are reckoned as $\frac{1}{2}$ and $\frac{1}{3}$ respectively. Call a form $[x, y, z]$ odd or even according as x, z are not both even, or are both even. Denote by $F(d)$ the class number of odd forms, and by $G(d)$ the class number of all forms. Then $G(d) - F(d)$ is the number of even forms.

If the binary quadratic form had been written as

$$[x, y, z]' = xX^2 + yXY + zY^2 \tag{20}$$

of discriminant $-d$, and so

$$4xz - y^2 = d,$$

we write $H(d)$ for the class number. Then $[2x, y, 2z]$ is an even form of determinant $-d$, and so

$$H(d) = G(d) - F(d).$$

While there is no difficulty in finding a few obvious solutions of equation (17) for special forms of d, the association with the class number suggests that it may be difficult to find others.

A famous difficult problem is: when does the quadratic field $Q(\sqrt{-d})$ have class number one, i.e. when is $H(d) = 1$? This requires that d should satisfy various congruences, e.g. $d \equiv 3 \pmod 8$. It is easy to see that d must be 1 or a prime, and the nine values

$$d = 1, 2, 3, 7, 11, 19, 43, 67, 163$$

are known. It was known that there was at most one other value of d. It has recently been shown by H. M. Stark by analytic methods that this does not exist. In fact, a proof had been given by Heegner which seemed to depend upon an unproved assertion. However, it has been shown by Birch, Siegel and Dering that Heegner's method of proof is essentially sound.

When $d \equiv 3 \pmod 8$,

$$G(d) = \tfrac{4}{3}F(d), \qquad H(d) = \tfrac{1}{3}F(d). \tag{21}$$

Then if $H(d) = 1$, $G(d) = 4$, and so there can only be twelve solutions of equation (17). These are typified by six solutions $(1, 0, d)$ each of weight $\tfrac{1}{2}$, three solutions $(1, 1, (d - 1)/2)$ if $d > 1$, and six solutions $(1, 3, (d - 3)/4)$ if $d > 7$. When $x = 1$, and so $(y + 1)(z + 1) = d + 1$, there would be other solutions unless $\tfrac{1}{4}(d + 1)$ is a prime. By Stark's result, there are other solutions when $d > 163$.

Theorem[4] 2

The number of solutions of

$$yz + zx + xy = d, \quad x \geqslant 0, y \geqslant 0, z \geqslant 0, \tag{22}$$

is $3G(d)$ if a weight $\tfrac{1}{2}$ is attached to a solution with $xyz = 0$.

To prove Theorem 2, we establish a 1–1 correspondence[5] between the reduced quadratic forms $[A, B, C]$ of determinant $-d$, and the solutions x, y, z of equation (20) given by

$$A = x + y, \qquad |B| = x, \qquad C = x + z.$$

The reduced forms are given by

$$B = 0, \qquad A < C, \tag{23}$$

$$B = 0, \qquad A = C, \quad \text{weight } \tfrac{1}{2}, \tag{24}$$

$$B > 0, \qquad [A, \pm B, C], \quad B < A < C, \tag{25}$$

$$B > 0, \qquad [A, A, C], \quad C > A, \tag{26}$$

$$B > 0, \qquad [2A, A, 2A], \quad \text{weight } \tfrac{1}{3}. \tag{27}$$

For (23) $x = 0$, $z > y$. By permuting, we have six solutions, each of weight $\tfrac{1}{2}$. For (24) $x = 0$, $z = y$. By permuting, we have three solutions, each of weight $\tfrac{1}{2}$.
For (25) we have six solutions for x, y, z.
For (26) we have $y = 0$, and so six solutions each of weight $\tfrac{1}{2}$.
For (27) we have $x = y = z = A$, one solution.

In each of these cases, the number of solutions is three times the number of the corresponding reduced forms. Hence the theorem follows.

It may be remarked that results such as Theorem 2 had their origin in the researches of Hermite and Liouville who also found the number of solutions for some assigned residues r of $x + y \pmod 4$. We note[4] that N the number of solutions of equation (17) is $3G(d) - 3F(d)$ when $r = 0$, and that $N = F(d)$ when $r = 1, 2, 3$, provided that d is not a perfect square when r is odd.
3. We now come back to the equation

$$z = f(x, y) = f_1(x, y)/f_2(x, y), \tag{28}$$

where $f_1(x, y), f_2(x, y)$ are polynomials with integer coefficients which have no polynomial as a common factor.

When $f_1(x, y)$ and $f_2(x, y)$ are homogeneous polynomials of the same degree, there is no loss of generality in supposing that $(x, y) = 1$. Since the possible common divisors d of $f_1(x, y), f_2(x, y)$ divide their resultant, the finding of the integer solutions of equation (28) reduces to solving $f_2(x, y) = d$ in integers. By Thue's Theorem, Chapter 22, there will be only a finite number of integer solutions except possibly when $f_2(x, y)$ is a power of a linear or quadratic form.

We may suppose now that $f_1(x, y), f_2(x, y)$, are not both homogeneous forms. In general, it is difficult to prove the existence of solutions of equation (28). In some cases, an infinity of solutions can be found, e.g. when $f_2(x, y) = xy$. Then by division if need be, we may suppose without loss of generality that

$$f_1(x, y) = g(x) + h(y) + c = zxy, \tag{29}$$

where $g(x), h(y)$ are polynomials in x, y respectively, without a constant term. We may suppose that $(x, y) = 1$, for if $(x, y) = d$, then $d \mid c$, and so we have a finite number of equations similar to (29) with $(x, y) = 1$.

The equation (29) is equivalent to the congruence

$$g(x) + h(y) + c \equiv 0 \ (\text{mod } xy), \tag{30}$$

or to the pair

$$g(x) + c \equiv 0 \ (\text{mod } y), \qquad h(y) + c \equiv 0 \ (\text{mod } x). \tag{31}$$

The conditions (31) are necessary, but they are also sufficient. For suppose

$$g(x) + c = uy, \qquad h(y) + c = vx. \tag{32}$$

Then a solution of (29) is given by

$$zxy = uy + vx - c, \quad (x, y) = 1,$$

for z is an integer since $(x, y) = 1$ and $uy - c$ is divisible by x etc. The method of solution of equation (29) will be sufficiently illustrated if we consider a congruence arising in the discussion[6] of integer solutions of a ternary cubic equation, namely,

$$ax_1^3 + bx_2^3 + c \equiv 0 \ (\text{mod } x_1 x_2), \tag{33}$$

where $(a, b, c) = 1$. We have supposed $(x_1, x_2) = 1$ and we now also suppose that $(x_1, c) = 1, (x_2, c) = 1$. These conditions involve no loss of generality. Thus if $(x_1, c) = d, x_1 = dX_1, c = dc_1$ and

$$ad^3 X_1^3 + bx_2^3 + dc_1 \equiv 0 \ (\text{mod } dX_1 x_2),$$

or

$$ad^2 X_1^3 + bx_2^3/d + c_1 \equiv 0 \ (\text{mod } X_1 x_2).$$

Since $(X_1, x_2) = 1$, we have $d \nmid x_2$ and so $d \mid b$.

11*

We now replace congruence (33) by the pair of congruences

$$bx_2^3 + c \equiv 0 \ (\text{mod } x_1), \tag{34}$$

$$ax_1^3 + c \equiv 0 \ (\text{mod } x_2). \tag{35}$$

The existence of an infinity of solutions of (34), (35) is proved by means of a recursive algorithm for a sequence $x_1, x_2, x_3, \ldots$, and congruences for $n \geqslant 2$ of the form

$$x_{n+2}^3 + A_{n+1} \equiv 0 \ (\text{mod } x_{n+1}) \tag{36}$$

$$x_{n+1}^3 + A_n \equiv 0 \ (\text{mod } x_{n+2}). \tag{37}$$

We satisfy (34) by putting

$$bx_2^3 + c = x_1 x_3, \tag{38}$$

where x_2 will be presently assigned with $(x_2, c) = 1$, and taking for x_1 any divisor of $bx_2^3 + c$ prime to c, e.g. $x_1 = 1$. Clearly $(x_2, x_3) = 1$.

To satisfy (35), we see from (38),

$$a \left(\frac{bx_2^3 + c}{x_3} \right)^3 + c \equiv 0 \ (\text{mod } x_2), \tag{39}$$

or
$$x_3^3 + ac^2 \equiv 0 \ (\text{mod } x_2), \tag{40}$$

and
$$bx_2^3 + c \equiv 0 \ (\text{mod } x_3). \tag{41}$$

From (40), (41), a particular solution for x_1, x_2, x_3 can be deduced by taking

$$x_2 = x_3^3 + ac^2, \qquad b(x_3^3 + ac^2)^3 + c \equiv 0 \ (\text{mod } x_3),$$

and so
$$ba^3c^5 + 1 \equiv 0 \ (\text{mod } x_3).$$

If we take for x_3 any divisor of $ba^3c^5 + 1$, then $(x_3, ac) = 1$ and so $(x_2, x_3) = 1$. Take

$$x_3 = ba^3c^5 + 1, \qquad x_2 = (ba^3c^5 + 1)^3 + ac^2.$$

Then from (38)

$$x_1 x_3 = bx_2^3 + c = b(x_3^3 + ac^2)^3 + c,$$

and so
$$x_1 = bx_3^8 + 3abc^2 x_3^5 + 3a^2 bc^4 x_3^2 + c.$$

We can deal more generally with (40), (41).

Write
$$x_3^3 + ac^2 = x_2 x_4. \tag{42}$$

Then
$$b \left(\frac{x_3^3 + ac^2}{x_4} \right)^3 + c \equiv 0 \ (\text{mod } x_3).$$

Suppose now that $(x_3, x_4) = 1$ which is so if $(x_4, ac) = 1$.

Then
$$x_4^3 + a^3bc^5 \equiv 0 \;(\mathrm{mod}\; x_3) \tag{43}$$

and
$$x_3^3 + ac^2 \equiv 0 \;(\mathrm{mod}\; x_4). \tag{44}$$

These congruences are similar to (40), (41).

A particular solution is given by
$$x_3 = x_4^3 + a^3bc^5, \qquad a^8b^3c^{13} + 1 \equiv 0 \;(\mathrm{mod}\; x_4),$$

and then $(x_3, x_4) = 1$.

The process can be continued and thus an infinity of solutions arise for x_1, x_2 as polynomials in a, b, c.

It can be shown that
$$A_n = a^{\lambda_n} b^{\mu_n} c^{\nu_n}, \quad n = 1, 2, \ldots,$$

where λ_n, μ_n, ν_n are given by the sequences
$$\lambda = 0, 1, 3, 8, 21, \ldots$$
$$\mu = -1, 0, 1, 3, 8, \ldots$$
$$\nu = 1, 2, 5, 13, 34, \ldots.$$

These are practically sequences of alternate Fibonacci numbers
$$0, 1, 1, 2, 3, 5, 8, 13, 21, \ldots.$$

4. Some interesting results can be found for the equation $z = f_1(x, y)/f_2(x, y)$, when $f_1(x, y)$ and $f_2(x, y)$ are special quadratic polynomials. These are due to Barnes[7], Goldberg et al.[8], Mills[9,10,11]. There may be an infinity of comparatively trivial solutions. Apart from these, there are only a finite number of possible values for z. For such z, we have a quadratic equation $zf_2(x, y) = f_1(x, y)$. The values of x, y are either finite in number or, if not, can be found from a Pell equation or an equivalent recursive algorithm.

We consider the case when
$$\left. \begin{array}{l} z = f_1(x, y)/f_2(x, y), \\[4pt] f_1(x, y) = ax^2 + bxy + cy^2 + dx + ey + f, \\[4pt] f_2(x, y) = pxy + qx + ry + s, \end{array} \right\} \tag{45}$$

where the coefficients are integers, subject to $ac \neq 0$, and to the divisibility conditions
$$a \mid (b, d, p, q), \qquad c \mid (b, e, p, r). \tag{46}$$

When $p = 0$, the equations (45) can be replaced by the equation,
$$f_1(x, y) = cy^2 + ey + f, \qquad f_2(x, y) = qx + s,$$

by a change of variables and division.

This defines the quadratic character of $qx + s \pmod{e^2 - 4fc}$, and the solution presents no difficulty.

Let now $(x, y, z) = (u_0, u_1, v)$ be a solution, and so

$$f_1(x, u_1) = vf_2(x, u_1) \tag{47}$$

is a quadratic in x with roots $x = u_0, u_2$ where u_2 is given by

$$a(u_0 + u_2) = pu_1v + qv - bu_1 - d. \tag{48}$$

From (46), u_2 is an integer. Hence $(x, y, z) = (u_2, u_1, v)$ is also an integral solution of (47). Continuing in this way, we obtain a sequence ... $u_0, u_1, u_2,$ ..., extending infinitely in both directions, and defined by

$$a(u_{2n} + u_{2n+2}) = pu_{2n+1}v + qv - bu_{2n+1} - d, \tag{49}$$

$$c(u_{2n-1} + u_{2n+1}) = pu_{2n}v + rv - bu_{2n} - e. \tag{50}$$

Also $(x, y, z) = (u_{2n}, u_{2n \pm 1}, v)$ are solutions of (45) for all integers n.

Lemma

If $|u_2| \geqslant |u_0|$, then either

$$pu_1 + q = 0, \quad or \quad |u_0| \leqslant |c/a|^{1/2}|u_1| + k,$$

where k is a constant depending only on the coefficients of $f_1(x, y)$, $f_2(x, y)$.

Since u_0, u_2 are the roots of the equation (47) in x, we have not only (48) but also

$$au_0u_2 = cu_1^2 + eu_1 + f - v(ru_1 + s).$$

Eliminating v from these equations, we find

$$au_2f_2(u_0, u_1) + au_0(ru_1 + s) = cpu_1^3 + Q(u_1),$$

where $Q(u_1)$ is a quadratic polynomial with coefficients depending upon those in $f_1(x, y)$, $f_2(x, y)$. Since $|u_2| \geqslant |u_0|$,

$$|cpu_1^3 + Q(u_1)| \geqslant |au_2f_2(u_0, u_1)| - |au_0(ru_1 + s)|$$
$$\geqslant |au_0^2(pu_1 + q)| - 2|au_0(ru_1 + s)|.$$

If $pu_1 + q \neq 0$, we deduce from this quadratic inequality in u_0 that

$$|pu_1 + q||u_0| \leqslant |ru_1 + s| + \{|ru_1 + s|^2 + |a^{-1}(pu + q)(cpu_1^3 + Q(u_1))|\}^{1/2}.$$

Hence $$|u_0| \leqslant k + |c/a|^{1/2}|u_1|,$$

where k is a constant depending only on the coefficients of $f_1(x, y)$ and $f_2(x, y)$.

We now arrange the sequences $u_0, u_1, u_2, \ldots$ in four classes:

I. Those where either $f_2(u_{2n}, u_{2n+1}) = 0$ or $f_2(u_{2n}, u_{2n-1}) = 0$ for some integer n. Such sequences exist if and only if the equations $f_1(x, y) = 0$,

$f_2(x, y) = 0$ have an integral solution. Then solutions of (45) exist for every z, and there are at most four sequences for any z.

II. For these

$$pu_{2n+1} + q = 0, \qquad ru_{2n+1} + s \neq 0$$

for some integer n. This implies

$$p \mid q, \qquad ps \neq qr, \qquad f_1(u_{2n}, -q/p) = v(ps - qr)/p,$$

and so the congruence

$$pf_1(x_1, - q/p) \equiv 0 \bmod (ps - qr)$$

has integral solutions. Then sequences exist for every integer z which can be represented by $pf_1(x, -q/p)/(ps - qr)$ with integer x.

III. Similar results hold when

$$pu_{2n} + r = 0, \qquad qu_{2n} + s \neq 0.$$

IV. These are sequences not of the comparatively trivial classes I, II, III. We now prove

Theorem 3

There exist sequences of type IV *for only a finite number of values of* v.

On interchanging x and y if need be, we may suppose without loss of generality that u_1 is an element of the sequence with least absolute value, and also that $|u_0| \leqslant |u_2|$. Since the sequence (u_n) is not of types I or II, $pu_1 + q \neq 0$, and so from the lemma,

$$|u_1| \leqslant |u_0| \leqslant |c/a|^{1/2}|u_1| + k.$$

Two cases arise. First,

$$|pu_0u_1| \leqslant 2|qu_0 + ru_1 + s|,$$

and so $\qquad |pu_0u_1| \leqslant 2(|q||c/a|^{1/2} + |r|)|u_1| + 2|q|k + 2|s|.$

If $u_1 \neq 0$, then from this, $|u_0| \leqslant k_1$ for some constant k_1, and if $u_1 = 0$, $|u_0| \leqslant k$. Hence u_0, u_1 are both bounded, and so there are only a finite number of possibilities for v.

Secondly, $\qquad |pu_0u_1| > 2|qu_0 + ru_1 + s|.$

Now $\qquad |f_2(u_0, u_1)| > \tfrac{1}{2}|pu_0u_1|, \quad u_0u_1 \neq 0,$

and so

$$|pv| = \frac{|pf_1(u_0, u_1)|}{|f_2(u_0, u_1)|} < \frac{2|au_0|}{|u_1|} + 2|b| + 2|c| + 2|d| + 2|e| + 2|f|.$$

Then v is bounded since $|u_0/u_1| \leqslant |c/a|^{1/2} + k$.

We now discuss the solutions of equations (45) for given $z = v$. Put

$$b' = b - pv, \qquad d' = d - qv, \qquad e' = e - rv, \qquad f' = f - sv.$$

Then equation (47) becomes

$$ax^2 + b'xy + cy^2 + d'x + e'y + f' = 0,$$

and the divisibility conditions (46) give,

$$a \mid (b', d'), \qquad c \mid (b', e'). \tag{51}$$

Also equations (49) and (50) become

$$a(u_{2n} + u_{2n+2}) = -b'u_{2n-1} - d', \tag{52}$$

$$c(u_{2n-1} + u_{2n+1}) = -b'u_{2n} - e'. \tag{53}$$

On eliminating u_1 from

$$a(u_0 + u_2) = -b'u_1 - d',$$

$$au_0u_2 = cu_1^2 + e'u_1 + f',$$

then $G(u_0, u_2) = 0$ where,

$$G(X, Y) = X^2 + BXY + Y^2 + DX + DY + F,$$

$$B = 2 - b'^2/ac, \qquad D = (2cd' - b'e')/ac,$$

$$F = (cd'^2 + b'^2f' - b'd'e')/a^2c.$$

From conditions (51), B and D are integers and so F is also an integer. Eliminating $u_{2n \pm 1}$ from (52), (53), we obtain

$$ac(u_{2n} + 2u_{2n+2} + u_{2n+4}) = -b'c(u_{2n+1} + u_{2n+3}) - 2cd'$$

$$= b'^2u_{2n+2} + b'e' - 2cd'.$$

Hence
$$u_{2n} + u_{2n+4} = -Bu_{2n+2} - D. \tag{54}$$

It follows that $x = u_0, u_4$ are the roots of $G(x, u_2) = 0$, and so

$$u_0u_4 = u_2^2 + Du_2 + F. \tag{55}$$

We may suppose now without loss of generality that $|u_2| \leqslant |u_{2n}|$ for all n, and in particular that $|u_0| \geqslant |u_2|, |u_4| \geqslant |u_2|$. Then from equation (55),

$$u_0 = \varepsilon u_2 + \delta, \qquad u_4 = \varepsilon'u_2 + \delta',$$

where
$$\varepsilon = \pm 1, \quad \varepsilon' = \pm 1, \varepsilon u_2\delta \geqslant 0, \varepsilon'u_2\delta' \geqslant 0. \tag{56}$$

Substituting in (54) with $n = 0$ and in (55), we obtain

$$- Bu_2 - D = (\varepsilon + \varepsilon')u_2 + \delta + \delta', \tag{57}$$

$$u_2^2 + Du_2 + F = \varepsilon\varepsilon'u_2^2 + \varepsilon\delta'u_2 + \varepsilon\delta'u_2 + \delta\delta'. \tag{58}$$

From (56), all the non-zero terms on the right-hand side of (58) have the same sign. Then for $\varepsilon\varepsilon' = \pm 1$,

$$|Du_2 + F| \geqslant |\delta'u_2| + |\delta u_2|. \tag{59}$$

If $u_2 \neq 0$, then from (59),

$$|\delta| + |\delta'| \leqslant |D| + |F|,$$

and so there are only a finite number of possibilities for $\varepsilon, \varepsilon', \delta, \delta'$.

For fixed $\varepsilon, \varepsilon', \delta, \delta'$, there are at most two values for u_2 from (57), (58), unless

$$\varepsilon + \varepsilon' = -B, \qquad \delta + \delta' = -D,$$

$$\varepsilon\varepsilon' = 1, \qquad \varepsilon\delta' + \varepsilon'\delta = D, \qquad \delta\delta' = F. \tag{60}$$

Suppose that (60) is not satisfied. Then each value of u_2 leads to at most one v sequence. Hence there are only a finite number of v sequences. This also holds for $u_2 = 0$. The sequences can be found from the above.

When (60) is satisfied, then $\varepsilon = \varepsilon' = \pm 1$. It can now be shown that there are only a finite number of v sequences for fixed v except in some special cases when the sequences are of order 1, 2, or 4, with one exception.

It can be shown from (54), that the v sequence is cyclic if $B = 0, \pm 1, 2$, and then it has period 1, 2, 3, 4, 6, 8, 12.

We now give few particular results.

The equation

$$x^2 + y^2 + 1 = xyz.$$

We suppose the u_n in the sequence $u_0, u_1, u_2, \ldots$ to be positive, u_1 minimal and $u_2 \geqslant u_0$. Now $(u_0u_2, u_1) = 1$. We cannot have $u_1 > 1$, for then

$$u_0u_2 \geqslant (u_1 + 1)^2 > u_1^2 + 1 = u_0u_2.$$

Hence $u_1 = 1, u_0u_2 = 2, u_0 = 1, u_2 = 2$. The u sequence becomes 5, 2, 1, 1, 2, 5, 13, ... with $z = 3$. Hence x, y are consecutive terms in the sequence of alternate terms of the Fibonacci sequence 1, 1, 2, 3, 5, 8, 13, 21....

The equation

$$x^2 + y^2 + x + y + 1 = xyz, x > 0, y > 0,$$

Here $\qquad x \mid y^2 + y + 1, \qquad y \mid x^2 + x + 1,$

and x, y are consecutive terms of the sequence $1, 1, 3, 13, \ldots$ where $u_n = 5u_{n-1} - u_{n-2} - 1$.

The equation

$$x^2 + y^2 - x - y + 1 = xyz, x > 0, y > 0,$$

Now $x \mid y^2 - y + 1,$ $y \mid x^2 - x + 1,$ and $x = y = 1.$

We conclude by noting that when the divisibility conditions (46) are not satisfied, the problem becomes a very difficult one. Thus for $z(1 + xy) = x^2 + 2y^2$, the only procedure seems to be to try if there is a solution for various values of z, e.g.,[7] when $z = 43$, $x = 30905$, $y = 663738$.

5. *The equation* $x^m - y^n = 1$
This equation seems to have been first noticed by Catalan who proposed in 1842 the

Conjecture
   The only solution in integers $m > 1, n > 1, x > 1, y > 1$ *of the equation*

$$x^m - y^n = 1 \tag{61}$$

is $m = 3,$ $n = 2,$ $x = 2,$ $y = 3.$ \hfill (62)

This still remains unproved. An alternative form of the conjecture is
If p and q are prime numbers and $x > 1, y > 1$, a similar result holds for

$$x^p - y^q = 1. \tag{63}$$

Very few really general results are known, and even when they are simple, their proofs are usually rather complicated and often out of place here. Some of the results give estimates for possible values of m, n, p, q.
   Perhaps the most general result is Cassels'[12]

Theorem 4
   If in equation (63), $p > q > 2$ *or* $q > p > 2$, *then* $q \mid x, p \mid y$.
   Another proof has been given by Hyyrö[13]. The result when $p = 2$ is due to Nagell[14].
   Most of the other results deal with the cases when some of the variables p, q, x, y are given. Thus Le Veque[15] established a result proved later by Cassels[16] as the

Theorem 5
   Suppose that (x, y) *are given in* (61), *and* (62) *is excluded. Let* μ, ν *be the least positive solution of*

$$x^\mu \equiv 1 \ (\text{mod } Y), \qquad y^\nu \equiv 1 \ (\text{mod } X),$$

where X, Y are the products of the odd primes dividing x, y respectively. Then
$m = \mu, n = \nu$, *except that* $m = 2, n = 1$ *may occur if* $\mu = \nu = 1$ *and* $x + 1$ *is a power of* 2.

When m, n are given in equation (61), the equation has only a finite number of solutions but these are not easily found. This is a particular case of Siegel's Theorem in Chapter 25. The result also follows from Mahler's[16a] result.

Theorem 6

The greatest prime factor of $ax^m + by^n$, $ab \neq 0$, $(x, y) = 1$, $m \geqslant 2$, $n \geqslant 3$ *tends to infinity as* $\max(|x|), (|y|)$ *tends to infinity.*

Proofs for equation (61) when m, n are primes satisfying various conditions have been given by LeVeque by using the methods for dealing with Fermat's last theorem.

Suppose next in equation (63) that p and q are given odd primes. Then Hyyrö[17] has shown that all the solutions can be given explicitly in terms of the convergents to the simple continued fraction for $q^{1-1/p}p^{1-1/q}$.

There are many results for special values of m, n and some are now given.

The equation $y^2 + 1 = x^p$, *p an odd prime.*

This was proved impossible for $x > 1$ in 1850 by Lebesgue[18]. A slightly dissimilar proof was given by Cassels[16]. Clearly $y \equiv 0 \pmod 2$, $x \equiv 1 \pmod 2$. Then from

$$(1 + iy)(1 - iy) = x^p,$$

$$1 + iy = i^r(u + iv)^p \quad r = 0, 1, 2, 3.$$

$$x = u^2 + v^2.$$

The factor i^r can be absorbed in the pth power, and so we need only consider $r = 0$. Then

$$1 = u^p - \frac{p.p - 1}{2!} u^{p-2}v^2 + \cdots \pm puv^{p-1}.$$

Hence $u = \pm 1$, and from a congruence mod 4, since v is even, $u \equiv 1 \pmod 4$ and so $u = 1$. Then

$$\frac{p.p - 1}{2!} - \frac{p.p - 1.p - 2.p - 3}{4!} v^2 + \cdots \pm pv^{p-3} = 0. \tag{64}$$

Then, since v is even, the general term can be written for $k \geqslant 1$ as

$$(-1)^{k-1} \frac{p.p - 1. p - 2.p - 3.....p - 2k + 1.}{(2k - 2)!} \frac{1.2v^{2k-2}}{2k - 1.2k}. \tag{65}$$

To prove that equation (64) is impossible (which is obvious if $(p.p - 1)/2$ is odd since v is even), we need only show that for $k > 1$ the term (65) is divisible by a higher power of 2 than for $k = 1$. The first two parts of (65) are integers. Also 2 cannot occur in the reduced denominator of the third part since, for $k > 1$,

$$2^{2k-2} > 1 + 2k - 2 > k.$$

The equation $y^2 - 1 = x^p$

The special case $p = 3$ of the equation

$$y^2 - 1 = x^p \tag{66}$$

was considered by Euler. The only solutions are $x = 0, -1, 2$.

We may suppose now that p is a prime > 3. The first general results are due to Nagell[14,19]. He proved very simply that p must be $\equiv 1 \pmod 8$ and $y \equiv 0 \pmod p$. He showed that equation (66) leads to

$$y \pm 1 = 2x_1^p, \qquad y \mp 1 = 2^{p-1}x_2^p,$$

and so
$$x_1^p - 2^{p-2}x_2^p = \pm 1. \tag{67}$$

Since $y \equiv 0 \pmod p$, it is easy to see that $(x + 1, x^p + 1) = p$, and $(x^p + 1)/(x + 1) \equiv 0 \pmod p$ but $\not\equiv 0 \pmod{p^2}$.

When $p \equiv 1 \pmod 8$, Nagell[14] showed by cyclotomic considerations applied to equation (68) that a necessary condition for solvability is that $u + v \equiv 1 \pmod 8$, where $u + v\sqrt{p}$ is the fundamental unit > 1 in the field generated by $\sqrt{p}$. This condition is equivalent to his other one that 2 is a biquadratic residue of p. Since Nagell proved the impossibility of equation (66) when $p \equiv 3, 5, 7 \pmod 8$, he thus showed that equation (66) is impossible for a set of primes of density $\frac{1}{4} + \frac{1}{4} + \frac{1}{4} + \frac{1}{8} = \frac{7}{8}$.

It may be noted that from (67), estimates (rather large ones) had been found for the magnitude of possible p, x_1, x_2 by Obláth[20], Hyyrö[17] and Inkeri[23].

Some thirty years after Nagell's results, Chao Ko[24] proved the impossibility of equation (66). We give his proof which for $p \equiv 3, 5, 7 \pmod 8$ is similar to Nagell's but not so simple.

It easily follows from (66) that

$$x + 1 = py_1^2, \qquad \frac{x^p + 1}{x + 1} = py_2^2, \tag{68}$$

where
$$y = py_1y_2 \text{ is odd.}$$

Suppose first that $p \equiv 5, 7 \pmod 8$, and so $p = 8n + a, a = 5, 7$. Then from (67), $x \equiv a - 1 \pmod 8$. Write (66) as

$$y^2 = (x^2 - 1 + 1)^{4n}x^a + 1$$

$$\equiv x^a + 1 \pmod{x^2 - 1}.$$

Hence the quadratic character

$$\left(\frac{x^a + 1}{x - 1}\right) = \left(\frac{2}{x - 1}\right) = 1.$$

This is impossible since $x - 1 \equiv 3, 5 \pmod 8$.
Suppose next that

$$p = 8n + 3 = 24m + a, \quad a = 11, 19.$$

Now
$$y^2 = (x^3 - 1 + 1)^{8m} x^a + 1,$$

$$\equiv x^a + 1 \pmod{x^3 - 1}.$$

Hence
$$\left(\frac{x^a + 1}{x^3 - 1}\right) = 1.$$

Suppose first that $a = 11$ and so $x \equiv 2 \pmod 8$. Since $x^{11} - x^2 = x^2(x^9 - 1)$,

$$1 = \left(\frac{x^2 + 1}{x^3 - 1}\right) = \left(\frac{x^3 - 1}{x^2 + 1}\right) = \left(\frac{-x - 1}{x^2 + 1}\right) = \left(\frac{x^2 + 1}{x + 1}\right) = \left(\frac{2}{x + 1}\right) = -1.$$

Take $a = 19$, $x \equiv 2 \pmod 8$, and then

$$1 = \left(\frac{x^{19} + 1}{x^3 - 1}\right) = \left(\frac{x + 1}{x^3 - 1}\right) = -\left(\frac{x^3 - 1}{x + 1}\right) = \left(\frac{2}{x + 1}\right) = -1.$$

There remains $p \equiv 1 \pmod 8$, and now from (68), $x \equiv 0 \pmod 8$.
From (68),

$$py_2^2 = x^{p-1} - x^{p-2} + \cdots - x + 1. \tag{69}$$

Let $q < p$ be a positive odd integer. Write $p = kq + a$, $0 < a < q$, and so
$(a, q) = 1$.

Put
$$E(t) = \frac{(-x)^t - 1}{(-x) - 1},$$

and so $E(t) \equiv 1 \pmod 8$. By (68),

$$py_2^2 = \frac{x^p + 1}{x + 1} = \frac{x^{kq + a} + 1}{x + 1}.$$

Since $x^a + 1 = (x + 1) E(q)$, this becomes

$$py_2^2 = \frac{((x + 1) E(q) - 1)^k x^a + 1}{x + 1}$$

$$\equiv \frac{(-1)^k x^a + 1}{x + 1} \equiv E(a) \pmod{E(q)}, \tag{70}$$

since $k \equiv a + 1 \pmod 2$. Now

$$(E(a), E(q)) = \frac{(-x)^{(a,q)} - 1}{-x - 1} = 1.$$

We show that the quadratic character $(E(a)/E(q)) = 1$. We apply the Euclidean algorithm

$$q = k_1 a + r_1, \quad 0 < r_1 < a$$

$$a = k_2 r_1 + r_2, \quad 0 < r_2 < r_1$$

$$r_1 = k_3 r_2 + r_3, \quad 0 < r_3 < r_2$$

$$\cdot \; \cdot \; \cdot \; \cdot \; \cdot \; \cdot \; \cdot \; \cdot$$

$$r_{s-1} = k_{s+1} r_{s-1} + r_{s+1}, \quad 0 < r_s < r_{s-1}$$

$$r_s = k_{s+2} r_{s+1}.$$

Then since $\qquad E(k_1 a + r_1) - E(r_1) \equiv 0 \pmod{E(a)},$

$$\left(\frac{E(a)}{E(q)}\right) = \left(\frac{E(q)}{E(a)}\right) = \left(\frac{E(k_1 a + r_1)}{E(a)}\right) = \left(\frac{E(r_1)}{E(a)}\right)$$

$$= \left(\frac{E(r_{s-1})}{E(r_s)}\right) = \left(\frac{1}{E(r_s)}\right) = 1.$$

From (70),

$$\left(\frac{pE(a)}{E(q)}\right) = 1, \qquad \left(\frac{p}{E(q)}\right) = 1.$$

Since $x \equiv -1 \pmod p$ from (67),

$$\left(\frac{p}{E(q)}\right) = \left(\frac{E(q)}{p}\right) = \left(\frac{q}{p}\right).$$

We have a contradiction if q is taken as an odd quadratic non-residue of p. This proves the result.

We conclude this section by mentioning the impossibility of the equations

$$y^3 = x^p + 1, \quad |x| > 1, \quad \text{Nagell}[24]$$

$$y^3 = x^p - 1, \quad |x| > 2, \quad \text{Nagell}[24]$$

$$y^4 = x^p + 1, \qquad\qquad \text{Selberg}[25].$$

The last result is now a special case of Chao Ko's theorem.

REFERENCES

1. Leon Bernstein. Zur Lösung der diophantischen Gleichung $m/n = 1/x + 1/y + 1/z$ insbesondere im Fall $m = 4$. *J. reine angew. Math.*, **211** (1962), 1–10.
2. R. Obláth. Sur l'équation diophantienne $4/n = 1/x_1 + 1/x_2 + 1/x_3$. *Mathesis.* **59** (1949), 308–316.

3. K. Yamamoto. On the diophantine equation $4/n = 1/x + 1/y + 1/z$. *Mem. Fac. Sci. Kyushu University.* Ser. A, **19** (1965), 37–47.

3a. L. A. Rosati. Sull'equazione diofantea $4/n = 1/x_1 + 1/x_2 + 1/x_3$. *Boll. Union Mat. Ital.*, (3) **9** (1954), 59–63.

4. L. J. Mordell. On the number of solutions in positive integers of the equation $yz + zx + xy = n$. *Am. J. Math.*, **45** (1923), 1–4.

5. R. F. Whitehead. On the number of solutions in positive integers of the equation $yz + zx + xy = n$. *Proc. Lond. Math. Soc.*, (2), **21** (1923), xx.

6. L. J. Mordell. The congruence $ax^3 + by^3 + c \equiv 0 \pmod{xy}$, and integer solutions of cubic equations in three variables. *Acta Math.*, **88** (1952), 77–83.

7. E. S. Barnes. On the diophantine equation $x^2 + y^2 + c = xyz$. *J. Lond. Math. Soc.*, **28** (1953), 242–244.

8. K. Goldberg, M. Newman, E. G. Straus, and J. D. Swift. The representations of integers by binary quadratic rational forms. *Archiv Math.*, **5** (1954), 12–18.

9. W. H. Mills. A system of quadratic diophantine equations. *Pacific J. Math.*, **3** (1953), 209–220.

10. W. H. Mills. A method for solving certain diophantine equations. *Proc. Am. Math. Soc.*, **5** (1954), 473–475.

11. W. H. Mills. Certain diophantine equations linear in one unknown. *Can. J. Math.*, **8** (1956), 5–12.

12. J. W. S. Cassels. On the equation $a^x - b^y = 1$, II. *Proc. Camb. Phil. Soc.*, **56** (1960), 97–103. This contains a history of the conjecture and many references.

13. S. Hyyrö. Über die Gleichung $ax^m - by^n = z$ und das Catalansche Problem. *Ann. Acad. Sci. Fennicae*, Series A. 1, 355 (1964), 39–48.

14. T. Nagell. Sur l'impossibilité de l'équation indéterminée $z^p + 1 = y^2$. *Norsk Mat. Forenings Skrifter.*, **1** (1921), Nr. 4.

15. W. J. Le Veque. On the equation $a^x - b^y = 1$. *Am. J. Math.*, **74** (1952), 325–331.

16. J. W. S. Cassels. On the equation $a^x - b^y = 1$. *Am. J. Math.*, **75** (1953), 159–162.

16a. K. Mahler. On the greatest prime factor of $ax^m + by^n$. *Nieuw Arch. Wisk.*, (3) **1** (1953), 113–122.

17. S. Hyyrö. Über das Catalansche Problem. *Ann. Univer. Turku*, Series A, **79** (1964), 3–9.

18. V. A. Lebesgue. Sur l'impossibilité, en nombres entiers, de l'équation $x^m = y^2 + 1$. *Nouv. Ann., Math.*, (1) **9** (1850), 178–181.

19. T. Nagell. Sur une équation à deux indéterminées. *Norsk Vid. Selsk Forh.*, **7** (1934), 136–139.

20. R. Obláth. Sobre ecuaciones diofánticas imposibles de la forma $x^m + 1 = y^n$. *Riv. Mat. Hispano-Am.*, **14** (1), (1941), 122–140. This contains many references.

21. C. L. Siegel. Die Gleichung $ax^n - by^n = c$. *Math. Ann.*, **114** (1937), 57–68.

22. R. Obláth. Über die Zahl $x^2 - 1$. *Mathematica Zutphen*. **B8** (1939), 161–172.

23. K. Inkeri and S. Hyyrö. On the congruence $3^{p-1} \equiv 1 \pmod{p^2}$ and the diophantine equation $x^2 - 1 = y^p$. *Ann. Univer. Turku*, Series A, **50** (1961), 3–4.

24. Chao Ko. On the diophantine equation $x^2 = y^n + 1$, $xy \neq 0$. *Scientia Sinica* (Notes), **14** (1964), 457–460.

25. T. Nagell. Des équations indéterminées $x^2 + x + 1 = y^n$ et $x^2 + x + 1 = 3y^n$. *Norsk. Mat. Forenings Skr.* Series I, **2** (1921), 12–14.

26. S. Selberg. Sur l'impossibilité de l'équation indéterminée $z^p + 1 = y^2$. *Norsk. Mat. Tidskrift*, **14** (1932), 79–80.

Bibliography

References to books on Diophantine equations and to books on number theory containing important sections on Diophantine equations.

1. P. Bachmann. "Niedere Zahlentheorie", II. B. G. Teubner (1910).
2. P. Bachmann. "Das Fermatproblem in seiner bisherigen Entwicklung". Walter de Gruyter & Co., Berlin und Leipzig (1919).
3. S. I. Borevich and I. R. Shafarevich. "Number Theory". Academic Press, New York and London (1966).
4. R. D. Carmichael. "Diophantine Analysis". Mathematical Monographs No. 13, Wiley, New York (1913). Reprint by Dover Corporation.
   R. D. Carmichael. "Analyse Indéterminée". Les Presses Universitaires, Paris (1929).
5. B. N. Delone and D. K. Faddeev. "The Theory of Irrationalities of the Third Degree", Vol. 10. Translations of Mathematical Monographs, American Math. Soc., Providence, Rhode Island (1964).
6. L. E. Dickson. "History of the Theory of Numbers", Vol. 2, Diophantine Analysis. Carnegie Institution of Washington (1920). Reprint Chelsea.
7. L. E. Dickson. "Introduction to the Theory of Numbers". Univ. Chicago Press, Chicago (1929).
8. L. E. Dickson. "Modern Elementary Theory of Numbers". Univ. Chicago Press, Chicago (1939).
9. A. O. Gelfond. "The Solution of Equations in Integers". Freeman & Co., San Francisco and London (1961).
10. G. H. Hardy and E. M. Wright. "The Theory of Numbers". Clarendon Press, Oxford (1945).
10a. M. Kräitchik, Théorie des nombres III, Analyse diophantienne et applications aux cuboides rationnels, Gauthier Villars et Cie, Paris (1947).
11. E. Landau. "Vorlesungen über Zahlentheorie (I) und (III)". S. Hirzel, Leipzig (1927).
12. E. Landau. "Diophantische Gleichungen mit endlich vielen Lösungen"—neu herausgegeben von Arnold Walfisz. VEB. Deutscher Verlag der Wissenschaften Berlin (1959).
13. S. Lang. "Diophantine Geometry". Interscience, New York (1962).
14. W. J. LeVeque. "Topics in Number Theory", (II). Addison-Wesley Publishing Co. Inc., Reading, Massachusetts (1956).
15. L. J. Mordell. "Three Lectures on Fermat's Last Theorem". Cambridge University Press, Cambridge (1921).
    L. J. Mordell. "Le Dernier Théorème de Fermat". Les Presses Universitaires de France, Paris (1929).
16. L. J. Mordell. "A Chapter in the Theory of Numbers". Cambridge University Press, Cambridge (1947).
17. T. Nagell. "L'analyse indéterminée de degré supérieur". Gauthier Villars et Cie, Paris (1929).
18. T. Nagell. "Introduction to Number Theory". Almqvist and Wiksell, Stockholm; John Wiley and Sons Inc., New York (1959).
19. W. Sierpinski. "Elementary Theory of Numbers". Panstwowe Wydawnictwo Naukowe. Warsaw (1964).
20. T. Skolem. "Diophantische Gleichungen". Springer, Berlin (1938).
21. J. V. Uspensky and M. A. Heaslet. "Elementary Number Theory". McGraw Hill Book Co. Inc., New York (1939).

List of Equations and Congruences

Degree 3

Homogeneous

Inhomogeneous

$y^2 = x^3 + k$ —continued

$k = n^3 - lm^2$		238–241
$k = 2a^3 - 3b^3$		244–245
$k = 4a^3 - 3b^3$		245
$k = 3a^3 - 3b^3$		245–246
$k = -432$	247	
-144	251	
-105	251	
-78	251	
-69	251	
-48	247	
-42	251	
-33	251	
-31	244	
-24	246	
-15	247	
-7	247	
-4	123	
-2	124	
1	247	
7	242	
17	246	
34	242	
45	239	
58	242	
70	242	

$x_1^3 = a + bx_2$	3–4, 9
$ax^3 + by^3 + cz^3 + dxyz = e$	110
$ax^3 + ay^3 + bz^3 = bc^3$	102
$x^3 + y^3 + z^3 - axyz = b$	106–110
$ax^3 + by^3 + cz^3 + d = 0$	101–103
$ax^2 + by^2 + cz^2 = 2dxyz$	6
$a(x^3 + y^3) + b(z^3 + c^3) = 0$	59
$x^3 + y^3 + z^3 = n$	83, 100–101
$n = 1$	84
$(x + y + z)^3 - dxyz = m$	83
$z^2 = f(x, y), f$ cubic	85–87, 103–106
$z^2 = p^2 + lx + my + ax^2 + bxy + cy^2 + Ax^3 + Bx^2y + Cxy^2 + Dy^3$	104
$z^2 = p^2 + lx + my + ax^3 + bx^2y + cxy^2 + dy^3$	103
$z^2 = ax^3 + bx^2y + cxy^2 + dy^3$	112
$z^2 = ax^3 + by^3 + c$	104–106, 115–116
$z^2 = X^3 - GXY^2 - G_3Y^3$	233
$z^2 = x^3 + y^3$	235

$2z^2 = x^3 + y^3$ 235

$y^2 - ax^2 = z^3 + bz + c$ 113

$z^3 = p^3 + lx + my + ax^2 + bxy + cy^2$ 103

$z^3 = ax^2 + by^2 + c$ 106, 113–114

$z^3 = x^2 + ky^2$ 215–217

$x^3 + y^3 + z^3 + w^3 = n$ 58, 182

$x_1^3 + x_2^3 + x_3^3 = 9x_4 \pm 4$ 7

$x_1^3 + x_2^3 + \cdots + x_s^3 = n$ 181

$x^2 + y^2 + 1 = xyz$ 299

$x^2 + y^2 \pm x \pm y + 1 = xyz$ 299–300

Degree 4

Homogeneous

$k_1(ax^2 + by^2 + cz^2)(a_1x^2 + b_1y^2 + c_1z^2) =$
     $k_2(px^2 + qy^2 + rz^2)^2$ 25

$\left(\dfrac{br - cq}{a}\right)^3 x^4 + \left(\dfrac{cp - ar}{b}\right)^3 y^4 + \left(\dfrac{aq - bp}{c}\right)^3 z^4 = 0$ 27

$(a_1x_1^2 + a_2x_2^2 + a_3x_3^2 + a_4x_4^2)(b_1x_1^2 + b_2x_2^2 + b_3x_3^2 + b_4x_4^2)$
     $= 2k(c_1x_1^2 + c_2x_2^2 + c_3x_3^2 + c_4x_4^2)(d_1x_1^2 + d_2x_2^2 + d_3x_3^2 + d_4x_4^2)$ 6

$a_1x_1^4 + a_2x_2^4 + a_3x_3^4 + a_4x_4^4 = 0$ 5, 90–94

$a(x^4 - y^4) + c(z^4 - w^4) = 0$ 91

$x^4 + y^4 = z^4 + w^4$ 90

$x^4 + y^4 + z^4 = w^4$ 94

$xy(mx^2 + ny^2) = zw(mz^2 + nw^2)$ 91

$f(x) + f(y) + f(z) - 4(f(u) + f(v) + f(w)) = 0$ where
     $f(x) = x_1^4 + x_2^4 + x_3^4 - x_2^2x_3^2 - x_3^2x_1^2 - x_1^2x_2^2 - x_1x_2x_3(x_1 + x_2 + x_3)$ 10

Inhomogeneous

$Ax^4 + Bx^3y + Cx^2y^2 + Dxy^3 + Ey^4 = 1$ 236–237

$ax^4 - by^4 = c$ 274

$x^4 - Dy^4 = \pm 1$ 275–276

$x^4 + y^4 = 1$ 116–117

$x^4 - 2y^4 = 1$ 207

$x^4 - 8y^4 = 1$ 208

$ky^2 = ax^4 + bx^3 + cx^2 + dx + e$ 268–272

$y^2 = ax^4 + bx^3 + cx^2 + dx + e$ 69–70, 74, 77, 268

$dy^2 = ax^4 + bx^2 + c$ 63–64, 236, 268–272

$py^2 = 2x^4 + 1$ 74

$py^2 = 4x^4 - 1$ 74

$py^2 = 8 - x^4$ 74

$y^2 = Dx^4 \pm 1$ 269–271

$Y^2 = X^4 + 1$ 17

$y^2(ax^2 + bx + c) + y(a_1x^2 + b_1x + c_1) + a_2x^2 + b_2x + c_2 = 0$ 70

$$\left(\frac{x(x-1)}{2}\right)^2 = \frac{y(y-1)}{2} \quad 268$$

$ax^4 + bx^3y + cx^2y^2 + dxy^3 + cy^4 = z^2 \quad 138$

$ax^4 + bx^2y^2 + dy^4 = cz^2 \quad 16\text{--}25$

$b = 0 \quad 23\text{--}25$

$c = 1 \quad 22$

$(ax^2 + by^2)^2 - 2k(cx^2 + dy^2)^2 = z^2 \quad 5$

$x^4 - py^4 = 2z^2 \quad 25$

$x^4 - 2y^4 = \pm z^2 \quad 72\text{--}74$

$x^4 - y^4 = z^2 \quad 17$

$x^4 + y^4 = 2z^2 \quad 18$

$x^4 + kx^2y^2 + y^4 = z^2 \quad 19$

$k = 0 \quad 16$

$\quad = \pm 6 \quad 18$

$\quad = 1 \quad 19$

$\quad = -1 \quad 20$

$\quad = 14 \quad 21$

$$\sum_{r,s=0}^{2} a_{rs}x^r y^s = dz^2 \quad 97$$

$z^2 = k^2 + x^2(ax^2 + by^2) \quad 97$

$ax^4 + by^4 + c = z^2 \quad 95$

$z^2 = U_1^2 + U_2 U_3$, where $U_r = a_r x^2 + h_r xy + b_r y^2 + f_r x + g_r y \quad 96$

$x^4 + y^4 + 4z^4 = 1 \quad 94$

$x^4 + y^4 + z^4 = 2 \quad 95$

$x^4 + ay^4 + bz^4 = z^2 \quad 95$

$(x^2 + a)(y^2 + a) = (az^2 + b^2)^2 \quad 95$

Degree > 4

Homogeneous

$\quad x^l + y^l = z^l \quad 137, 280\text{--}286$

Inhomogeneous

$\quad f(x) = m, f$ homogeneous of degree d in n variables $\quad 174\text{--}180$

$\quad a_0 x^n + a_1 x^{n-1}y + \cdots + a_n y^n = m \quad 157\text{--}163, 186\text{--}199, 218$

$\quad ax^n - by^n = c \quad 273\text{--}275$

$\quad c = \pm 1 \quad 274\text{--}275$

$\quad x^n - Dy^n = \pm 1 \quad 274\text{--}276$

$\quad n = 5 \quad 275$

$\quad f(x, y) = 0 \quad 262\text{--}263, 276\text{--}277$

$\quad y^2 = f(x) \quad 263\text{--}265$

$\quad ay^2 + by + c = dx^n \quad 265$

$\quad y^m = x(x + 1)\cdots(x + n) \quad 267\text{--}268$

$\quad m = 2 \quad 267$

$\quad ax^m - by^n = c \quad 272\text{--}276, 300$

Miscellaneous equations

Pure and Applied Mathematics

A Series of Monographs and Textbooks

Edited by PAUL A. SMITH and SAMUEL EILENBERG,
Columbia University, New York

In preparation

HANS FREUDENTHAL and H. DE VRIES. Linear Lie Groups.

J. DIEUDONNÉ. Foundations of Modern Analysis (*enlarged and corrected printing*)

WILLIAM F. DONOGHUE, JR. Distributions and Fourier Transforms

MARSTON MORSE and STEWART S. CAIRNS. Critical Point Theory in Global and Differential Topology.

J. BARKLEY ROSSER. Simplified Independence Proofs: Boolean Valued Models of Set Theory.